Se
Gua

THE MORNING AFTER
by
Michelle Reid

A WOMAN OF PASSION
by
Anne Mather

RENDEZVOUS WITH REVENGE
by
Miranda Lee

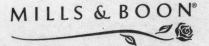

MILLS & BOON®

*MILLS & BOON and MILLS & BOON with the Rose Device
are registered trademarks of the publisher.
Harlequin Mills & Boon Limited,
Eton House, 18-24 Paradise Road, Richmond, Surrey, TW9 1SR*

SEDUCTION GUARANTEED
© by Harlequin Enterprises II B.V., 2000

The Morning After, A Woman of Passion and *Rendezvous with Revenge*
were first published in Great Britain by Harlequin Mills & Boon Limited
in separate, single volumes.

The Morning After © Michelle Reid 1996
A Woman of Passion © Anne Mather 1995
Rendezvous with Revenge © Miranda Lee 1996

ISBN 0 263 82416 0

05-0006

*Printed and bound in Spain
by Litografia Rosés S.A., Barcelona*

Michelle Reid grew up on the southern edges of Manchester, the youngest in a family of five lively children. But now she lives in the beautiful county of Cheshire with her busy executive husband and two grown-up daughters. She loves reading, the ballet, and playing tennis when she gets the chance. She hates cooking, cleaning, and despises ironing! Sleep she can do without, and produces some of her best written work during the early hours of the morning.

THE MORNING AFTER
by
MICHELLE REID

CHAPTER ONE

ANNIE wanted to scream. She *tried* to scream! But every time she opened her mouth he covered it with his own.

It was horrible. A violation. She felt sick.

And it was dark in the room—very dark. The air hot and stifling, filled with the laboured breathing of their uneven struggle. Hands grappling against intrusive hands—her strangled sobs mingling with his thick, excited groans. Alien sounds, smells and textures swamping her senses to hold her trapped in a terrifyingly black void of wretched helplessness.

Suffocating—she felt as if she was suffocating. She couldn't breathe. She couldn't think beyond that vile, thrusting tongue. She could feel her heart pounding in wild fear. It throbbed in her chest, her head—thundered in her ears.

Her clothes had gone. She didn't know where or even how they had gone—but they were no longer covering her body.

Louis Alvarez was. Big, strong and repulsively naked. His greedy hands touching everywhere—*everywhere*.

It didn't help that she was slightly drunk from the amount of champagne that she had swallowed. She felt weak and dizzy, her head swimming as she tossed it from side to side in an effort to evade his awful mouth.

He dealt with this by reaching out to grasp a fistful of her silken gold hair, using it to clamp her twisting head to the bed. Her whimper of pain brought his smothering mouth back onto hers.

And then the real nightmare began.

His free hand, shifting to cover one madly palpitating breast, moulding, squeezing before moving on, palm sliding over quivering flesh, eager, hungry. Fingers searching, probing, hurting until, on a sudden surge of sexual urgency, he thrust a knee between her thighs and wedged them wide apart.

Then he was there, heavy on her, his mouth dragging sideways away from hers on a rasping sigh of pleasure as his swollen manhood made contact with her warm flesh.

And at last from somewhere—from nowhere—she didn't know where—she found the ability to scream. Her body arching away from the invading thrust of his body, her slender neck arching away from the sickening threat of his thrusting tongue—

Then a door was opening, a burst of light flooding like acid through her tortured mind. And the scream came, thick and wretched—a cry from hell, filling the air around her...

The flash bulbs began popping even before the limousine drew to a halt outside the hotel. Annie Lacey and Todd Hanson were big news at the moment. And the paparazzi were out in force.

The car stopped, a uniformed attendant stepped forward to open a door and the flash bulbs went wild, catching frame by frame the appearance of a strappy gold shoe and one long, long silk-clad female leg. Then a head appeared, breast-length, die-straight wheat-blonde hair floating around a physically perfect female face, followed by the rest of the exquisite creature, wearing nothing more than a shimmering short scrap of pure white silk that seemed held to her body only by the thin gold belt she had cinched into her narrow waist.

Annie Lacey. Tall, blonde and leggy. A lethal combination. Beautiful, with a pair of cool, cool pure blue eyes which were so disconcertingly at odds with her shockingly sensual siren's mouth. She was the present-day super-sought-after supermodel. And super-tramp to those who believed slavishly every word printed by the tabloid Press.

They envied her, though. Love or despise her for her morals, they envied her how she looked and what those looks had brought her.

Fame. Fortune.

Gods, to a lot of people. Unreachable dreams to most. To Annie herself?

Well, she used that gorgeous mouth to smile for the cameras while those blue eyes gave nothing away of what was going on behind them. What Annie thought or felt about most things was kept a close secret—which was why the Press had such a field-day where she was concerned. They could say and print what they liked about her, safe in the knowledge that she wouldn't retaliate.

Smile and say nothing, was her motto. Because whatever you did say would be taken down and twisted into something completely different—mainly something more likely to sell papers. And that meant lies, sex and the inevitable scandal—a lesson she had once learned the hard way.

A man—a big, blond-haired, blue-eyed man who was as handsome as she was beautiful—rounded the car to arrive at her side, and instantly the media interest intensified.

'Mr Hanson—Mr Hanson! It is true that Annie got the *Cliché* contract as a direct result of her relationship with you?'

Todd's hand settled about Annie's waist, drawing her close as the next question hit.

'Are you lovers, Mr Hanson?'

'Will Susie Frazer return to the States now she's lost both you and the *Cliché* contract, Mr Hanson?'

'Is there any truth in the rumour that Miss Frazer dumped you because you refused to dump Miss Lacey?'

'I hate you for setting us both up for this,' Annie threw at Todd through gritted teeth.

'Just keep smiling and ignore them,' was all he replied, pressing her into motion towards the hotel. 'They're just fishing. They don't really know anything.'

'What, with Susie feeding them their lines?' she drawled.

'She's a bitch,' he allowed, 'but not that big a bitch.'

'Was that a joke?' Annie mocked him. 'She's out for blood. My blood preferably.'

'I wish you two could have become friends,' he sighed as they stepped through the hotel doors.

'And pigs might fly,' was her only reply to that.

There never had been any love-loss in evidence between the two top models from the moment they'd first met. That had been just over six months ago, when Susie Frazer had come to London from her native Los Angeles to attend the British Advertising Awards.

Annie had been there with Todd that time too, he in his role as head of Hanson Publications and more specifically as representative of *Cliché* magazine—one of the top British monthly glossies on the present-day market—and Annie because she was featured in that month's issue of *Cliché* wearing that season's latest from the Paris shows.

Susie had taken one look at the dynamically handsome Todd Hanson and fallen like a ton of bricks—had seen that he had none other than the notorious Annie Lacey hanging on his arm and declared outright war on the spot.

'Who does she think she is, looking at you as if you're dirt?' Todd had demanded furiously.

'My reputation goes before me, darling,' she'd drawled mockingly in reply. 'But, you have to admit, she does look rather spectacular glaring at me like that.'

Tall and reed-thin, the brilliant flame of her gorgeous red hair forming the most wonderful halo of fire around her exquisite face, spectacular Susie certainly had looked. And despite his anger Annie had been able to tell by the sudden gleam in his eye that Todd had thought so too. So she hadn't been that surprised to discover a few weeks later that Susie had moved into Todd's apartment with him.

LUCKY DEVIL HANSON HAS THE PICK OF THE CROP! the tabloids had read that week, featuring accompanying photos of Todd with Annie and Todd with Susie, both women gazing adoringly into his handsome face. Annie had thought it rather amusing, but Susie hadn't. She was spoiled, vain, jealous and possessive. And she wanted Annie cut right out of Todd's life. The fact that she had never managed to achieve this aim made her animosity towards Annie almost palpable. So when Annie had been chosen over Susie to promote *Cliché's* launch into Europe earlier this week Susie had retaliated by walking out on Todd.

Which was why Annie was here tonight with Todd, instead of Susie. He was still stinging from the way that Susie had walked out on him, and his self-esteem had hit rock-bottom. He needed a beautiful woman hanging on his arm to bolster his ego and—no vanity intended—Annie was undoubtedly it!

'Susie will be there,' he'd said, explaining his reason for wanting her here with him tonight. 'She's accused me often enough of having something going with you. So let her think she was right! It will certainly hit her where it will hurt her the most—in her over-suspicious little mind!'

It hadn't been the best incentive that Annie had ever been offered to attend something she did not want to go to. But what the heck? she'd decided ruefully; her own reputation had been shot to death years ago when she'd been named as the other woman in the much publicised Alvarez divorce. And Annie owed Todd—owed him a lot for bringing her through that wretched ordeal a reasonably sane woman.

Like the rock she had always likened him to. Todd had stood by her right through it all, not caring if some of her dirt rubbed off on him. But, most precious of all, he'd believed her—believed her in the sight of so much damning evidence against her, and for that she would always be grateful. Grateful enough to do anything for him—even play the outright vamp if he asked it of her.

Which was exactly what she was here to do. But...

'Just remember I'm here only as a big favour to you,' she reminded him as they paused in the open doorway to the huge reception room to take in the glittering array of those already gathered there, who were considered best and most powerful in the advertising fraternity. 'Once I'm sure Susie has taken note that we are a pair I'm off home. I hate these kinds of do's.'

But, champagne glass in hand, she moved with Todd from group to group, smiling, chatting, smoothly fielding the light and sometimes not so light banter came their way, and generally giving the impression that she was thoroughly enjoying herself, while her eyes kept a sharp lookout for Susie.

It was then that she felt it—a sharp, tingling sensation in her spine that caught at her breath and made her spin quickly to search out the originator of the red-hot needles at present impaling themselves in her back.

She expected to see Susie. In fact, she had been so sure it would be Susie that it rather disconcerted her to find herself staring across the crowded room at not a red-haired witch with murderous green eyes but a man. A strange man. The most darkly attractive man she had ever encountered in her life before.

Dressed in a conventional black bow-tie and dinner suit, he stood a good head and shoulders taller than anyone else. His hair was black—an uncompromising raven-black, dead straight and shiny, scraped severely back from a lean, darkly tanned face. A riveting face. A face with eyes that seemed to be piercing right into her from beneath the smooth black brows he had lowered over them. Thin nose, straight, chiseled mouth and chin—he had the haughty look of a Spanish conquistador about him. And he possessed the neat, tight body of a dancer, slim but muscled, lithe like a dancer—a Spanish dancer, she found herself extending hectically.

Something like a small explosion of feeling took place deep inside her stomach, and hurriedly she looked away, going to wind herself closer to Todd, as though his reassuring bulk could soothe the disturbing sensation away.

'What's the matter with you?' Todd murmured, turning from the conversation he was having with a couple of business cronies to frown at the way she was suddenly clinging to his arm.

'Nothing,' she denied, feeling decidedly agitated. 'Where's Susie?' she snapped with a sudden impatience. 'I would have thought she'd have shown her face by now.'

Todd smiled—a thin, hard parody of a smile. 'She's over there,' he said, nodding his head in the direction in which Annie had just seen the stranger. 'Playing vamp to that guy from the Rouez Sands Group.'

'Who—Josh Tulley?'

'Mmm,' he confirmed, hiding his jealousy behind that casual reply.

But Annie wasn't fooled. She knew how crazy Todd was about Susie. She knew how much this was hurting him, and her eyes clouded in gentle sympathy. 'You have been living like man and wife for the last six months, darling,' she reminded softly. 'Maybe she has a right to feel rejected by you over this *Cliché* thing.'

If Annie had been hoping that her defence of Susie would help soften his heart towards the woman he loved, it didn't. If anything it only helped to annoy him. 'I'm a businessman, not a pimp,' he clipped. 'My boardroom is not in my bedroom. She knew that before she decided to try her luck in either.'

But that is not what the papers are saying, is it? Annie contemplated heavily. And once again it would be Annie Lacey who was going to carry the mucky can. Then she was instantly disgusted with herself for worrying about her own bad press when Todd had not worried about the mud thrown at him during her fall from grace four years ago!

'Love you,' she murmured softly, and reached up to press a tender kiss to his cheek.

Then she almost fell over when those red-hot needles returned with a vengeance. They prickled her spine, raising the fine, silken hairs on the back of her neck, drying her mouth, tightening tiny muscles around her lungs so that she found breathing at all an effort.

She must have actually stumbled because suddenly Todd exclaimed, 'What the hell—?' He made a grab to steady her, his blue eyes narrowing into a puzzled frown as he peered down into her unusually flushed face. 'Are you tipsy?' he demanded, sounding almost shocked.

It was a shock she well understood. Todd knew as well as Annie did that she had not consumed more than half a glass of anything alcoholic in any one evening in over four years.

Not since the Alvarez affair, in fact.

She shuddered on the name. 'No. I just feel a bit flushed, that's all.' Hamming it up, she began fanning herself with a hand. 'It's so damned hot in here. Oh, look! There's

Lissa!' she cried, wanting to divert him. Why, she wasn't sure. 'I'll leave you to your boring businessmen and go and have a chat. Is Susie still in evidence?'

Todd glanced over Annie's shoulder then away again swiftly. 'Yes,' he said, and she could tell by the sudden tensing of his jaw that he hadn't liked what he'd seen.

'Then I want a kiss,' Annie commanded, reaching up to wind her arms around his neck.

He grinned, relaxing again, and gave it.

'Take that, you bitch,' she murmured to the unseen Susie as they drew apart.

Todd shook his head with a wry smile of appreciation for the act that she was putting on for him. 'You,' he murmured, 'are a dangerous little witch, Annie Lacey.'

'Because I love you and don't mind showing it?' she questioned innocently.

'No,' he chuckled. 'Because you love me one way but enjoy presenting it in another. Now, stop laying it on with a trowel and go and talk to Lissa.'

He gave her a light tap on her rear to send her on her way and she fluttered her lashes at him as she went, his laughter following behind her.

The sound was like manna from heaven to Annie, who hadn't heard him laugh like that in days. And she decided it was worth all the speculative looks that she was now receiving from those around them who had witnessed their little staged scene just to know that he had got his sense of humour back.

And that included the dark, brooding look that she was receiving from one man in particular, she noted on a sudden return of that hot breathlessness.

He was now standing on the other side of the room— though how he'd got there that quickly through this crush Annie didn't know.

Her heart skipped a beat.

That look was very proprietorial.

Who did he think he was, looking at her like that?

Her chin came up, her famous, cool blue eyes challenging him outright.

He smiled, his chiselled mouth twisting wryly, and he gave a small shrug of one broad shoulder as if to say, I have no right but—what the hell?

Arrogant devil! With a toss of her beautiful hair she spun away and went to join her agent. But right through the next half-hour she was acutely aware of him, what he was doing and who he was talking to.

And even more acutely aware of every time his glance came her way.

It was weird, oddly threatening yet disturbingly intimate.

Todd joined her, and after a short while they moved off through the crush, eyes with varying expressions following their slow progress as they paused several times to speak to people they knew. Some envied Todd Hanson the delicious woman curved to his side, and some envied her the attractive man she was with. But few could deny that they complemented each other perfectly—she with her long, softly rounded, very feminine body, he with his tightly packed, muscled frame, both with their fair-skinned, blond-haired, aggravatingly spectacular looks.

They ended up in another room where a buffet had been laid out. It was the usual kind of spread expected at these functions—finger food, high on calories and low on appetite satisfaction. Todd loaded up a plate with Annie's help, then they found a spot against a wall to share their spread, the plate full of food balanced between them on the flat of Todd's palm.

It all looked very cosy, very intimate, with Todd feeding Annie her favourite devilled prawns while she held a chicken drumstick up for him to bite into. But the conversation between them was far from cosy.

'Well, did you get to speak to her?' Annie asked him bluntly.

'She collared me.' Todd shrugged offhandedly. 'It wasn't the other way around.'

'After waiting until I was safely out of the way, of course. Bite—you've missed a tasty bit there…' He bit, sharp white teeth slicing easily into succulent chicken. 'So, what did she have to say?'

Another shrug. 'Nothing worth repeating,' he dismissed.

Which meant, Annie surmised, that Susie had spent the time she'd had alone with him slaying Annie's character. He fed her a mushroom-filled canapé and she chewed on it thoughtfully for a while, then said firmly, 'All right, tell me what you said to her, then.'

For a moment his eyes twinkled, wry amusement putting life into the pure blue irises. 'Just like that,' he murmured ruefully. 'She could just have been enquiring about your health, you know.'

'And we both know she was not,' Annie drawled.

He huffed out a short laugh. 'Do you have any false illusions about yourself at all, Annie?' he asked curiously.

'None that I know of.' She pouted, then, like him, shrugged a slender shoulder. 'They wouldn't be much use to me if I did have them, would they?' She was referring to the fact that people believed what they were conditioned to believe, and the Alvarez affair had done the conditioning on her character four years ago.

His blue eyes clouded at her candid honesty about herself, a grim kind of sympathy replacing the moment's amusement. 'I wish…' he began, but she stopped him by placing sticky fingers over his lips.

'No,' she said, her eyes suddenly dark and sombre. 'No

wishes. No heart-searching or self-recriminations. They serve no useful purpose. And we know what we are to each other, no matter what everyone else wants to believe.'

'I love you,' he murmured, and kissed the tips of her fingers where they lay lightly against his mouth.

'Now that,' she decided, 'has just earned you the right to use me whenever you want to. Business or pleasure, my love. I am at your service!'

A sudden movement on the very periphery of her vision had her head twisting in that direction just in time to catch sight of her stranger turning away from them, and that odd feeling went chasing down her spine again.

'Have you any idea who that man is?' she asked Todd.

'Which one?' he prompted, glancing in the direction that she was looking, but already the stranger had disappeared through the door which led into the main function room.

'It doesn't matter.' She turned back to face Todd. 'He's gone.' And she made a play of cleaning her sticky fingers on the damp towels provided, aware that Todd was frowning at her, wondering why she'd felt driven to remark on the person at all. He knew that it wasn't like her; she usually showed a distinct lack of interest in the male sex in general. So her sudden interest in one man in particular intrigued him. But just when he was going to quiz her further a colleague of his joined them, and the moment was lost.

A fact for which Annie was thankful, because she didn't think that she could give Todd a reason why the stranger was bothering her as much as he was. He was impertinent, certainly. The way he had been watching her all evening made him that. And arrogant too, because he didn't even bother to look away when she caught him doing it!

But...

She had no answer to her 'but'. And on a sudden burst

of restlessness she excused herself from Todd and his companion with the excuse that she was going to the bathroom.

She began threading her way through the crowd towards the main foyer, a tall, graceful mover with the kind of figure that was now back in fashion—slender but curvy, with high, firm breasts, a narrow waist and sensually rounded hips.

Being so blonde meant that the white and gold combination of her outfit suited her, the silk clinging sensually as she walked, advertising the distinct lack of underwear beneath it. But although she was well aware of the admiring glances that she was receiving she acknowledged few of them, smiling only at people she knew but giving them no chance to waylay her.

The foyer was almost as busy as the function rooms, with people milling about or just standing in small groups chatting, and Annie paused by the doorway, her blue gaze searching for the direction of the ladies' room. She spied it way across on the other side of the thickly carpeted foyer, but had barely taken a small step in that direction when she caught a flashing glimpse of flame-red hair and sighed when she realised that Susie was going in the same direction.

In no mood for a cat-fight in the Ladies, she watched Susie disappear from view, then turned, feeling a bit at a loss as to what to do next and wondering if she dared just walk out of here without telling Todd.

She'd had enough now and wanted to go home. The tall dark stranger had unsettled her. And the fact that Todd had already had his confrontation with Susie, and that Susie was completely aware of whom Todd was here with, made her reasons for being here at all redundant.

And, to be honest, her bed beckoned. In her line of business early nights were a fact of life, and her body clock was telling her that she was usually tucked up and fast asleep by now.

Quite how it happened she didn't know, but all of a sudden a noisy group came bursting out of the room she'd just left, forcing her to take a quick step back out of their way—which brought her hard up against the person standing behind her.

She turned quickly to apologise—only to stiffen on a fiercely indrawn breath as something icy cold and very wet landed against her chest...!

CHAPTER TWO

'*OH*…!' she gasped out shrilly.

'Damn,' a deep voice muttered. 'My apologies.'

But Annie was too busy trying to catch her breath to listen to any apology as she watched what looked like the full contents of a tall, fluted glass of champagne drip down the honeyed slopes of her breasts. Ice-cold bubbles were fizzing against her heated skin, the chilled liquid soaking into the thin white silk of her bodice.

The fabric darkened, then turned transparent before her very eyes, plastering itself so tightly to her breasts that anyone within a vicinity of ten feet would now know that she was definitely not wearing a bra! And to top that humiliating exposure her nipples, always so annoyingly sensitive to quick changes in temperature, burst into tight, prominent buds, pushing against the wet fabric in sheer, affronted surprise!

'Hell,' the culprit muttered, making her wretchedly aware that he was seeing exactly what she was seeing—and from a better vantage point than anyone else, including herself. In a delayed act of modesty she snapped her arms across her breasts at the same time as her head came up to receive the second stunning shock in as many seconds.

It was the man who had been watching her all evening—the same man who had filled her with such strange, unsettling feelings—and she just stared at him blankly, her lovely mouth parted while her body quivered badly enough for anyone to see that she was suffering from a severe state of shock.

19

Then flash bulbs began to pop, and the next thing she knew a male chest of a rock-like substance was blocking her off from view as a strong arm whipped around her waist to pull her hard up against his muscle-packed frame.

'Pretend you know me!' he muttered urgently. And before she could begin to think what he meant his mouth took fierce possession of her own.

Annie froze, this shock invasion, coming on top of all the other shocks she had just received, holding her so stiff and still that she simply let him get away with it!

But the shock did not stop her from being intensely aware of the way his mouth seemed to burn against her own, or the way he was holding her so tightly that her wet breasts were being crushed against the silky fabric of his dinner jacket. And she could feel his breath warm against her cheek, smell the slightly spicy scent of him that teased her stammering senses.

She was panting for breath by the time he drew away, giving only enough space between their lips so he could speak to her softly and swiftly. 'At the moment only you and I know about the champagne.' His voice held the finest hint of an accent—American tinged with something else… 'Keep up the pretence of knowing me and those greedy cameras will merely believe that Annie Lacey has just been greeted by one of her many lovers. You understand?'

Many lovers? She blinked, still too shocked, too bewildered by a mad set of events to begin to think clearly.

Then more flash bulbs popped, and she closed her eyes as tomorrow's headlines played their acid taunt across the inside of her lids: ANNIE LACEY BARES ALL IN CHAMPAGNE CLASH!

'Oh, God,' she whispered shakily.

He shifted slightly, accepting her response as acknowledgement of his advice, a large hand splaying across the base of her spine to ease her more closely to him. 'Smile,' he instructed brusquely.

Obediently she fixed a tight, bright smile to her throbbing lips.

'Now reach up and kiss me in return.'

Her eyes widened, then darkened in dumb refusal. He read it, and his own eyes flashed a warning. Green, she realised quite out of context. His eyes were green.

'Do it!' he commanded harshly. 'Do it, you fool, if you want this to look natural!'

More flash bulbs popped, congealing the horror in her shock-paralysed throat when she realised that her choices were few. She either complied with this frightening man's instructions or she faced the humiliation that she would receive at the hands of the gutter Press.

It was no contest really, she decided bleakly. The Press would be cruel—too cruel. This man—this frightening stranger—could never hurt her as deeply as a ruthless Press could do.

So with a dizzy sense of unreality washing numbly through her, her eyes clinging like confused prisoners to the glinting urgency in his, her tense fingers began sliding up his chest and over his broad shoulders, and her slender body stretched up along the ungiving length of his as she went slowly up on tiptoe to bring her reluctant mouth into contact with his.

Only, her mouth never made it as she received yet another shock—a shock which made her wet breasts heave against his hard chest in surprise, and sent her blue eyes wider, her quivering mouth too—when her fingers made accidental contact with something at his nape.

His hair was so long that he had it tied back with a thin velvet ribbon!

He gave a soft laugh deep in his throat, white teeth flashing between beautifully moulded lips, sardonically smiling in amusement at her shock.

Then he wasn't smiling, his green eyes darkening into something that stung her with a hot, dark sense of her own femininity and had her body stiffening in rejection even as he arched her up against him and closed the gap between their mouths.

She stopped breathing. Her fingers coiled tensely around that long, sleek tail of dark, silken hair as fine, pulsing jets of stinging, hot awareness sprayed heat across her trembling flesh.

For all her carefully nurtured reputation, for all the juicy rumours about her personal life, Annie rarely allowed herself to be properly kissed, rarely let any man close enough to try—though those who wished to would rather have died than admit such a thing to anyone, which was why her image as a man-killer stayed so perfectly intact.

So to have this man kiss her—not superficially but with enough sensual drive to have her own lips part to welcome him—seemed to throw her into a deeper state of shock, holding her completely still in his arms as she felt her response like a lick of fire burning from mouth to breasts then, worse, to the very core of her sex. Her muscles contracted fiercely in reaction, her lips quivering on yet another helpless gasp.

Then, thankfully, she was free—thankfully because in all her life she had never experienced a response like that! And the fact that she had done so with this perfect stranger both frightened and bewildered her.

'Right,' he muttered. 'Let's get the hell out of here.'

Crazily she found herself leaning weakly against him, sponge-kneed and dizzy with the strange cacophony of reactions taking place inside her. Her mouth was throbbing, her heart trembling and her damp breasts quivering where they were being pressed tightly against his chest.

Inside she was fainting—it was the only way her muzzy head could think of describing that odd, dragging feeling that seemed to be trying to sink her like liquid to the ground. Even the roots of her hair reacted stingingly as his chin brushed across the top of her head when he moved to glance around them.

He shifted her beneath the crook of his powerful arm, and he was big—big enough to fit her easily beneath his shoulder, even though she was no small thing herself. Her hand slid from the long lock of his hair to flutter delicately down his back to his lean, tight waist, her other pressing against the front of his white dress shirt where she was made forcefully aware of the accelerated pounding of his heart beneath the sticky dampness where her wetness had transferred itself to him.

The whole scene must have looked powerfully emotional to anyone watching all of this take place—the notorious Annie Lacey meeting, throwing herself upon and leaving hurriedly with a man who could only be an old and very intimate friend by the way he held her clasped so possessively to him. But, huddled against him as she was, at that moment she could only be glad of his powerful bulk because it helped to hide what had happened to her from all those curious eyes.

But when she felt the cooling freshness of the summer night air hit her body she at last made an effort to pull her befuddled brain together.

'Wait a minute!' she gasped, pulling to a dead stop in front of the row of waiting black cabs. 'I—'

'Just get in,' he instructed, transferring his grip to her elbow and quite forcefully propelling her inside the nearest cab.

Annie landed with less than her usual grace on the cheap, cracked leather seat.

'What the hell do you think you're doing?' she exclaimed with shrill indignity as he climbed right in behind her.

He didn't bother to answer, but instead, and to her horror, began stripping off his black silk evening jacket!

Annie made an ungainly scramble into the furthest corner of the seat, blue eyes revealing the real alarm she was now beginning to feel.

'Where to, mate?'

'Tell the guy,' the man beside her commanded. 'Then put that on—' the jacket landed on her trembling lap '—before his eyes pop out of his head.'

Annie glanced sharply at the cabby to find his eyes fixed on her breasts so shockingly outlined against the sodden fabric of her dress. Dark heat stung along her cheeks as hurriedly she dragged the jacket around her slender shoulders and clutched possessively at its black satin lapels.

'Your address,' her accoster prompted, after having watched sardonically her rush to cover herself up.

Annie flashed him a fulminating look, frustratedly aware that she had no choice but to comply. Well, she did have a choice, she acknowledged bitterly. She could toss this alarming man back his jacket, climb out of the cab and walk back into the hotel to face all those eagerly speculative eyes while she went in search of Todd.

But the very idea of doing that made her feel slightly sick. All those eyes with their amused, knowing looks, and sly sniggers from people who would see the whole thing as yet another Annie Lacey sensation.

Reluctantly she muttered her address, then subsided stiffly into her corner of the cab while he leaned forward to repeat it to the cabby.

Annie followed the lithe movement of his long body with her eyes.

Who is he? she wondered tensely. Though he sounded American there was an added hint of a foreign accent in his deep, gravelly voice that she couldn't quite place. And his skin wore a rich, smooth olive tint that suggested foreign climes—like the colour of his raven-black hair with its outrageous pony-tail lying smoothly along the pure silk of his bright white dress shirt between well-muscled shoulderblades.

What is he? Even in profile his face showed a hard-boned toughness of character that somehow did not go with the flamboyant style of his hair.

He gave a conflict of impressions, she realised, and wondered if it was a deliberately erected façade aimed to put people off the track where his true personality was concerned.

And why did she think that? Because she did it herself and therefore could recognise the same trait in others.

Instruction to the cabby completed, he slid the partitioning window shut then sat back to look at her.

Instantly those strange sparks of awareness prickled along the surface of her skin—an awareness of his firm, sculptured mouth that had so shockingly claimed her own, of lips that made hers tingle in memory, made her throat go dry as they stretched into a smooth, mocking smile.

'A novel way of meeting, don't you think?' he drawled.

Not gravel but velvet. She found herself correcting her description of the liquid tones of his voice. And laced with a hint of—what? Contempt? Sarcasm? Or just simple, wry amusement at the whole situation? Annie flicked her wary glance up to his eyes. Strange eyes. Green. Green eyes that again did not go with the dark Latin rest of him, and were certainly alight with something that kept her senses alert to the threat of danger.

Danger?

'You were watching me earlier,' she said half-accusingly. 'And you know my name.'

He smiled at that, the wry—yes, it was wry—amusement deepening in his eyes. 'But you are a very beautiful woman, Miss Lacey,' he pointed out. 'Your face and your body can be seen plastered on billboards all over the world. Of course I know your name.' He gave a small shrug of those wide, white-clad shoulders. 'I would expect every red-blooded man alive to recognise you on sight.'

'Except that all those other men do not make a point of stalking me all evening,' she pointed out.

His attention sharpened. 'Are you by any chance trying to imply something specific?' he enquired carefully.

Was she? She was by nature very suspicious of men in general. This one seemed to have gone out of his way to be where he was right now.

'Perhaps you suspect me of spilling the champagne deliberately?' he suggested, when Annie did not say anything.

'Did you?' Cool blue eyes threw back a challenge.

He smiled—the kind of noncommittal smile that tried to mock her for even thinking such a thing about him. But she was not convinced by it, or put off.

'Things like it have happened before,' she told him. 'In my business you collect nut cases like other people collect postage stamps.'

'And you see me as the ideal candidate for that kind of weird behaviour?' He looked so amused by the idea that it made her angry.

'You can't tell by just looking at them, you know,' she snapped. 'They don't have "crazy man" stamped on their foreheads to give me a clue.'

'But in your business, Miss Lacey, you must surely accept that kind of thing as merely par for the course.'

'And therefore relinquish the right to care?'

He offered no answer to that, but his eyes narrowed thoughtfully on her as though he was making a quick reassessment of something he had already set in his mind about her, and a small silence fell.

Annie turned her head away to stare out the cab window so that she did not have to try and read what that reassessment was about. Why, she wasn't sure, except...

She sighed inwardly. She knew why. She'd looked away because he disturbed her oddly. His dark good looks disturbed her. The way he had been staring at her earlier disturbed her. His shocking kisses had disturbed her, awakening feelings inside her that she had honestly believed she did not possess.

The black cab rumbled on, stopping and starting in London's busy night traffic. People were out in force, the warm summer night and the fact that it was tourist season in the city filling the streets with life. Pub doors stood wedged open to help ease the heated air inside rooms packed with casually dressed, enviably relaxed people. Cafés with their pavements blocked continental-style by white plastic tables had busy waiters running to and fro, and the sights and smells and sounds were those of a busy international metropolis, all shapes, sizes, colours and creeds mingling in a mad, warm bustle of easy harmony.

She sighed softly to herself, wishing that she could be like them, wishing that she could walk out and mingle inconspicuously with the crowd and just soak up some of that carefree atmosphere. But she couldn't. Her looks were her fortune, and therefore were too well-known—as the man sitting beside her had just pointed out. Dressed in jeans and a T-shirt with a scarf covering her head, she would still be recognised. She knew because she'd tried it.

The trouble was, she decided heavily, she was becoming weary of the life she led, the restrictions that life placed on her. Tired of an image that she had created for herself which meant her always having to be on her guard with people—people like the man sitting beside her.

'The champagne caught your hair.' The sudden touch of light fingers on a sticky tendril of hair just by her left ear had Annie reacting instinctively.

She jerked violently away from his touch. He went very still, his strange eyes narrowing on her face with an expression that she found difficult to define as he slowly lowered his hand again, long, blunt-ended fingers settling lightly on his own lap.

A new silence began to fizz between them, and Annie did not know what to say to break it. There was something about this man that frightened her—no matter how much she tried to tell herself that she was being paranoid about him. Even that touch—that light, innocent brush of his fingers against her hair—had filled her with the most incredible alarm. Her heart was hammering too, rattling against her ribs with enough force to restrict her breathing.

She bit down on her lower lip, even white teeth pressing into lush, ruby-coloured flesh, and her dusky lashes lowered to hide her discomfort as warm colour began to seep into her cheeks.

Then the cab made a sharp turn, and she saw with relief that they were turning into a narrow cobbled street of pretty, whitewashed cottages, one of which was her own.

Almost eagerly she shifted towards the edge of the seat so that she could jump out just as soon as they stopped. The sound of soft laughter beside her made her throw a wary glance at her companion.

He was smiling, ruefully shaking his sleek dark head. 'I am not intending to jump on you, you know,' he drawled. 'I assure you I do possess a little more finesse than to seduce my women in the back seats of black cabs. And,' he went on, before Annie could think of a thing to say in reply, 'I did think my behaviour exemplary enough to give me gallant-knight status if nothing else.'

He thought those kisses in the hotel foyer exemplary behaviour? She didn't. And he could sit there smiling that innocently mocking smile as long as he wanted to, but she would not lower her guard to him. Her senses were just too alert to the hidden danger in him to do that.

'I'm sorry,' she said coolly. 'But gallant knights are so few and far between that a girl does not expect to meet one these days.'

The taxi came to a stop outside her tiny mews cottage then—thankfully. Because she was suddenly very desperate to get away from this strange, disturbing man.

But as she went to slip off his jacket and opened her mouth to utter some polite little word of thanks for his trouble he stopped her.

'No.' His hand descended onto her shoulder to hold his jacket in place. 'Keep it until we arrive at your door,' he quietly advised, sending a pointed glance at the cab driver. 'One can only imagine what the champagne has done to the fabric of your dress by now.'

She went pale, remembering that awful moment when she'd caught the cab driver's gaze fixed on her breasts, so transparently etched against her sodden dress.

'Thank you,' she whispered, clutching the jacket back around her.

He said nothing, opening the taxi door and stepping out, then turning to help her join him before he bent to pass some money through the driver's open window. Annie supposed that she should offer to pay the fare, but somehow this man gave the impression that he would not appreciate such egalitarian gestures. There was an air of the old-fashioned autocrat about him—an indomitable pride in the set of those wide shoulders flexing beneath the white dress shirt as he straightened and turned back to face her.

She shuddered, feeling oddly as though something or someone had just walked over her grave.

'Y-you should have held the taxi,' she murmured stiffly as the black cab rumbled off down the street, belching out pungent diesel fumes as it went.

If he picked up on her unspoken warning—that if he was standing in the belief that she was going to invite him into her home then he was mistaken—he did not show it, merely shrugging those big shoulders dismissively as he turned towards her black-painted front door.

'Your key?' he prompted.

Disconcerted by his calm indifference to any hint she had given him, she decided grimly not to argue, lowering her pale head to watch her fingers fumble nervously with the tiny catch on her soft gold leather evening bag to get at the key. The quicker she got the door open, the sooner she could get rid of him, she decided, wondering crossly what the heck was the matter with her. She didn't usually feel like this.

She didn't usually get herself into crazy situations like this one either. She was very careful not to do so normally.

Normal. What was normal about any of this?

Refusing to allow her fingers to tremble, she fitted the key into the lock, pushed open the door, then forced herself back around to face him. 'Thank you,' she said firmly, 'for bringing me home. And—' she allowed him a small, dry smile '—for saving my embarrassment.'

'Think nothing of it.' He sent her a little bow that was

pure, old-fashioned gallantry and befitted somehow this tall dark man who reminded her so much of a throwback from another age. South American, maybe? she wondered curiously, then shuddered, not wanting him to be. She had a strange, unexplainable suspicion that it would actually hurt her to find that he might be the same nationality as Alvarez.

If he was aware of her curiosity he did not offer to relieve it. Instead, and with another one of those bows, he held his hand out towards her as though he were going to grab hold and push her into the house.

Defensively she took a big step back, bringing herself hard up against the white-painted stone wall behind her, and almost choking on an uplift of clamouring fear.

'My jacket,' he reminded her softly.

Oh, God. Annie closed her eyes, angry with herself because she knew that she was behaving like an idiot and really had no reason for it. He had, as he had pointed out, shown her exemplary behaviour over the whole messy incident!

Except for those kisses, she reminded herself tensely. Those kisses had not been exemplary at all.

Lips pressed tightly together over her clenched teeth, she slipped off the jacket and handed it to him. 'Thank you,' she murmured without looking at him.

'My pleasure,' he drawled, his long fingers sliding delicately over hers as he took the jacket from her. Her own began to tingle, fine, sharp showers of sensation skittering across the surface of her skin to make her tremble as she whipped her arm across her body in an effort to hide herself from those terribly disturbing eyes.

Casually he hooked a finger through the loop and draped the jacket over his shoulder, his lazy stance showing no signs that he was going to go away.

Annie waited, praying fiercely that he was not standing

here expecting her to invite him in. No man other than Todd had ever stepped a single foot inside her home. And only Todd had done so because he had proved time and time again that she could trust him with her very life.

She thought of this house as her sanctuary—the only place where she felt she could relax and truly be herself. She didn't want to give way to the compelling urge he seemed to be silently pressing on her to break that rule and invite him to enter.

Panic began to bubble up from the anxious pit of her stomach—panic at the man's indomitable refusal to be brushed off by her, and panic at the knowledge that if he kept this small, silent battle up she was going to be the one to give in.

Then he touched her.

And, good grief, everything vital inside her went haywire—muscles, nerves, senses, heart, all clamouring out of control as his hand cupped gently at her chin, lifted it, forcing her wary blue gaze to meet the probing expression in his.

He didn't say anything, but a frown marred that high, satin-smooth brow as though he was reassessing—again— and was still not sure what he was seeing when he looked at the infamous Annie Lacey.

'Beautiful,' he murmured almost to himself, then bent suddenly, blocking out the dim lamplight as his mouth swooped down to press a soft, light kiss to her trembling mouth. 'More than beautiful,' he extended as he straightened again. 'Dangerous.' Then he said, 'Goodnight, Miss Lacey,' and simply turned and walked away, leaving her standing there staring at his long, loose, easy stride with his jacket thrown over one broad shoulder while that shocking pelt of raven hair rested comfortably along his straight spine.

And she felt strangely at odds with herself—as though she had just let go of something potentially very important to her and had no way of snatching it back.

CHAPTER THREE

IT WAS crazy, she told herself later as she pulled a smooth satin robe over her freshly showered body.

It had been a crazy night with a crazy end that had left her with this crazy sense of deep disappointment that she couldn't seem to shake off.

What's the matter with you? she asked herself impatiently. You should be feeling relieved, not disappointed that he didn't take advantage of a situation most men would have leapt at if they'd found Annie Lacey beholden to them for something!

Or maybe, she then found herself thinking, it was *because* she was the notorious Annie Lacey that he had not taken advantage. Perhaps he was the kind of man who did not involve himself with the Annie Laceys of this world.

Perhaps, for once, your reputation has worked against you.

What?

No.

'That's sick thinking, Annie,' she muttered to herself.

And anyway, you cannot be feeling annoyed about a lost opportunity you had no intention of taking up yourself!

Remember Luis Alvarez, she told herself grimly. Remembering him was enough to put any woman off all those dark Latin types for good!

With that levelling reminder, she tightened her robe's belt around her waist and flounced out of the bedroom, aware that there was more than a little defiance in the way she slammed the door shut on the thoughts she had left on the other side.

Her house was not big, really nothing more than an old-fashioned terraced cottage renovated to modern-day standards. The upper floor housed her one bedroom, which had been carefully fitted to utilise minimum space for maximum storage, and a rather decadent bathroom, with its spa bath and pulse-action shower that could massage the aches out of the worst day's modelling. The stairway dropped directly into her small sitting room-cum-dining room, where the clever use of lighting and pastel shades made it a pleasure to her eye each time she entered.

The kitchen was a super-efficient blend of modern appliances and limed oak. Annie padded across the cool ceramic floor to fill the kettle for a cup of good, strong tea.

The best panacea to cure all ills, she told herself bracingly. Even the ills of a silly woman in conflict with no one but herself!

Crazy. Crazy, crazy, she sighed to herself as she leant against a unit to gaze out on the dark night while she waited for the kettle to boil.

Most of her life had been lived in busy high profile. Her ability to act and her photogenic looks had been picked up on and used from a very early age. While Aunt Claire had been alive she had been buffered from most of the flak that went with a well-known face by a woman who had been fiercely protective of Annie's privacy. But after her aunt had died and with what came afterwards Annie had suddenly found herself the constant cynosure of all eyes.

Which was why she loved her little house so much. She loved the sense of well-being and security that it always filled her with to be shut alone inside it. It was here and only here that she felt able to relax enough to drop her guard and be herself—though, she then thought, she was not really sure she knew who or what that person was, having never really been given the time or chance to find out.

Was it that sombre-faced person she could see staring back at her in the darkened reflection of the kitchen window? she wondered. She hoped not. Those eyes looked just a little too lost and lonely for her peace of mind, and her mouth had a vulnerable tilt to it that unsettled her slightly because she did not consider herself vulnerable to anything much—except contempt, she conceded. Others' contempt of her could still cut and cut deeply.

As could rejection, she added. Or—to be more precise—cold rejection, usually administered by women who felt threatened by her, but sometimes by men. Men of that stranger's calibre. Cool, self-possessed, autocratic men who—

She pulled herself up short, a frown marring the smooth brow she could see in the window. Now why had her mind skipped back to him again? He had not held her in contempt—or if he had he had not shown it. Nor had he rejected her—not in the ice-cold way she'd been musing about just then.

He was a stranger—just a mere, passing stranger who had helped her out of an embarrassing spot then quietly gone on his way, that was all.

The trouble with you, Annie Lacey, she told herself grimly, is that you've become so damned cynical about the opposite sex that you actually expect every one of them to take advantage of you whenever they possibly can!

And could it be that you're feeling just a teeny bit miffed because he did *not* take advantage of the situation?

I wish…

And just what do you wish? that more sensible side of her brain derided. For a nice, ordinary man to come along to sweep you off your dainty feet and take you away from all of this? Two things wrong with that wish, Annie. One—you made this particular bed you are now lying so uncomfortably on. And two—that man was no ordinary man. He was strong, dark and excitingly mysterious.

And you fancied him like hell, she finally admitted. But he obviously did not fancy you!

And that's what you're feeling so miffed about!

She grimaced at that, and was glad that the kettle decided to boil at that moment so that she could switch her thoughts to other things.

She was just pouring tea into her cup when the telephone began to ring.

Todd, she decided. It had to be. He would be ringing up to find out just what had happened to her, and a rueful smile was curving her mouth as she took her cup of tea with her into her sitting room and dropped into the corner of a soft-cushioned sofa before lifting the receiver to her ear.

'What the hell happened to you?' It was Todd, sounding angry and anxious all at the same time, God bless him. 'One minute you were off to the loo, the next I'm being informed that you were seen in a mad, passionate clinch with some guy, then disappearing out of the door with him! Who the hell is he? And what the hell were you doing just walking out on me like that?'

She shifted uncomfortably, taking her time curling her bare toes beneath her while she tried to decide how to answer all of that. There was no way she was going to admit the truth, that was for sure. it was bad enough knowing what a fool she'd been, getting into a taxi with a complete stranger, but telling Todd of all people that not only had she done exactly that but she'd also let the stranger kiss her in front of half of London's best would make him think that she'd gone temporarily insane!

Crazy. The whole thing was crazy.

'Oh, just an old friend from way back,' she heard herself say lightly. 'And we weren't kissing,' she lied. 'We were plotting because some stupid fool had spilled a full glass of champagne down my front, and you don't need much imagination to know what that must have done to my dress.'

'God, yes!' he gasped, obviously not lacking the imagination needed to guess what the skimpy silk would have looked like wet. 'Are you all right? Why didn't you come and get me? Is he still there with you now?'

Annie had to smile at the quick-fired set of questions. 'I'm fine,' she replied. 'I didn't come and get you because quite frankly, darling, I was not in a fit state to go anywhere but straight home. And no, he is not still here.'

'You said an old friend,' he murmured thoughtfully. 'I didn't know you had any male friends but me.'

'Well, there's conceit for you,' she drawled, thinking, He's right, I don't. And she felt suddenly very empty inside.

'Who?' Todd demanded. 'What's his name?'

'No one you know,' she dismissed, realising with a start that she hadn't even bothered to ask his name!

Crazy. You really are going crazy, Annie!

'A male model,' she said, forcing her mind back to Todd's question. 'I met him on that promo I did for Cable last year. Who told you I was kissing him?' she demanded with commendable affront, to throw him off the track.

There was a short pause before his deriding, 'Guess,' came down the line at her.

'Susie,' she sighed. She should have known.

'She took great delight in telling me how she'd seen you lost in a heated clinch with another man before you walked off and left me,' he related grimly. 'Then had the bloody gall to suggest I see her home instead!'

'To which you replied?' she prompted.

'Guess again, darling,' he drawled. 'I'm still here at this wretched mêlée if that gives you a clue.'

Yes, it gave her a big clue, and Annie's heart ached for him.

'If she thought she could walk up to me and start slandering you in one breath then expect me to fall back into her arms in the next then she soon learned otherwise,' he went on tightly. 'She eventually left with that guy from the Rouez Sands Group.'

'And made sure you saw her leave with him, of course.'

'Oh, yes,' he sighed.

'You OK?' she asked him gently.

'No,' he said. 'But I'll live.'

Annie smothered a sigh, wishing that she could ease the pain she knew he was suffering right now. But only Susie could do that, and the foolish woman was too jealous of Annie to see that by blackening Annie to Todd she was only making things worse for herself.

In all fairness Annie didn't completely blame Susie for being suspicious about their relationship. It did look suspicious to anyone looking in on it. But even though she'd urged Todd often enough to tell Susie the truth he'd refused, going all stiff and adamant in a way that told her that Susie's suspicions offended his pride. 'It cuts both ways,' was all he ever said. 'If she can't trust my word that there is nothing intimate between you and me, then why should I trust her with the full truth about us?'

Stalemate, and likely to stay that way while both of them remained so pig-headed about it all.

'Give me a call soon,' he murmured as a conclusion to the conversation, then added as an afterthought, 'But not during the rest of this week, because I'll be in Madrid trying to whip up that extra injection of cash I need to secure *Cliché* Europe's safe launch.'

Annie frowned, having forgotten all about that. Todd had told her about it only this evening—the surprising and worrying fact that he was taking a big risk publishing a new glossy in the present economic climate. 'The trouble is,' he'd explained ruefully, 'I stagnate if I don't and stand to lose everything if I do.'

'What I need,' he murmured thoughtfully now, 'is something really exclusive to front the first issue—something that will guarantee sales and therefore appeal to my backers. I just haven't come up with what that exclusive something is yet.'

'You will,' she stated, with soft confidence in his ability. 'And if all else fails I could always pose nude,' she suggested. 'That'll be a world first and guarantee you a complete sell-out.'

'You'd do it too, wouldn't you?' he murmured curiously, hearing the note of seriousness threading through her lighter tone.

'For you?' she said. 'I would sell my very soul for you, my darling, and that's the truth. But I would much rather not,' she then added. 'So try to come up with something less—sensational for me, will you?' she pleaded.

'I promise,' he laughed. 'Not that the idea of you posing nude does not appeal,' he teased. 'But I think I should be able to come up with something more—subtle. So take care, and be good while I'm away.'

When am I ever anything else? Annie thought as she replaced the receiver and grimaced at the dark sense of dissatisfaction that began niggling at her nerves.

And all because a stranger managed to get beneath that protective skin you wear? she mocked herself.

'Goodness me, Annie,' she muttered aloud, and then thought, You must be feeling starved of affection to have one small incident affect you as much as you're allowing this to do.

Bed, she decided. Bed before you become even more maudlin than you already are!

But she didn't sleep well, her dreams seeming haunted by a tall dark figure who kept insisting on kissing her, his warm mouth constantly closing over her own every time she tried to speak! But, worse than that, she didn't try to fight him but always, always welcomed him—helplessly, eagerly! Then she ended up waking in a breathless state of shock at her own wanton imagination.

It was terrible. She was ashamed of herself! 'Sex-starved, that's what you are,' she muttered, and gave her pillow an angry thump before settling down to experience the self-same dream all over again!

Consequently she was not in a very good frame of mind when her phone began ringing at what felt like the break of dawn that morning.

Grumbling incoherently to herself, she tried to ignore it at first, stuffing her head beneath her pillow and pretending the noise was not there. But it didn't stop, and after a while she sighed, sat up, rubbed at her gritty eyes then reached out with a lazy hand to lift the receiver.

'Annie!' Lissa's excited voice hit her eardrums like the clash from a hundred cymbals. 'Get our neat botty out of that bed! *Cliché*'s got its launch. And we have one hell of a panic on!'

A panic. She would call it more than a panic, Annie decided grumpily as she dragged herself to the transit lounge at Barbados's Grantley Adams airport over twelve hours later.

'But I'm due in Paris on Tuesday!' she'd exclaimed in

protest when Lissa had finished giving her the hurried details of Todd's great coup.

'All changed, darling,' her agent had said. 'Everything cancelled for the next two weeks in favour of this.'

'This' being Todd's brainwave—which had apparently hit him after he had been talking to her on the phone last night.

Or—to be more precise—someone else had hit him with it.

The great and glorious Adamas, no less.

And, even despite not wanting to be, Annie was impressed.

Adamas jewellery was the most expensive anyone could buy. The man who worked under that trade name was a legend because he designed and produced every single breathtakingly exquisite piece himself, using only the finest stones and setting them in precious metal. All the world's richest women clamoured to possess them.

He was a genius in his field. His last collection had taken five years to put together, and had sold out in five minutes. That must have been—Annie frowned, trying to remember—four years ago at least.

And late last night, it seemed, Todd had found himself talking to none other than Adamas himself! He hadn't known, of course, whom he was sharing a nightcap with. Hardly anyone alive on this earth knew who the real Adamas actually was, because the man was some kind of eccentric recluse!

But, according to Lissa, during this chat over a drink Todd's journalistic mind must have been alerted by something Adamas had said, and he'd begun to suspect just whom he was drinking with. So he had gone for it—asked the man outright—and, lo and behold, found out that he was right!

One thing had led to another, and a few drinks later Todd had discovered that the guy had just completed his latest collection. And that had been when his brainstorm had hit. A blind shot, he'd called it. He'd suggested what a coup it would be if *Cliché* launched with Annie Lacey wearing the latest Adamas collection. And to his surprise the great man had agreed!

And that, neatly put, was why Annie had just spent the last twelve hours travelling.

Adamas had agreed, but only on his own strict terms— one being that the whole thing had to take place immediately or not at all, another that he chose the location and— something insisted on because of the priceless value of the subject matter in hand—that the whole thing must be carried out in the utmost secrecy!

Which was also why she was now stuck in transit, waiting to find out what the rest of her travel arrangements were. Lissa had only been privy to Annie's travel plan this far. The rest was to be revealed.

But that would not be before she'd had a chance to change out of the faded jeans and baggy old sweatshirt that had been part of her disguise along with a sixties floppy velvet hat into which she'd had her hair stuffed for the last twelve hours to comply with his demand for secrecy, she decided grimly.

She was hot, she was tired, and she felt grubby. And, grabbing her flight bag, she made her way to the ladies' room, deciding that any further travelling could wait until she felt more comfortable.

Half an hour later, and dressed more appropriately for the Caribbean in a soft white Indian cotton skirt and matching blouse, with her hair scooped into a high topknot, she was being ushered out into the burning sun and across the tarmac towards a twin engined, eight-seater aeroplane which was to take her to Union Island, the gateway to the Grenadines, or so she'd been informed by the attendant who'd come to collect her.

An hour after that she found herself standing in the shimmering heat of her third airport of the day, where a beautiful young woman with perfect brown skin and a gentle smile was trying to usher her towards a waiting helicopter!

'But where am I supposed to be going to?' she demanded irritably, growing tired of all this cloak-and-dagger stuff.

'To one of our beautiful smaller islands, privately leased from our government by your host,' the young woman informed her smoothly, and strode off in the wake of Annie's luggage, which was being carried by an airport lackey.

'Host,' she muttered tetchily. Did anyone know the actual name of the great Adamas? Or did his desire for privacy mean that even his name was a carefully guarded secret?

Her luggage had been stowed by the time she reached the helicopter, its lethal blades already rotating impatiently. She was instructed to duck her head a little as she ran beneath them, then was helped to clamber in beside the pilot.

With a smile and a gesture of farewell the young woman closed the door, and the sudden change from deafening noise to near silence was a shock. Annie straightened in her seat, smoothed down the soft folds of her skirt, blinked a couple of times in an effort to clear her bewildered head, then turned to look at the pilot.

And almost fainted in surprise.

Long black hair, tied back at the tanned nape by a thin black strip of ribbon, lean dark face with green eyes smiling sardonically at her.

It was her rescuer from the night before.

And the man she had let seduce her all night long in her dreams.

'You!' she gasped, feeling an upsurge of guilty heat burn her insides when her eyes automatically dropped to his shockingly familiar mouth.

'Good afternoon, Miss Lacey,' he drawled, enjoying the reaction he was having on her.

'But—what are you doing here?'

'Why, I live here,' he smoothly replied, and touched something that sent a burst of power into the engines. 'Please fasten yourself in; we are about to take off.'

'But…' She couldn't move for the shock of it. 'You're a helicopter pilot?' she choked out eventually.

'Among other things.' He smiled, humour leaping to that magnetically attractive mouth at what, Annie realised almost as soon as she'd said it, was about the most stupid thing she had ever said. 'Your belt,' he prompted. 'We will talk later.'

Then he was flicking the headset he had resting around his neck up over his ears and dismissing her as he turned his attention to the task in hand, leaving her to fumble numbly with her belt while he spoke smoothly to air-traffic control. Then, without warning, they were up in the air.

Annie gasped at the unexpectedness of it, staring with wide eyes as the ground simply dropped away beneath them. Her heart leapt into her mouth, her lungs refused to function, and, of course, the slight numbing effect of jet lag was not helping her discern what the heck was going on here.

They paused, hovering like a hawk about to swoop, then shot forwards in a way that threw her back into her seat. He glanced at her sharply, then away again, a small smile playing about his lips which seemed to err more towards satisfaction than anything else.

Then suddenly she was covering her eyes as they seemed to shoot directly towards the bright orange ball of sun hanging low in the sky.

Something dropped on her lap. Peering down, she saw a pair of gold-rimmed sunglasses and gratefully pushed them on. Able to see again without suffering for it, she turned to look curiously at him.

He too had donned a pair of sunglasses; gold-rimmed like her own pair, they sat neatly across the bridge of his long, thin nose, seeming to add a certain pizzazz to an already rivetingly attractive face.

Last time she'd seen him he had been standing at her front door wearing a severely conventional black dinner suit and bow-tie. He had seemed alarmingly daunting to her fanciful mind then.

Now those same sparks of alarm came back to worry her, darting across her skin, because here in this contraption, with the full blast of the Caribbean sun shining on his face, he had taken on a far more dangerously appealing appearance. His skin looked richer, his features more keenly etched. The thin cream shirt he was wearing was tucked into the pleated waist of a pair of wheat-coloured linen slacks, offering a more casual view of him that made her want to back off even while she was drawn towards it.

'Why are you here?' she asked as her nerves began to steady. 'Or—' she then clarified that '—why am I here with you?'

'You do not know?' He flicked her a glance before returning his attention to what he was doing, but the look had been enough to make her stupid mind click into action, and she sat there staring at him in utter disbelief.

'You—are Adamas?' she gasped.

He didn't answer—didn't need to. It was written in that small smile that touched briefly at the corner of his mouth.

'We are going to my island,' he informed her smoothly instead. 'It sits just beyond the main string of islands, lapped by the Caribbean on one side and the Atlantic on the other…'

Annie was barely listening; she was still staring unblinkingly at him, trying to fit her impression of what the Adamas man should look like to the one he actually was!

An eccentric recluse? This—Adonis of a man with more muscle than fat and an air about him that still made her think more of the Spanish Inquisition than an artistic genius. Blinking, she found herself staring at his hands—long hands, strong hands with the signs of manual labour scored into the supple palms, long fingers, blunt-ended, with neatly shorn nails. The hands of a man who worked fine metal into those intricate designs that she had been privileged to glimpse once around the neck of a very wealthy woman?

'I don't believe it,' she muttered, more to herself than to him.

But he shrugged carelessly, as if her opinion did not bother him. 'I am what I am, Miss Lacey,' he drawled indifferently. Then almost too casually he went on, 'As you are what you undoubtedly are.'

An insult—Annie didn't even try to mistake it for anything but what it was. But before she could challenge him about it again they veered sharply to one side, sending her heart leaping into her mouth again when she found herself staring sideways out of the helicopter onto a half-moon stretch of glistening silver sand.

'My home,' he announced. 'Or one of them,' he then added coolly. 'The island is a quarter of a mile wide and half a mile long. It has a shape like a hooked nose which is where it gets its name—Hook-nose Island. My villa sits in the hook—see?'

Dipping the helicopter, he swooped down towards the

island, bringing the two-storey white plantation-style house swinging dizzyingly up towards them. Then, before she had time to catch her breath at that little bit of showmanship, he levelled the helicopter off and hovered so that she could focus on the palm-tree-lined lawns that swept down from the house to the silver beach she had seen first.

'Hook-nose Bay is a bathers' paradise,' he said. 'The natural curve of the land itself and the coral reef at the bay's mouth protect it from the worst of the weather and any unwelcome aquatic visitors with sharp teeth.'

'Sharks?' she asked nervously.

He nodded. 'These islands are famous for their resident Nurse Sharks. But it is safe to bathe there in the bay— though the rest of the island is not so safe,' he warned. 'Strong currents and sometimes angry seas can make bathing on any of the other little coves you see quite dangerous. Especially on the Atlantic side.'

As he turned them neatly to face in the opposite direction Annie gazed curiously down to where a thick tropical wood clustered around a hump in the centre of the island, at the bottom of which the house nestled against its lushly carpeted slope. On the other side of the hill sheer drops of craggy rock fell abruptly downwards to jagged inlets where the Atlantic tossed itself against them in foaming white crests.

This side of the little island was a stark contrast to the other softer, more gentle side that the house faced. It would be an unlucky sailor who came upon this island from that direction, she noted with a small shudder.

Then she gasped as they began to drop like a stone towards the ground. They landed gently, though, her sigh of relief bringing a mocking look from the man beside her before he turned his attention to shutting down the engine and going through some kind of mental check-list before he opened his door and jumped out.

He came around to help her, having to stoop low beneath the slowing blades and warning her to do the same as his hands circled her slender waist to assist her. Then they were running free, both bent almost double, Annie with a hand covering her eyes to stop the whirls of dust from blowing into them.

Pulling to a halt about ten yards away from the helicopter, he turned to watch as she dusted down her clothes with her hands. They'd landed on a natural plateau of rock not far away from the house. But, sand being sand, it had found its way up here, blown probably by the trade winds that acted like natural air-conditioning to most of these islands.

'Come,' he said when she'd concluded her tidy-up by brushing light fingertips over her hair and cheeks. 'I will bring your luggage later. But now you must be in dire need of a drink.'

She was and didn't demur, following him across a neatly kept lawn and up the few steps which took them into the lower veranda's shade.

The two solid wood front doors stood open in welcome. He led the way into a deliciously cool entrance hall, where Annie paused to catch her breath and study with still slightly bewildered eyes the blatant luxury of Aubusson thrown down on top of richly polished wood.

For a mere hallway it was huge—as big as any other room in a house of this size. 'Grand' was the word that slid into her mind. Old masters with a nautical theme hung in heavy gold frames on plain, white-painted walls and a great staircase swept up from its central location to a galleried landing that seemed to form a circle around the whole upper floor.

A woman appeared from the back of the house. Short,

thin and wiry, with greying hair swept away from a severe
face, she was wearing all black. She greeted her employer
with some words in what Annie half-recognised as Spanish,
to which he replied in the same language, his voice seeming
to grow more liquid, more sensually disturbing to Annie's
agitated mind.

'Margarita,' he informed Annie, watching as the two
women exchanged shy, slightly stiff smiles. 'Between
them, she and her husband Pedro take care of everything
here. If you will please come this way—' he held out an
arm in invitation '—Margarita will bring us some refresh-
ment.'

As the woman bustled off towards the back of the house
Annie followed her host across the hall and into a large,
bright, sunny room with full-length French-style windows
standing open to the gentle sea breeze.

Momentarily diverted, she moved over to look at the
view, and stood transfixed by what she saw. Before her lay
a dramatic mix of lush green lawns rolling down towards
a crescent of silver sand, followed by the pale aquamarine
shades of shallow waters deepening to rich gentian-blue.
Several beautiful flame-trees with their branches laden with
vivid red blooms were scattered around the grounds. The
sun was hanging low—a deep golden globe shimmering in
a melting turquoise sky.

And when she heard movement behind her she turned an
enraptured smile to the man she found propped up against
the closed door, mockery and arrogance in every line of his
body as he stood there with one neat ankle crossed over
the other, arms folded across his big chest.

'Well, well,' he drawled. 'So the notorious Miss Lacey
can still experience a childlike enchantment at something
beautiful and unspoiled. Who would have thought it?'

Annie went still, her smile dying as she was suddenly

assailed by a cold, dark sense of menace, his lazy masculine stance, his insolent expression and his deriding words all helping to remind her of something that she should have never let herself forget. Men were the enemy. And this particular man was no different.

'Who are you?' she demanded quietly.

'Who am I?' he repeated, the mockery hard and spiked. 'Why, I am Adamas,' he informed her lazily. 'Loosely translated, it means diamond-hard—impenetrable. But in this case we shall call me a—rock,' he decided. 'A rock on which you, Annie Lacey, have just been neatly marooned.'

CHAPTER FOUR

'MAROONED.' Annie frowned at him, trying to decide whether he was just attempting a very poor joke. But his face held no hint of humour, only a smile that sent the blood running cold through her veins.

Marooned, she repeated silently and slowly to herself. Abandoned. Isolated without resources. He had used the word quite deliberately.

It hit her then that this was no simple commission in which the great Adamas employed the notorious Annie Lacey to promote his priceless gems. She had been brought here under false pretences—brought here and isolated from the rest of the world by this man for some specific purpose of his own.

A sick sense of *déjà vu* washed over her, filling her eyes with unmistakable horror as Luis Alvarez's hot face loomed up in her mind, and for a moment—a small moment—she lost control, face paling, breasts heaving, eyes haunted as they glanced around for somewhere to run.

'Perfect,' he drawled, making her blink at the soft-voiced sensuality that he managed to thread into the one simple word. 'That look of maidenly panic must have taken hours of practice in front of your mirror to cultivate. Allow that gorgeous mouth to quiver just a little,' he suggested, 'and you will be well on the way to convincing me that the well-seasoned vamp is actually a terrified virgin.'

Margarita used that moment to knock on the door. He moved smoothly, loose-limbed and lazily controlled, to open the door and stand aside while his shyly smiling ser-

52

vant wheeled in a trolley laid out with coffee things and some daintily prepared sandwiches.

Annie watched, unable to so much as move a muscle as the other woman murmured in Spanish to her employer and he answered in deep casual replies. The trolley was wheeled over to stand beside a low table between two big, soft-cushioned sofas of a pale coral-pink. Then Margarita was leaving again, murmuring what must have been her thanks to her employer for holding the door for her.

'Who are you really?' Annie demanded once they were alone. 'And will you kindly explain what this—stupid charade is all about?'

'I am who I said I am,' he replied with infuriating blandness. 'I am Adamas. I told you no lies, Miss Lacey.' Moving gracefully, he went over to the trolley then turned a questioning look at her. 'Tea—coffee?' he asked. 'Margarita has prepared both.'

Impatiently Annie shook her head. She wanted nothing in this house until she got some answers. Nothing. 'Is that supposed to make sense to me?' she snapped out impatiently.

'No,' he conceded. 'But then—I never meant to.' A brief smile touched his mouth before he turned his attention to pouring himself a cup of dark, rich coffee. The aroma drifted across the room to torment Annie's parched mouth, forcing her to swallow drily, but other than that she ignored the temptation to change her mind. 'Won't you at least sit down?' he offered politely.

Again she shook her head—for the same reason. 'I just want you to tell me what is going on,' she insisted.

He studied her for a moment, those strange green eyes glinting thoughtfully at her from between glossy black lashes, as if he was considering forcing her to sit and drink. Whatever, the look had the effect of pushing up her chin, her blue eyes challenging him just to try it and see what he got!

Though what he would get if he did decide to force her physically, she wasn't sure. She was tall, but this man seemed to fill the whole room with his threatening presence. And she couldn't help quailing deep down inside because she knew that if he did call her bluff she would have no choice but to do exactly what he wanted her to do.

And it is that, Annie, she told herself grimly, which keeps you standing as far away from him as you can get! He reminds you of Luis Alvarez—the same height, the same colouring, the same arrogance that made men like them believe that they could say, be and do anything they liked! And if he was Adamas then he also possessed the same money and power in society to have anything nasty about himself that he would not wish the world to hear covered up.

Like the abduction of unwilling females.

She shuddered, unable to control herself. She should have known from the moment she laid eyes on him last night—had known! Her well-tuned instincts had sent out warning signals straight away! But she had let his easy manner lull her into a false sense of security. And, dammit, she'd liked him! Actually allowed herself to like him for the way he had behaved!

She had never been able to say that for Luis, she remembered bitterly. Luis Alvarez had turned her stomach from the moment she'd found herself alone with him. But then, Luis Alvarez had been at least ten years older than this man, his good looks spoiled by ten years' more cynicism and dissolution.

This man did not turn her stomach in that same way, she realised worriedly. And maybe that was one of the reasons why he frightened her perhaps more than Alvarez had ever done. He frightened her because she was reluctantly attracted to him. His calculating study of her frightened her. His softly spoken words that held so many hidden messages frightened her. But, above all, the actual air she was breathing was frightening her—simply because it was filled with the appealing scent of him.

Did he know it? she wondered anxiously. Could he tell what kind of effect he was having on her? His eyes were burning over her—burning in a way that told her that, whatever else was going on here, he too liked what he saw.

The air thickened, became impossible to breathe as the silence between them grew hot and heavy. Then, without warning, he looked down and away.

It was like having something vital taken from her, and Annie had to measure carefully the air she dragged into her suddenly gasping lungs in case she should hyperventilate.

'OK,' he conceded coolly. 'We talk.'

He brought those green eyes to hers again, and there was something overwhelmingly proud in the way his chin lifted along with the eyes.

'My name,' he announced, 'is César DeSanquez. Adamas is merely a name under which I trade…'

DeSanquez, DeSanquez, Annie was thinking frowningly. The name rang a rather cold bell inside her head. It was a name that evoked an image of great wealth and power—an image wrapped in oil and gold and diamonds and—

'I am American-Venezuelan by birth, but my roots are firmly planted in my Venezuelan links.'

And it hit. It hit with a sickening sense of understanding that made her sway where she stood.

'Ah,' he murmured. 'I see you are beginning to catch on. Yes, Miss Lacey,' he softly confirmed, 'Cristina Alvarez is my sister. And you made the quick connection, I must assume, because your—affair with my brother-in-law took place in the DeSanquez apartment. The media made quite a meal out of these—juicy facts, did they not? In fact, their attention to detail was quite remarkably concise—the way they told of Annie Lacey lying with her lover in one bed while her lover's wife lay asleep in another bedroom of her brother's apartment. My apartment, Miss Lacey,' he enunciated thinly. 'My bed!'

Annie sank tremulously into a nearby chair, his anger, his contempt and his disgust breaking over her in cold, sickening waves while she fought with her own sense of anger and disgust—disgust for a single night in her life that would always, it seemed, come back to haunt her for as long as she lived.

She had gone to that apartment by invitation, to a party being held by a man called DeSanquez—a wealthy young Venezuelan who had expressed a desire to meet the sweet Angel Lacey, as everyone had called her then. She never had actually met the Venezuelan, she remembered now in surprise, because she hadn't given him a thought after meeting Alvarez instead.

Alvarez. She shuddered.

'Quite,' he observed. 'I acknowledge your horror. It was a revolting time for all of us. Not least my sister,' he pointed out. 'Having to walk into my bedroom and find you in my bed, not with me—it would not have mattered if it had been me,' he drawled. 'But to find you with her own husband was a terrible shock. It effectively ruined her marriage and ultimately almost ruined her life.

'For this alone,' he explained with a hateful coolness, 'I feel perfectly justified in demanding retribution from you—and indeed would have done so at the time this all happened if my sister had not begged me to let it be. So, for Cristina's sake, and for Cristina's alone,' he made absolutely clear, 'I went against my personal desire to strangle the unscrupulous life out of you right there and then. But— that is not the end of it.'

Turning, he moved to place his coffee-cup on the top of the white marble fireplace then rested his arm alongside it. Every move he made, every unconscious gesture was so incredibly graceful that even in the middle of all of this Annie found herself drawn by him.

'I mentioned my dual nationality for a good reason,' he continued, his tone—as it had been throughout—utterly devoid of emotion. 'For although my father was Venezuelan my mother was, in actual fact, American. Now,' he asserted, as though relaying a mildly interesting piece of history, 'her name before she married my father was Frazer— Ah, I see you are quick. Yes.' He smiled thinly as Annie licked her suddenly dry lips. 'Susie is my cousin. Quite a coincidence, is it not, that you should happen to be the woman trying to ruin her life just as carelessly as you ruined my sister Cristina's?'

Annie closed her eyes, shutting out the crucifying blandness of his expression as he watched her. She had been wrong before when she'd believed him to be of the same ilk as Luis. He was in actual fact very different, if only because Luis had cared only for his own rotten neck while this man seemed to hold himself personally responsible for the necks of others.

Which in turn made him very dangerous because, in deciding to make himself an avenger, it was obvious that he was quite prepared to endanger his own neck to get retribution for those he loved. Blindly loved, she added heavily to herself. And she suddenly felt very, very sorry for him.

To each his Achilles heel, she mused starkly, opening her eyes to show him a perfectly cool expression. Luis Alvarez's Achilles heel had been his inflated ego, and the arrogant belief that power and money could buy for his bed any woman he'd desired. Cristina's had been her blindness to what her husband actually was. And Susie's was her need to have everything her selfish heart desired.

This man's was his fierce love for his family.

She then found herself wondering what her own Achilles heel was. She didn't know, but she had a horrible feeling that in this man's hands she was going to find out.

'You have nothing to say?' Her calmness was irritating him; she could see the annoyance begin to glint in his strange green eyes.

Green. 'No,' she answered. 'Not a single thing.' And another realisation hit her squarely in the face. Susie had green eyes—the same green eyes. Which seemed to tie the whole situation off neatly for her. She didn't have a cat-in-hell's chance of making this man with those eyes see anything from her point of view, so she wasn't even going to try. 'Perhaps you would, therefore, like to continue?' she invited, knowing with certainty that he had not offered her all of this information just for the fun of it.

His sudden burst of angry movement at her seeming indifference took her by surprise, because he had been so purposefully controlled up until then. His hand flicked down from the mantel, his body straightening tautly. 'Has nothing I have said managed to reach you?' he demanded harshly.

'It would seem not,' she said. 'All I've heard until now is a potted description of your family tree. Very interesting, I'm sure,' she drawled, 'but nothing for me to get fired up about.'

He didn't like it. He didn't like the fact that she could maintain a cool façade and even go as far as mocking him.

It served him right, she thought, for his arrogant supposition that he had a right to speak to her like this! If he had taken the trouble to find out about her—really find out instead of restricting his knowledge to pure tabloid gossip and the malicious judgement of his thankless family—then he would have discovered that few people managed to rile Annie Lacey with mere words. Out of sheer necessity she had grown a thick skin around herself to protect her from the cruel thrust of words, and it would take a better man than he to pierce that protective skin.

'When they say you possess none of the finer senses they are right, aren't they?' he muttered. 'Do you feel no hint of compassion for others at all?'

'It would seem not,' she said again, fielding his contempt with blue eyes that gave away nothing of what she was thinking or feeling inside. Then sheer devilment made her cock a golden eyebrow at him. 'Is there any in you?' she challenged right back.

'For you, you mean?' He shook his sleek dark head. 'No, Miss Lacey, I am sorry to inform you that I harbour not an ounce of compassion for you.'

'Then you have no right to expect more from me than you are willing to give yourself,' she said, and got up, her slender body no less sensuous in movement because it was stiff with control. He couldn't know, of course, that she had been through this kind of character-slaying before, and at far more lethal hands than his, or he would not be trying this tactic out on her.

'Where do you think you are going?' he demanded as she walked towards the door.

'Why, to the one place you obviously expect me to go,' she replied. 'To the devil. But by my route, Mr DeSanquez, I will do it by my own route.'

He moved like lightning, had to to reach the door even before she had a chance to turn the handle. His hand, big and slightly callused, closed around her own. Even with the light clasp he exerted, the hand managed to intimidate her.

'And how do you mean to get there?' he enquired silkily. 'Fly on your broomstick as witches do? Or are you more the snake, Miss Lacey, prepared to slither your way across the ocean to your devil's lair?'

'Funny,' she jeered, having to force herself to retaliate through the stifling breathlessness that she was suddenly experiencing at his closeness. 'But I thought this was the devil's lair?'

'I am merely his servant, Angelica,' he stated grimly. 'Merely his servant.'

There was nothing 'mere' about this man. He was larger than life itself—in size, in presence, in the sheer, physical threat of the man.

'I want to leave here,' she informed him coldly.

'But I've not finished with you yet.' The taunting words were murmured against her cheek, dampening her skin with his warm spicy breath.

'But I have finished with you!' she snapped, turning to anger to cover up the hectic effect his closeness was having on her. 'I demand that you fly me back to Union Island!' She tried to prise his fingers from her other hand. 'Now— before this silly game gets out of hand!'

He responded by snaking a hard arm around her waist and lifting her off the ground. Ignoring the way she twisted and struggled and kicked out with feet made ineffectual by the way he was carrying her, he walked over to the sofa and dropped her unceremoniously into the soft coral-coloured cushions, then came to lean threateningly over her.

'Now listen to me,' he commanded. 'And listen well, for this is no game. I mean business, Miss Lacey—serious business. You are here on my island for one purpose only, and that is to put you right out of circulation. From now on I am going to ensure personally that you form no danger to anyone in my family again!'

He was talking about Susie now, of course, Annie realised. 'And how do you intend to do that?' she asked, blue eyes flashing a scornful challenge at green, absolutely refusing to let him see how very frightened she was. 'By ruining my good reputation when everyone knows I don't have one? Or do you have murder in mind, Mr DeSanquez?' she taunted dangerously.

His anger flared at her refusal to take him seriously, his bared teeth flashing bright white in a cruel dark face as he reached for her again. 'Murder is too easy an escape for you, you little she-devil,' he muttered. 'Perhaps this will teach you to have a healthy fear of me!'

She didn't expect it, which was why he caught her so totally off guard when his hard fingers curled tightly on her shoulders and he brought her wrenchingly upwards to meet the punishing force of his mouth.

It lasted only seconds, but it was long enough for her to feel again the hectic sensation of her whole body burning up, as though something totally alien had invaded her.

She didn't move, did not so much as breathe or blink an eyelash in response, yet, as she had been the evening before, she was suddenly and excruciatingly aware of him—aware of his strength, of the power behind the muscles that strained angrily against her, of the subtle, pleasing scent of him, the smooth texture of his tight, tanned skin.

Her mouth was burning, her soft lips throbbing where he pressed them bruisingly back against her tightly clenched teeth. And her breasts—the damning traitors that they were—were responding to the heated pressure of his hard chest, the sensitive tips hardening into tight, tingling sensors of pleasure as they pushed eagerly towards him.

He muttered something in his throat and whipped a hand

around the back of her neck so that he could arch her backwards, the other hand coming up between them to let a
throbbing nipple push against his palm.

Annie gasped at the shocking insolence of the action,
trying to pull away from him. But her gasp gave him entry
into her mouth, and the next thing she knew she was being
flung into a heady vortex of hot, moist intimacy.

Never—never since Alvarez—had she let a man kiss her
like this. The very idea of it had always appalled her. But
with this man it was the most achingly sensual experience
of her life!

And that appalled her. It appalled her to know that she
could be so receptive to a man who held her in such open
contempt! And when he eventually lifted his head it was
an act of sheer self-preservation that made her stare up at
him with apparent indifference to the attack when in actual
fact she was slowly and systematically collapsing inside.

'Well, well, well,' she heard herself murmur with an inner horror at her own gall. 'So you too are prepared to use
sex to get what you want. And there I was, thinking you
way above that kind of thing. How very disappointing.'

He stiffened violently at the taunt, then smiled ruefully
when her meaning sank in. 'Ah,' he drawled. 'You are
implying that we are similar creatures. But that is not the
case,' he denied. 'You see, I do not sleep around—especially with promiscuous bitches who run a high risk of contamination.'

That cut—cut hard and deep. Not that she let him see it,
her bruised and trembling mouth taking on a deriding twist
as she taunted softly right back, 'Then I think you should
tell your body that, because it seems to me that it's quite
fancying a bit of contamination right now.' And she let her
eyes drop to where the evidence of his own response to the
kiss thrust powerfully against Annie's groin.

He dumped her so suddenly that she flailed back into the soft cushions behind her, but she barely noticed because her gaze was fixed incredulously on his hard, angry face.

He'd flushed—he'd actually flushed! She had absolutely thrown him by daring to point out his own sexual response, and elation at managing to get to him made her eyes flash with triumph.

Spinning away from her, he went to pour himself a drink—not coffee this time, but something stronger from a crystal decanter standing on a beautiful mahogany sideboard by the fireplace.

Annie got to her feet, studying him with more curiosity than fear now as that small revelation helped her to diminish the godlike proportions she had been allowing herself to see in him.

How old was he? she found herself wondering curiously. Thirty-one—thirty-two? Not much older, she was certain, though her original impression last night—had it only been last night?—had been of a much older, more mature man.

'Don't you think it's time you told me exactly what it is you do want from me?' she suggested when the silence began to drag between them.

He turned with glass in hand. 'What I want from you is quite simple,' he said, having got his temper back under control, she noted. 'I want you taken right out of Hanson's life, and I intend personally to make sure it happens.'

Todd? She stared at him, amazed that she could have forgotten all about Todd! Even when he'd brought Susie into this Annie had only connected the other girl with their modelling war. Susie's connection with Todd had not even entered her head!

Stupid! she berated herself. How damned stupid can you get? Of course this was all about Todd and Susie, and not just Susie and the *Cliché* contract!

It was like being on a see-saw, she likened heavily. One minute feeling the uplift of her own confidence returning before she crashed down again so abruptly that she was starting to feel dizzy.

'How long have you known Hanson?' he asked her suddenly.

Almost all my life, Annie thought, with a smile that seemed to soften the whole structure of her face. Then she shrugged, slender shoulders shifting inside the white cotton top. 'None of your business,' she said.

He grimaced, as if acknowledging her right to be uncooperative. Yet he tried again—on a slightly different tack. 'But you have been lovers on an off for—what—four years, is it now?'

'No comment.'

He took a sip at his drink, green eyes thoughtful as they ran slowly over her. Annie fixed him with a bland stare; she was determined to give him no help whatsoever.

'You are very beautiful,' he remarked, making her eyelashes flicker in memory of the way he had said that to her the night before. 'Incredibly so for someone who has led such a chequered life. It is no wonder my brother-in-law lost his head over you.'

'Something you are determined not to do,' she reminded him, smiling although the fact that just thinking of Luis Alvarez was enough to turn her stomach.

'And Hanson,' he continued, as if she had not spoken. 'He cannot seem to help himself where you are concerned.'

'Is this conversation supposed to be leading somewhere?' she asked. 'Only, if it is, would you kindly get to the point so I can get out of here? I am tired and would like to get off this island so I can book into a hotel somewhere and get some sleep tonight.'

'Oh, you will get your sleep, Miss Lacey,' he assured

her smoothly. 'Plenty of it—in the bed already waiting for you upstairs. You see...' He paused—entirely for effect, Annie suspected. 'As from tonight you became my mistress, and therefore will sleep wherever I sleep.'

'*What*—?' Annie began to laugh. She couldn't help it; the whole thing was getting so ridiculous that she was truly beginning to believe that she must be stuck in some real-as-life nightmare—one of those where nothing made any sense!

'Oh, not in the physical sense of the word,' he inserted coolly into her laughter, 'since we have already established that I have no wish to go where too many men have been before me.'

'Have we?' Her blue eyes mocked him. He lifted his chin and ignored the silent taunt.

'It is, therefore, simple logic to assume that I mean to create the illusion of intimacy—solely for the minds of others.'

'And I'm supposed to meekly go along with all of this, am I?' she murmured with rueful scorn.

Funnily enough, instead of getting angry with her again, he grimaced. 'No,' he conceded. 'Not meekly, I do acknowledge. But I fail to see what you can do about it since this is my island, and the only form of transport off it is in my helicopter. And,' he continued while Annie grimly took all of that in, 'considering I hold the very success of Hanson's launch into Europe in the palm of my hand, I think I can—persuade you to do exactly what I want you to do. If only for Hanson's sake,' he added carefully.

Annie's spine straightened slowly, her attention well and truly fixed now. 'What is that supposed to mean?' she demanded.

'Exactly what it said.' He rid himself of his glass then shoved his hands into the pockets of his lightweight trousers. The action drew her eyes unwillingly downwards to that place where the evidence of his arousal had been so obviously on show.

Not so now. The man was back in control of his body, his stance supremely relaxed. 'As I suppose you must already know, Hanson has overstretched his resources going into Europe,' he went on smoothly. 'He is in dire need of a world exclusive to get his new magazine off the ground. Convincing me to let him publish my new collection is undoubtedly that world exclusive. Using your body to display that collection means he cannot fail. And indeed,' he went on while Annie stood taking it all in, 'I have no wish for him to fail. It would not suit my cousin, you see, for the man she loves to be a failure,' he pointed out. 'But,' he then warned chillingly, 'I am prepared to have him fail if you are not prepared to do exactly what I say.'

The bottom line, Annie recognised as he fell into a meaningful silence. They had just reached the bottom line—as far as any protest from her went anyway. Because from the moment he said he was able to hurt Todd she had been beaten. She would do anything for Todd. Lay down her life for Todd.

Prostitute herself for Todd.

'Tell me exactly what you want me to do,' she said huskily, and at last gave him his victory over her spirit by letting her shoulders wilt in defeat.

Oddly, rather than pleasing him it seemed to have the opposite effect, tightening his mouth and putting an impatient glint into his strange green eyes.

'Look,' he exhaled irritably, 'why don't you avail yourself of some of that coffee? You are obviously jet lagged and no doubt dehydrated. Please…' He waved a hand towards the trolley, but when she still just stood there, looking like a slowly wilting flower, another sigh rasped from him and he came to grasp her arm, guiding her to one of the chairs and pushing her roughly into it.

Annie glanced at the hand on her arm, long-fingered and beautifully sculptured, then at his face, darkly intense and intimidatingly grim, and shivered, realising just how accurate her first impression of this man had been. Danger, her instincts had warned her. Danger—hard with resolve.

Dangerous on several levels, she acknowledged as her senses quivered beneath his touch. Then, as she let her tense body relax into the chair, she was filled with a sudden aching kind of sadness. For the first time in her adult life she had come upon a man whom she did not feel an instant physical revulsion for, and he wanted only to do her harm.

Lifting her hand, she began rubbing at her brow with weary fingers. Her head was beginning to ache, the long hours of travelling only to be faced with all of...this beginning to take their toll.

A minute later a cup of strong coffee was placed into her hand, then he stood over her, with those piercing eyes probing her pale face while she sipped at the strong, sweet drink.

'Please explain the rest,' she requested, once the drink had managed to warm a small part of her numbed body.

He looked ready to refuse, an oddly ferocious look tightening his lean face. Then, on a short sigh, he turned away. 'Hanson will get his exclusive for his magazine,' he assured her. 'Only—' he turned back to face her '—it won't be you wearing the Adamas collection, it will be Susie—after Hanson has begged me to allow her to take your place, of course, when you don't turn up in time for his deadline because you have disappeared with your lover.'

'You, I suppose.' Her smile was twisted with contempt.

'Of course.' He gave an arrogant half-nod of his dark head. 'It has to be convincing, after all. The man may have overstretched his resources in this economic climate, but he is no fool. He knows you well enough to suspect anything less than your assurance that the love of a very rich man has brought this decision on you.'

He paused, waiting for her to put up a protest or at least show some horrified response to his demands. But when she revealed nothing—nothing whatsoever—his frown came back, the first hint of puzzlement showing on his rock-solid, certain face.

'You understand what I am demanding of you?' he questioned. 'I am demanding that you cut yourself completely free of Hanson—both professionally and personally. No contact,' he made clear. 'Nothing. He loves my cousin, but he suffers an incurable lust for you. You cannot be allowed to go on ruining lives simply because that body of yours drives men insane!'

And whose fault is that? she wondered cynically. Mine for projecting exactly what they want to see? Or theirs for being such pathetic slaves to their wretched libidos?

She glanced at him from beneath her lashes, wondering curiously if this man had ever been a slave to his libido. And decided not. He was Adamas—the rock, the invincible one! And just too damned proud to let himself become a slave to anything—except his family, maybe.

And there, she realised suddenly, was his weakness! Hers was Todd and always would be Todd. His was his pride and abiding love for his family.

'You know…' she murmured thoughtfully, a small seed of an idea beginning to develop in her mind. If it worked— if she could swing it—there was a small chance that she could get herself out of this relatively unscathed. 'You've forgotten one rather obvious thing in all your careful planning,' she said. 'If, by your reckoning, I've had Todd at my beck and call for the last four years, despite the countless other men he knows have been falling in and out of my bed—then he isn't going to give up on me just because you've come along.'

That deep sense of personal pride took the shape of haughty arrogance on his face. 'He will if I insist upon it,' he said.

'Enough to make him turn to Susie for comfort?' she charged. 'Enough to make him thrust me from his mind? I'm sorry—' ruefully she shook her head '—but it won't happen. Todd loves me, you see,' she stated with a soft and sincere certainty. 'Loves me from the heart not the body. Or why else do you think he keeps coming back to me no matter what goes on in my life?

'Ask Susie if you don't believe me,' she prompted when deriding scepticism that anyone could love a promiscuous bitch like her turned his attractive mouth ugly. 'Ask her why all her other attempts to make Todd dismiss me from his life have failed. And ask yourself why a beautiful, desirable woman like Susie cannot win her man on her terms without having to bring you in to do it for her.

'Ask her—' she gently thrust her strongest point home '—if she's ever asked Todd why he refuses to give me up, and if she's honest, Mr DeSanquez, she'll tell you that she *has* asked him, and Todd had told her, quite clearly, that he loves me and will always love me until the day he dies—no matter what I do.'

Silence. She had him wondering, and Annie had to stifle the urge to smile in triumph. The way his sleek black brows were pulling downwards over the bridge of his long, thin nose told her that she had forced him to consider what she'd said.

'You could keep me here for six months—a year! but when I eventually went back Todd would be waiting for me with open arms. Is Susie prepared to live with that?'

she challenged. 'Knowing that, no matter how deeply she manages to inveigle Todd into her clutches, I will always be there like the shadowed wings of a hawk in their lives, waiting to swoop down and steal him right away from her?'

This felt good—really good! Annie thought with relish as he spun restlessly away. He poured another drink, swallowed it down in one go then turned, forcing her to smooth the pleased glow out of her eyes as he glanced sharply back at her.

'You really are the shrewd, calculating bitch my family label you, are you not?' he said grimly.

'I am what I am.' She shrugged, throwing his own words of earlier right back at him.

'And what made you what you are, I wonder?' he mused angrily.

'Oh, that's easy,' she said. 'There's a final ingredient in all of this which should clear that up.' She looked him straight in the eye. 'You see, I love Todd in exactly the same way that he loves me. Only, we are not allowed to show it because of Todd's mother. You do know who Todd's mother is, don't you?' she questioned tauntingly.

'She is Lady Sarah Hanson,' she provided the answer whether he knew it or not. 'A woman with pure blue aristocratic blood running through her veins. She would die rather than see her son align himself with a woman with my reputation.' Her soft mouth twisted on that little truism.

'Lady Sarah also suffers from a chronic heart condition,' she went on. Most of this was the absolute truth—most of it. 'Todd is strong—tough—but draws the line at killing his own mother.' She gave a helpless shrug. 'Your Susie doesn't stand a chance against a love like ours, Mr DeSanquez,' she concluded, 'and you would be doing her a bigger service by telling her that, rather than trying to blackmail me.'

At that she got up, mentally crossing her fingers that she'd managed to swing it. He was certainly not as confident as he had been, nor—oddly—as contemptuous of her as he studied her thoughtfully.

'No.' He shook his dark head and her heart sank. 'You are wrong. I have seen the way he looks at my cousin, and no matter what you believe about his feelings for you Hanson gazes at her like a man angrily frustrated in love. Whatever hold you may have on him, and I do not deny it is there,' he conceded, 'I think it is time—perhaps more than time—that both you and Hanson learned to forget each other.

'I saw the way you were with him the other night, watched the seductive way you utterly bewitched him, seducing him with your promising smiles and the sensual brush of your exquisite body.' Contemptuously his gaze raked over her. 'Susie has a chance with him with you out of the way,' he concluded. 'She stands none while you are around.'

'So what is your plan?' she scoffed at him deridingly, her mind tumbling over itself in an effort to find the hidden key that would stop all of this. 'To keep me here tonight and tomorrow night and the next and the next in the hopes that it will blacken me in his eyes? Didn't you hear a word I said?' she sighed. 'Todd doesn't care what I do or who I do it with! He will forgive me for you and he will forgive me for breaking my contract with *Cliché*!'

'Then you have a rather big problem on your hands, Miss Lacey,' he countered grimly. 'Because if you do not find a way of convincing him that you care nothing for him any more then I withdraw my support for his magazine. So now what do you suggest that we do?'

Catch twenty-two. Annie felt her heart sink in her breast.

CHAPTER FIVE

'I SEE I have managed to silence that quick little tongue of yours,' he taunted when the silence stretched out between them. 'But I would appreciate a suggestion as to how we overcome the stalemate we seem to have created.'

'I don't have one,' Annie admitted dully, eyes lowered so that he wouldn't see the frustration glittering there.

'I see,' he said silkily. 'Then it seems to be up to me to find it for you. That is, of course,' he then prompted, 'if you are prepared to do anything to save Hanson from ruin?'

'Yes,' she whispered, with a numbness that encompassed her whole being.

'I beg your pardon?' he drawled aggravatingly, coming to lean over her, bracing his hands on the arms of her chair. 'Was that a yes? I did not quite catch the word.'

'Yes—it was a yes!' she flared, her fingers clenching into tight fists of frustration on her lap. 'I'll do anything to save Todd from ruin!' Then, on a sudden flood of tears that blurred her beautiful eyes, she choked, 'Anything, damn you—anything!'

It was odd, but the tears seemed to throw him. His eyes widened, shocked surprise showing on his lean face before he suddenly jerked away from her as if those tears held poison in them and he was afraid of dying if they so much as touched his skin.

But anyone who knew Annie well would also have known that when tears flowed from her eyes so did her temper burn up to counteract them, and she jumped from her seat, those same tears glistening with a wretched, bitter anger.

'So what do you want me to do?' she demanded shrilly. 'Strip naked in public in the hopes I'll make him despise me? Or simply cut my own throat and put a quick end to all poor Susie's problems? Or maybe,' she went on while he just seemed to stand there struck by her sudden explosion, 'you would like me to strip naked in public *and* cut my own throat? That should do it!' she concluded thickly. 'Put a neat if messy end to the whole bloody lot!'

'Swearing doesn't help,' he said, as if that one expletive was the only part of what she'd thrown at him that had actually meant anything at all.

'Hah!' she choked, her temper almost shooting right out of the top of her head, then disappearing suddenly when she began to see the black humour of the situation. Here she was, offering to top herself for that cat Susie's sake! She couldn't believe that she could be sunk so low!

'I do not think we need take such drastic action—on either point,' he added calmly.

Or was it calmly? Annie focused her eyes on him at last, wary of the expression on his face that was neither gleeful nor, as she would have expected, contemptuous, but strangely—

No. She spun her back on him, arms wrapping tightly around her body in an age-old gesture of self-defence. She refused so much as to put a word to what her senses had told her that new look in his eyes meant!

'Then what the hell *do* you want me to do?' she muttered thickly.

There was a silence behind her that made the fine nerves lying along her spine prickle. She closed her eyes tightly, refusing—refusing to listen to what her senses were screaming at her. It was impossible. No man could find it arousing to have a woman swap insults with him! No woman could find it arousing to spar with a man like him!

Yet—

Oh, God, if he touched her now... And she could feel him fighting the urge to do just that, feel it with every instinct she possessed buzzing in warning that he was—

'You must convince Hanson that I mean more to you than he does.' The words came from a throat roughened by the battle he had just fought with himself and won. 'You must make him believe that I am the man who has managed to take his place in your heart!'

Annie had to swallow to clear the tension from her throat. 'And how am I supposed to do that?' she asked, without turning to face him. She didn't dare.

Didn't dare.

Another loaded pause shifted the tension upwards another notch. Then he said quietly, 'In two weeks Hanson will arrive here at my invitation. You will first convince him that you and I have become—passionate lovers, then I will hand him an envelope which will supposedly contain the photographs he desires so much. But before he has a chance to open it you will take it from him and rip it in two.'

'*What*?' That made her turn, her blue eyes dark with confusion as she levelled them at him. 'But what is that going to prove?' she gasped.

'It will prove that your love for me means more to you than your love for him, because you are prepared to ruin him rather than lose me. You see,' he went on, turning slightly to pick up his glass, 'I will have issued you with a decision to make. You can save him and lose me, or ruin him and have me. You will, of course, choose me.'

'But—I thought the whole point of all of this was *not* to ruin Todd?' she choked, utterly bewildered now.

'No—no,' he denied. 'The whole point of all of this is to pay you back for the ruin you have wrought in others' lives and to get you out of Hanson's life,' he corrected. 'And your taking away his best chance at success at the eleventh hour should alienate you completely,' he decreed with grim satisfaction.

'But will also lose you my agreement to co-operate,' she said. 'Or have you forgotten that I'm only doing this for Todd's sake?'

'No.' He shook his dark head. 'I have not forgotten. But you seem to have forgotten my cousin Susie waiting in the wings to step neatly into your shoes. Co-operate, and she will convince me to let her take your place. Susie will wear the Adamas collection for *Cliché*'s European launch, save Hanson from ruin and receive his undying gratitude in the interim. Refuse to co-operate,' he added smoothly, 'and I will simply keep you here out of harm's way until the very last moment—then pull out of the deal—' he gave an idle shrug '—leaving him with nothing—nothing to fall back on. You understand?'

Understand? Oh, yes, she understood, Annie thought bitterly. Susie gets everything at Annie Lacey's expense.

'My God!' she breathed. 'You're worse than Svengali, aren't you? And what happens to me once this little charade is all over?' she asked. 'Am I supposed to keep my mouth shut about the way you and Susie plotted this whole thing against me? Because I won't, Mr DeSanquez,' she warned him angrily. 'And by then *Cliché* will be launched and you won't be able to hurt Todd!'

His answering sigh was harsh and driven. 'Why can you not possess enough simple decency to see without the threats that it is time you let go of Hanson—for his sake if not your own?'

'You talk to me about decency,' she countered

scathingly. 'Where is yours while you stand here threatening me like this?'

'You need teaching a lesson,' he muttered, but she knew that her words had got through to him because he dropped his gaze from hers.

'Not in Susie Frazer's name, I don't,' she denied. 'And you're wrong to do this to me and wrong to do this to Todd simply on the evidence of that silly, deranged woman!'

Wrong thing to say, Annie realised as anger flared into his vivid green eyes and he took a threatening step towards her. 'You will take that back!' he insisted, thrusting his dark face close to her own.

For once he looked and sounded completely foreign— hard and dark and frighteningly alien, his anger so palpable that she could almost taste it. Annie quailed inside but refused to show it, her blue eyes clinging defiantly to his.

'I will take nothing back!' she spat at him. 'In your arrogant self-righteousness you like to believe that I've sinned against your rotten family when in reality it is they who've sinned against me!'

'Sin?' he repeated. 'You are sin, Annie Lacey. With your siren's body and your lush, lying mouth.'

'The lies are all yours, Adamas,' she threw back. 'And what do you think it will do to Susie's chances when Todd finds out what a lie this whole thing actually is?'

'And you intend to tell him so?' he demanded.

Annie stood firm in her defiance. 'What do you expect me to do once this is all over?' she snapped. 'Crawl into some dark corner and pretend I no longer exist? I have a life waiting for me out there, Mr DeSanquez. You can put it on hold for a few short weeks but not for ever! And, my God, I vow that the first thing I'll do with that life is save Todd from Susie's calculating clutches if it becomes the very last thing I am able to do!'

His anger shot up another notch, sent there, she suspected, by sheer frustration with her for defying him like this. 'By telling Hanson the truth?' He was demanding confirmation.

'About your lies? Yes!' she declared.

His hand whipped out, curling threateningly around the back of her neck. 'Then we will have to make the lies the truth,' he gritted, moving close so that his body pressed along the full length of hers. His breath was warm against her face, his green eyes glowing with a new and terrifyingly readable light. 'I shall bed you if I have to, Angelica Lacey,' he told her huskily. 'I will take your beautiful body and drown in its sinful lusts every night for the next two weeks if you continue to insist on telling the truth.'

'No,' she protested, trying to move away from him. The heat from his body was having a strange effect on her own, burning it, bringing it to life, disturbing all those delicate senses she had always so thoroughly locked away.

'Why not?' he whispered. 'Why not make the charade the truth? Two weeks is a long time for a woman like you to go without a man. And I find I am man enough to be— receptive to your charms. Why not?' he repeated, almost as though he was trying to convince himself rather than her. His mouth lowered to brush a tantalising caress along her cheek. 'I can feel you trembling,' he murmured. 'I can feel your breasts throbbing against my chest, smell the sweet scent of desire on your skin. You want me, Angelica.'

'No—'

'Yes,' he insisted. 'As much as I admit to wanting you.'

'No—' she denied again, trying to pull free because he was conjuring up all kinds of sensations that were totally, frighteningly foreign to her.

'You want proof?' Reaching down, he took hold of her

tightly clenched hands and grimly prised the fingers apart before forcing by sheer superior strength her tense palm to press against the hardening muscle between his thighs. 'Proof,' he muttered, and captured her shaken gasp with his hungry mouth.

For a few blinding, ecstatic moments Annie let herself sink willingly into the embrace, some small, sensible corner of her brain telling her that this had been coming from the moment they'd met the night before, that the violent exchange of words had merely been a vent for…this—this sudden greedy need to feel his mouth on hers again, to feel his body pulse against her, know his touch, his taste, the texture of his tight, tanned skin.

But it was only for a few hectic moments, then an icy darkness began closing her in—the darkness of bad memories, of man's physical power over woman and his ability to subdue her if she dared to protest.

And suddenly, instead of the warm, coaxing mouth of the man kissing her now, she was being stifled by the hot, wet pressure of another mouth—a cruel mouth—and cruel hands that hurt as they touched her. Hands which had her crying out, fighting for breath, straining to get free, struggling—struggling so desperately that she didn't even know that she was flailing wildly at César DeSanquez with her fists, didn't realise that he was no longer kissing her but frowning down at her, no longer holding her in an embrace but trying—unsuccessfully—to stop her from landing blows on his surprised face.

'Angel—'

It was all she heard. Not the full 'Angelica' he had actually said in husky concern but 'Angel' as Luis had husked at her—'Angel. I have a real angel in my bed.'

'No!' she ground out, and managed at last to break free,

her blue eyes wild as she turned like a terrified animal and ran.

Ran out of the open windows across the veranda and down the wooden steps. Ran—ran with no idea where she was running as her feet took her across the springy grass still warm from the long day's sun. It was almost dark outside now, but she didn't notice—didn't notice anything as she made her mindless bid for escape.

She came to a halt only when the balmy water of the Caribbean lapped around her thighs. Breathless from running, panting with fear, she lifted her dazed eyes to the miles of coral-washed water laid out in front of her and at last felt reality return.

Not Luis Alvarez but César DeSanquez. Not the darkened bedroom of a plush London penthouse but a Caribbean island basking in the embrace of a beautiful dying sun.

'Oh, God,' she choked out thickly. 'Oh, God.' And, limp-limbed suddenly, she dropped like a weighted sack onto her knees, then as the water closed in a lazy, silken swirl around her heaving shoulders she put her hands to her face and wept.

Whatever he would do about her stupid flight she didn't consider, but certainly she didn't expect him to come wading into the water after her, his dark eyes tight with fury as he hauled her angrily to her feet and began dragging her back onto dry land again.

It was only later that it occurred to her that it might well have looked to him as if she were trying to drown herself. Whatever, it gained her no sympathy whatsoever—no hint of remorse as he muttered something harsh and Spanish beneath his breath then picked her up in his arms and carried her back up the garden towards the house.

His step hardly altered as he carried her up a flight of

steps that led up the outside wall of the house and along the upper balcony into a room where he dropped her onto her unsteady feet before stalking off towards what she vaguely assumed was a bathroom.

Because this was a bedroom, she realised on yet another rise of panic—a bedroom with two full-length windows standing open either side of a huge coral-pink covered bed.

'Get those wet things off!' He came back with a fluffy white towel. Annie started, her blue eyes huge in her pale face as she stared blankly at him, unable to move a single muscle in case she fell down again.

With another Spanish curse he began stripping off her clothes, the bite of his fingers quelling any attempt she made at trying to stop him. She was shivering violently, though with shock rather than cold. Her top came off and was thrown down on the soft coral-coloured carpet, her arms wrenched away when they automatically crossed over her breasts. With rough hands he unclipped her bra and sent that flying too.

Then, as she stood there still half-numbed by her mind-blowing reaction to his kiss, the towel landed around her shoulders and he was kneeling in front of her, dark face stern as he ruthlessly began to strip the dripping wet skirt from her, followed instantly by her briefs.

'You stupid fool,' he bit out hoarsely. 'What made you do something as crazy as that?'

She didn't answer—couldn't. She just stood there huddling into the towel and shivering so badly that her teeth chattered. He cursed again, turning angrily away, and began wrenching off his own sodden clothes. His trousers landed on top of her skirt, the sleek, lean flanks of his buttocks flexing as he stripped away his briefs and sent them the same way before spinning back to face her, arrogant in his complete lack of modesty and misreading her new, white-

faced stillness as indifference to his exposure while he
railed at her once again.

'I should throttle the lovely life out of you for doing
something as stupid as that!'

With another rasping sigh he turned and walked back
into the bathroom while Annie stood staring after him, mesmerised by those exposed buttocks rippling as he moved.
He came back with another towel, his face no less angry
as he stripped his shirt over his head and slammed it down
onto the floor.

And Annie lost the ability to breathe.

Her eyes were fixed unblinkingly on that daunting junc-
ture between muscle-taut thighs where the shadowing of
crisp black chest hair arrowed to a thick cluster around his
potent sex.

He obviously felt no qualms about standing stark naked
in front of Annie Lacey. As far as he was concerned, she
had seen it all before—many times. But to her this was one
of the most critical occasions of her life. And she could
neither move, breathe nor speak as, dry-mouthed, she stared
at him, horrified by the slow, rumbling burn beginning to
erupt deep down inside her.

Desire—for a man who held her in such contempt. And
a fascination so strong that she couldn't even make herself
look the other way! Her eyes flickered, then shifted to graze
over wide shoulders and bulging biceps where the deeply
tanned skin shone like lovingly oiled leather.

His chest was wide and firm, covered by the thick mass
of black curling hair—hair that angled down over a stomach so tight that she felt she could throw a punch at it and
not make it give so much as a fraction. Then those hips—
those narrow, tight hips so arrogantly cradling the essence
of the man himself, a man endowed with such power that
she could almost feel its—

'Santa María…'

The softly uttered words barely impinged on her concentration. She was too lost in what was happening to him, too busy watching in paralysed awe as his body stirred, hardened, grew into full masculine arousal.

He let go of the towel and began walking slowly towards her. Annie took in a short, shaky breath and moistened her dry lips with her tongue. She couldn't move, was unable to do anything other than watch him fill with desire, and feel her own senses fill with the same.

'Sin,' he muttered tightly as his eyes glittered over her. 'You are sin, Angelica Lacey. Pure sin.'

Coming to a stop in front of her, his hand lifted, stroking across her shoulder on its way to capture the edge of her towel. She was trembling when it fell away—not shivering now, but most definitely trembling. There was a subtle difference, and it all had to do with the sensations she was experiencing inside.

His hand was on her waist, gripping, tugging—arrogant in his maleness as he lifted her up against him. She arched on an indrawn gasp as his manhood slid proudly between her trembling thighs. For a moment they stayed like that, their eyes locked, burning, darkened by feeling. Then he captured her parted mouth, widened it and plunged hungrily in.

And she surrendered—surrendered to the storm that had been building steadily from the moment their eyes had clashed across a crowded room…

Nothing—nothing in her vast and cynical if second-hand knowledge about the act of love had prepared her for what had actually taken place there in the growing darkness of that night.

Nothing. And she lay very still beside the man who had

just propelled her into true womanhood, not daring to move while she came to terms with the wreck it had left of her emotions—her senses! Her very soul.

César was lying beside her, stretched out on his stomach, his arms curved tensely around his dark head. His body was damp, layered with a fine film of perspiration. His shoulders, his hips, his slim, tight buttocks were trembling as he struggled to come to terms with what had just taken place.

He was shocked.

Dear God, *she* was shocked! But both for different reasons. She was shocked by the sheer, brutal reality of the act. His shock came from discovering that the woman he had just taken with such devastating power and sensuality was not the woman he had believed her to be.

And why should he have suspected? she asked herself bitterly. She was the notorious Annie Lacey, for goodness' sake. Used—more than used to experiencing what they had just done!

She had not even attempted to tell him the truth.

And would he have believed the truth if she had attempted to tell him?

Of course not. Who would? She was Annie Lacey. A product of her own making. She had set out to build a lie around herself and had succeeded so successfully that no one ever thought of questioning that lie.

But he could have been—kinder, she thought on a sudden well of anguish. No matter who or what he'd believed her to be, he still could have been kinder—couldn't he?

Tears lay like a film across her eyes, blurring her vision as the moon filtered through the darkness of the room. She hurt. She hurt in so many places that she did not know which one hurt the most—her body, still wearing the power of his physical imprint, her brain, grinding against her skull in stunned revelation, her senses, still quivering, flailing around in the morass of the aftermath, not quite knowing what had happened to them, and too shattered by it all even to attempt to regroup.

Then a hand reached out to touch her, and everything— mind, body, shattered senses—leapt upwards and together in a wild dovetailing of panic, sending her rolling from the bed to land, swaying, on her feet—feet that were already stumbling away, running from what she knew was bound to come next.

The post-mortem. No! Please! Just let me be!

Bathroom. A bathroom door had a lock on it, and she needed to put herself behind lock and key before he—

'Angelica…'

No! Bright balls of panic propelled themselves against the back of her eyes, and in one swift movement she leapt like a gazelle into the bathroom, closing and locking the door behind her before sliding heavily down its smooth, panelled white surface onto the cold, hard ceramic-tiled floor.

Her knees came up, her arms wrapping tensely around them, then her head was lowering, the silken tangle of her hair falling like a curtain all around her as she sat huddled, shivering. Exposed.

Exposed for exactly what she was.

A fraud.

For the last four years of her life she had been a complete fraud. She, the shrewd and cynical Annie Lacey, who had believed that she was playing a great game with other people's perception of her, now realised that she had only been deceiving herself. In her way, she'd believed that she was punishing them all for making her be that way when in actual fact she had been punishing herself—punishing herself for a whole range of things, Alvarez being only a small part in all of that, she now realised.

He had been the conductor, but not the whole orchestra.

'Oh, God.' The words came choking from a throat closed tight on tears of self-knowledge.

You hate yourself, Annie, she told herself wretchedly—not all those other people who only responded to what you gave them to respond to. You built Annie Lacey because you truly believe that persona the only one you're fit for.

Woman as whore. She shuddered nauseously. The fact that you never actually did whore around is incidental. It is what you believed yourself to be.

And now you are, she added starkly—the whore of a man who despises everything about you, even the fact that he could not stop himself from devouring the body he despised so much.

'Sin'. He had called her 'sin'.

'Angelica.' A tap at the door behind her accompanied the gruff reverberation of her name. 'Angelica, open the door.'

No. God, no, she thought, and stumbled to her feet, blue eyes so dark with emotion that they seemed black in her paste-white face. Sheer instinct sent her towards the glass door which housed the shower cubicle. She stepped in and switched on the jet, not caring that the water hissed down icy cold on top of her, then almost immediately stinging-hot.

The need to wash away the whole experience kept her locked beneath the shower, lost to everything but a grinding knowledge of utter self-disgust.

If he knocked or called her name again, she didn't hear him. And she stayed like that for long, long minutes, face lowered, water streaming onto her head until her long hair split and hung in two slick golden pelts from her nape.

Then, slowly, a sense of feeling began to creep back into her numbed flesh, the hot sting of water pulsing down on her urging her back to life, and she lifted her head, found a bar of soap and began methodically washing herself. Toes, feet, legs. Her thighs where his thrusting body had left marks on her fine, delicate skin.

She washed her hips and her buttocks—sore where the height of his passion had sent his fingers digging in. The smell of him and the feel of him still lingered languorously in the hot, steamy air.

Her belly felt tight and tender inside, her breasts alien parts of her that, when she smoothed soap over the taut, swollen mounds, brought a sharp gasp of reaction from her tight throat as her fingers brushed nipples still erect and raw from his hot, hungry kisses.

He had left his mark here in other ways too—in reddened blotches where his lips had nipped and sucked. Her throat had the same—several tender places where she knew she would bruise later on. It was the way of her skin—pale, delicate, it bruised at the slightest knock.

Her arms seemed to be the only part of her that had escaped the marks of his possession—except for her wrists, she noted as she stared at them, ringed pink where he had gripped them together over her head. Oh, not in a demand for submission, she grimly allowed, but in rough, angry passion. He'd wanted to stretch her out to her fullest so that he could taste every inch of her skin with his tongue, kneeling over her with his dark face fierce with desire.

A ripple fluttered over her skin—in memory of the pleasure he had given. Her mouth, full and throbbing, was still wearing his kisses even though she had washed her lips as well.

Sighing, she turned her face up to the spray then stood

there with her eyes closed, trying not to think of it any more.

Then her nails curled tensely into her palms as unwillingly she remembered what she had done to him, how the wild explosion of passion inside her had sent her fingers raking across his sleekly groomed head, searching for, finding and clutching at the slim tail of hair, then tugging—using it to pull him closer so that she could lose herself in his hot, marauding mouth.

Then later... She shuddered, remembering how those same fingers had scraped the ribbon right away, his hair falling like midnight silk around her as her fingers had moved on again, curling into tense claws to score down the full length of his long, muscular back as he'd entered her... Her impassioned cry of pain echoed now in the hollow place her mind had become.

Well, there was one thing, she mocked herself grimly when eventually she made herself move again, she had gone from virgin to experienced lover in one fell swoop, because there had been nothing that he hadn't shown her in that wildly hectic romp on the bed, nothing he had not been prepared to do to heighten their pleasure.

No gentle introduction for the virgin. No holds barred.

That point between her thighs quivered in response, and jerkily she pushed herself out of the shower before it all took too frightening a grip on her again.

Another huge white bath sheet hung folded on the rail. Picking it up, she wrapped it fully around herself then found another towel which she wrapped turban-style round her head.

It took a teeth-clenching gathering together of all her courage to make her unlock the door and step back into the bedroom.

CHAPTER SIX

CÉSAR WAS still there, standing by the open window on the other side of the bed, gazing out at a moonlit sea. He was dressed again, in a fresh white shirt and a pair of casual trousers. His hair had been severely contained once again.

Like the man, she decided hollowly—back under control.

Someone had removed the wet clothes, and the bed had been tidied. Not that it mattered. Nothing mattered.

Ignoring him, she moved over to a big, apricot-coloured easy chair and, snatching up the scatter cushion lying on it, sat down, curling herself into it, hugging the cushion to her breasts.

'Why?' he demanded quietly—nothing else. It really was not necessary to add anything else.

'People see what they want to see,' she answered flatly. She could have said more but didn't. She didn't want to talk at all. She just wanted to sit here and wallow in the aftermath of a holocaust.

He moved, turning his tense body a little so that he could look at her. The movement made her glance warily at him, her huge blue eyes that had lost all their self-protecting veils clashing with a tight, grim face emptied of most of its beautiful colour. He was holding his lips in a straight, tight line, as if the teeth behind them were fiercely clenched, his chiselled jaw set under the pressure.

His eyes were dark and sombre, the truth overlaying his earlier contempt with remorse.

No. She looked down and away again as compassion for

him began to swell inside her. But she was too full with her own dark thoughts just now to deal with his.

And anyway, even though she was aware that maybe half of the blame for what had taken place between them had to lie at her own feet—or those of the Annie Lacey she had so carefully deceived everyone with—she could not forgive him his soulless seduction.

Would not forgive him.

He had got her here to this island under false pretences. He had insulted and threatened her, then coolly blackmailed her before offering the final indignity of ruthlessly seducing her.

If he'd wanted his revenge, he had it. She only hoped that he was satisfied with his results.

Oh, God help me, she thought on a sudden well of absolute despair, and began to sob softly, brokenly into the protection of the cushion.

'Hell.' The thickened curse came from very close by. He was squatting down in front of her. 'I'm sorry,' he murmured deeply. 'What else can I say? I swear to you, I never meant to hurt you like this.'

No? He had set out to hurt her from the very moment they'd met. If it hadn't been this way then it would have been another. He'd seen only the persona, which made the rest of what had happened such a sick joke because, in the end, even he hadn't been able to keep his hands off Annie Lacey, the super-tramp.

And the angry way he'd lost control of himself had told her just how much he'd despised himself for it.

'Leave me alone,' she whispered. 'I just w-want to be left alone.'

He sighed, the heavy sound disturbing the air around her naked shoulders and she shivered.

'You're cold,' he said, with a kind of rough gentleness

that made her want to weep all the more. 'Let me help you into bed, then I will—'

'No!' His hand had come out to touch her; she reared away from him like a terrified animal. Her tear-washed face came out of the cushion, and in sheer self-preservation Annie Lacey surged furiously back to life. 'You've had what you wanted from me—now get out of here. *Get out*!'

Eyes as dark as the ocean beyond the window held onto stormy blue. He didn't flinch from the contempt she seared at him, did not respond to it. And for a moment out of time they stayed like that, he squatting there while she leaned accusingly towards him.

The damner being damned.

But even as she huddled there, flaying him with her eyes, she felt the lazy beginnings of other emotions start to flutter into corrupting life. Her pulse began to race, her aching breasts to stir, her senses pumping soft, sensual messages to the muscles around her sex.

His fault! He had done this to her—awoken demons she had believed so thoroughly shut away! And she hated him for that too, because it showed that no matter how degrading the revelation that had taken place in this room, she'd liked it, and wanted more.

Oh, God. 'Get out of here, you bastard,' she whispered thickly, and lowered her face again—though her senses were on full alert. Bastard he might be, but a proud one. And she was sure that he would not take kindly to having the word spat into his face.

Yet—he did take it; with only another heavy sigh he took it and drew himself grimly to his feet. 'At least get yourself into bed, Angelica,' he advised quietly. 'Or you will catch a chill sitting there like that. I will send Margarita up with some food.' He was walking towards the door. 'Perhaps by tomorrow you will be ready to talk. I will see you then.'

Annie waited until she heard the quiet click as the door closed behind him before she began crying all over again.

She was sitting on a rock, gazing emptily out to sea, when the skittering displacement of a pebble somewhere behind her warned her that she was no longer alone.

It was still quite early. Having surprisingly slept the sleep of the dead the night before, she had awoken just as dawn had been turning the sky from navy to blue. And on a restless urge to stop the events of the previous night from tumbling back into her head she'd got up, dressed in a simple pair of white shorts and a white T-shirt, then left her room via the French windows.

Glancing up, she saw César coming towards her. Barefoot, he moved easily across the light, pebbly ground, the solid gold bracelet of his watch glinting in the early morning light. Behind him his white-painted house stood in the shadow of a new day. Behind it stood the hill, with its thicket of trees reaching up towards a pure blue sky.

A beautiful place. Somewhere between Eden and paradise, she found herself thinking fancifully.

If César was the serpent Annie wasn't sure what that made her.

He was dressed in a light cambric shirt and a pair of thin white cotton beach trousers rolled up a little at the ankles. His hair was contained, his face wearing the sheen of a man who had just indulged in a close shave, and he looked devastatingly attractive.

A man who stood out on his own as special.

No. Firmly she squashed what was trying to take place inside her, and looked away again. She did not want to feel anything right now.

And she did not want to see the knowledge that she knew

would be written in his shrewd emerald eyes if she let her own eyes clash with them.

He came to drop down beside her. No smile, no greeting—no tension in him. He simply drew up his knees, spread them slightly, rested his deeply tanned forearms on top, and said, 'Right. It is time for explanations, Angelica. I want to know what made you into the absolute fraud you are.'

Just like that. She smiled to herself. Guilt and remorse done with the night before, he now demanded enlightenment.

'Looking for absolution, Mr DeSanquez?' she asked. 'You won't get it, you know,' she warned him. 'All you will do is discover that you are just like the rest of the human race—rarely looking beyond what you're expecting to see.'

'And you with your carefully prepared persona did not aid that deception?' he countered.

Annie's shoulders moved in a careless shrug. 'I am in the business of selling things,' she reminded him.

'Using your notoriety to do it.'

'A commodity you weren't above exploiting yourself to help sell your precious collection. Which,' she added before he could say anything else, 'I accept entirely as part of my job. But it never occurred to you to look beyond the façade to the real person beneath.'

'It wasn't merely the false image which made you the woman I saw you to be, Angelica,' he argued. 'There were other, far more convincing factors which did that. Alvarez, for instance,' he prompted quietly.

'Alvarez', she noted. Luis Alvarez had suddenly become the detached 'Alvarez' instead of the more familiar 'brother-in-law'.

She almost smiled at the irony of it, only her stiff lips

would not stretch to it. Instead she reached down to gather up a handful of pebbles from the side of her rock, then told him grimly, 'I am not going to bare my soul to you just because you've happened to discover my darkest secret.'

'It was not a dark secret, Angelica,' he countered gently. 'It was a sad one.'

Sad. A moment's moisture spread across her eyes then left again.

It was more than sad. It was pathetic, she thought bitterly as her mind flew back to that dark period in her life.

At sixteen years old she had to have been the most naïve female alive. A child actress with a fresh-faced, angelic image that had made people sigh when they'd seen her on their TV sets playing a role that had grown from a single ad for breakfast cereal into a three-year-long concept of how every parent would want their teenage daughter to look and behave.

The first ad had begun simply, with her sitting in a homely kitchen with the morning sunlight beaming down onto her pale gold head. She had been dressed for school in a neat lemon and white striped uniform and her face had shown the horrors that the voice-over had explained she was experiencing with the onset of her first day at a brand new school.

'Eat up,' her TV mother had commanded gently. 'Things won't look half so bad on a full stomach.'

Reluctantly she'd pulled the bowl of crunchy flakes towards her, dipped in her spoon and forced the first mouthful down; the next had not been quite so slow, the one after that almost eager. By the time she had finished the whole bowl her face had firmed, her small chin lifting determinedly, her thoughts—via the voice-over—having become more positive with each mouthful.

The next episode had shown her coming home again,

buoyant, alive, rushing into the kitchen to tell her mother about her first exciting day, and all the time she'd chatted the bowl had been coming off the shelf, the crunchy-flake box out of the cupboard, milk from the fridge. Then had come the blissful silence as she'd eaten, blue eyes shining, the voice-over explaining her instant success at her new school as she'd replayed it to her bowl of cereal.

Over the next three years her crunchy cereal, via the voice-over discussions she'd had with it, had solved all her teenage problems with a lesson well learned at the end of each ad, which had earned her the nickname 'The Angel'.

The ads had been thrown up at other teenagers as perfect examples of good moral behaviour. She had been kind to animals, old people and small children. Parents had loved her, grandparents had loved her, small children had loved her—teenagers had hated her. Which was why she'd had so few friends of her own age—that and the fact that she'd lived with an aunt who had kept her strictly to heel when she had not been working or at school.

Losing Aunt Claire at the vulnerable age of nineteen had been like losing the linchpin that had held her unnatural life together. It had also preceded her spectacular fall from grace—a fall which had left her with two options only. Either she crawled away to hide in shame or she lifted her chin and outfaced everything that her critics had to throw at her. She had chosen the latter. And, with Todd's support, countless surprise offers had flooded in to Lissa, her agent, for the kind of work which must have made her aunt turn in her grave.

It was only as César's hand reached out to cover her own that she realised she was sitting there pressing damp pebbles between two tense palms as if she were trying to grind them into dust.

She looked down at that hand—big and dark, and seeming to promise so many things that she had learned not to trust. A hand that now knew her more intimately than any hand. The hand that had drawn from her a woman she hadn't known existed inside her.

The hand of contempt, now the hand of consolation.

She pushed it away.

There was a moment's silence, in which they both stared bleakly out to sea. Then, on a soft sigh that revealed an until now banked-down frustration, he requested brusquely, 'At least tell me what Hanson is to you.'

'Todd?' She turned a glance on him, seeing for the first time how his shattered illusions had scored deep grooves of strain into his lean, dark face. He was not so calm and composed, nor was he finished with guilt and remorse, she added as his eyes caught hers and held, the sombre glow of regret dulling the usual incisive greenness. 'Well, he's not my lover, that's for sure,' she drawled with mocking irreverence, watched him wince, then turned her face away again to stare back out to sea.

'He's my half-brother,' she announced.

Well aware that she had just delivered the biggest shock she could have done she selected one of the tiny pebbles in her hand and threw it into the ocean.

'We share the same father,' she extended, launching another pebble. 'Though I didn't find out about him until my aunt died.' She paused, then added, tight-lipped and flatly, 'Only she wasn't my aunt. She was my mother.'

Another stone was launched into the clear blue water while she gave those few pertinent facts a chance to settle in the stunned air now surrounding them. Then she quietly began relating a story that she had never told anyone in her life before—though why she suddenly chose to tell this man was beyond her ability to understand.

'Not once during the eighteen years I lived with her did

she ever let me know that interesting little fact,' she told
him. 'I had to wait until she was dead to discover our true
relationship—via letters sent from Todd's father to her, laying out ground rules for the lump sum he settled on us both
which involved her holding her silence about his name.
Why she decided to include herself in that silence I don't
know.' And will never know now, she added bleakly to
herself. 'But discovering that far from being the orphan I'd
always believed myself to be I'd had not only a mother but
a father as well sent me a little crazy for a time.'

'You were hurt,' he defended her gently.

'And the rest,' she said, and huffed out a sound of scorn.
Hurt, angry, bitter, betrayed.

She hunched her body over her knees, a fresh handful of
pebbles clenched in her fist.

'I stormed into Giles Hanson's office and began shriek-
ing at him like a maniac,' she went on after a moment. 'I
accused him of just about everything I could accuse him
of, then set about telling him what I thought of him as a
man.'

The word 'man' emerged with enough contempt to make
any man wince. César winced.

'I had just got to the part where I was telling him how
I was going to reveal to the world how he and my mother
had treated me when Todd came into the room.'

She turned to look at him then, her gaze skimming over
his set, sober face. 'Your eyes are the same colour as
Susie's,' she remarked—quite out of context. 'I should
have made that connection a lot earlier than I did. And I'm
surprised now that I didn't.'

He glanced at her frowningly, not really understanding
what she was getting at. 'We have nothing else in common,' he said, almost as if he was defending himself
against a suspected insult. 'The eyes are the only legacy.'

'You think so?' Her expression was curious and damning at the same time. But she didn't elaborate, returning to the original subject instead. 'I took one look at Todd and saw myself,' she said. 'The hair, the eyes… We are so similar, in fact, that I am amazed that no one else has ever made the connection.

'Still—' she shrugged '—I didn't give a hoot about what he looked like then as I slammed into him as well as his father. He was shocked.' She grimaced, remembering that look of pained horror on Todd's face as clearly as if he were standing in front of her right now. 'Shocked enough for me to realise through my rage that he, like myself, knew nothing about his father's past indiscretion.

'But it was he who calmed me down, he who shut his father up when he began spitting all kinds of threats back at me about what would happen if I did open my mouth. And it was Todd who led me out of there, took me to his apartment, let me pour out the whole dirty story all over again, then set about convincing me that I would do no one any good by making it all public, but could actually do a lot of harm.'

Her mouth tightened, eyes glinting at some bitter memory of then that could still hurt her now. 'His mother really does suffer from a chronic heart problem,' she said huskily. 'And finding out about me would surely have killed her because she so foolishly believed that she had a marriage made in heaven.' Her cynicism was so tight and bitter that even Annie wanted to wince when she heard it in her tone.

'Todd didn't care what the scandal could do to his father. But he did care about his mother. So did I, funnily enough,' she admitted. 'Having known what it felt like to be betrayed by just about everyone who should love you, I had no wish to put a sick woman through the same kind of hell. So—'

another of those expressive shrugs '—I found myself shut out in the cold again.'

'Hanson shut you out also?' César said in surprise.

'I shut him out actually,' she amended. 'He had his loyalties, which did not include me or my feelings, so as far as I was concerned right then he could go to hell with the rest of them. I told you I'd gone a little crazy,' she reminded him. 'Anger, hurt, bitterness—you name it—' she grimaced '—he got the lot since his father had delegated responsibility to his son.'

'You say "his" father,' César remarked. 'But he was your father also.'

'Not so you'd notice,' she said. 'Not so you'd ever notice,' she then added tightly. 'He died last year never having so much as mentioned my name. Ironic really,' she tagged on ruefully, 'that he should precede his ailing wife to the grave after all he had been prepared to do to me to protect a slowly dying woman from more pain.

'Still—' another shrug '—perhaps that was the price he had to pay for being such a callous, devious swine. I don't regret his going, and I can't say I have any regrets now that he never acknowledged me for what I was to him. He was just a man—' again that contempt for men in general slithered into her tone '—like all the rest of them—vulnerable to his sexual urges but unwilling to accept the consequences of his weakness.'

'So you paid him back for his rejection of you by becoming someone he could never acknowledge even if he did change his mind.'

'The notorious Annie Lacey, you mean?' A soft laugh that fell nowhere near humour left her dry lips. 'Oh, no,' she denied. 'That honour goes to someone much closer to your home, Mr DeSanquez.' She turned her cheek on her arms to look directly at him. 'Luis Alvarez did that.'

He flinched but did not protest, and for a moment she studied the tight line of his profile, wondering how far ahead of her his mind had already taken him. It had to have skipped some way ahead on the simple knowledge that last night had given him. But how far he was willing to use his intelligence to work out the rest, she didn't know.

He was proud—too proud for his own good, probably. That pride might not be willing to take the full brunt of all of this without him at least putting up a token objection—like that of sacrificing her feelings for that of his family.

She knew all about that kind of thing, had experienced it before. She turned away, deciding that it was up to him to indicate whether or not she continued this. The trouble was, she accepted as she launched another stone into the clear blue sea, that what she said was going to make him appear as gullible as a babe in arms, and she had a feeling he knew that too.

'Please continue.'

He was going to take it all on board. Annie smiled grimly to herself.

'I was nineteen years old,' she reminded him, with the first hint of a wobble in her voice. 'And until my aunt—stroke mother,' she added deridingly, 'died I had been kept pretty much to heel by her overprotection and the kind of job I did alongside normal schoolwork.'

Her hands wrapped themselves around her legs again, shoulders hunching in as if to protect her from some unseen evil. 'And, as I told you, discovering all that dirt about myself sent me a little crazy for a time—discos, parties, anything to keep the bitterness away. Then I went to your party. It was *your* party, wasn't it?' She partly asked him, partly accused him.

He sighed heavily in answer, a nerve clenching at the side of his jaw. 'I was in London on business,' he explained. 'I happened to see you on television—playing a cameo role in a big period drama…'

Annie nodded, knowing exactly what drama he was referring to. It had been the first real acting role she'd been offered—and it had turned out to be the last, because her life had blown apart not long after that drama had been shown on TV.

'You were so beautiful,' he murmured gruffly, 'that I wanted to meet you. I knew the director. He promised to bring you to a party I was giving at my apartment.'

'You weren't there,' Annie stated with an absolute certainty. She would have known, she was sure of it. She would know if this man was in the same hemisphere as herself.

'I was called away on urgent business,' he said, confirming his absence. 'My sister and her husband were staying with me at the apartment. They offered to play host to my guests in my place, but Cristina was taken ill early on and apparently took to her bed, leaving Luis to play host alone.'

'Which is why I met him there instead of you.' She swallowed thickly, and lowered her face to watch her hand grind tiny pebbles in her palm again.

'You were starving for affection.' He turned his head to look at her with dark and sombre eyes. 'He offered it. You grabbed at it desperately with both hands.'

About to throw her fistful of stones, Annie paused to stare at him. 'You are joking, of course,' she gasped. 'He was old enough to be my father!'

César nodded. 'The father-figure you had been deprived of all your life.'

That made her laugh, not humorously but with a wincing mockery. 'He was a dissolute slob,' she derided with contempt, 'who tricked me into that bedroom then proceeded to attack me!'

She was on her feet suddenly, wiping her damp palms down her thighs in a tense, agitated kind of way that said she was reliving that dreadful moment in her life.

'He would have succeeded in raping me too,' she added thickly, 'if his wife hadn't walked in the room!'

And suddenly she was shaking, white-faced, the whole length of her slender frame from the top of her head to her curled toes trembling with a painful mixture of anger and sickening repugnance.

'But if this is true—why did you not tell someone?' He made a sharp, uncontrolled gesture of pained disgust that brought him jerkily to his feet. 'Call in the police?'

For that Annie turned a withering look of contempt on him. 'Are you really that naïve about your family?' she cried. 'Your sister was there, for goodness' sake!' She angrily drove home the point that he seemed to have ignored completely. 'But did she care about me and what I was being subjected to? Did she hell!' The words scored across his steadily greying face. 'She was too busy screaming in hysterics while the rest of your damned guests were falling over each other to get into the room to see what was going on!'

He muttered something beneath his tight breath, but Annie didn't hear it; she was reliving her worst nightmare and it held her stiff and shaking.

'I was labelled a cheap little tramp before I left your apartment.' Her breasts heaved up and down on a forced breath. 'No one bothered asking me for my side of the story. They just saw what they wanted to see,' she said bitingly. 'A nice juicy scandal where supposedly sweet Angel Lacey of all people was caught red-handed with another woman's husband!' She shuddered, feeling sick. 'They saw what they wanted to see,' she repeated thickly.

'I'm—sorry,' César dropped grimly into the throbbing silence.

She didn't acknowledge him. 'All I wanted to do was try to forget the whole ugly episode,' she went on after a while. 'Then the next thing I know I'm being cited as the other woman in your sister's divorce and my name is being splattered all over the place! Who was going to believe my side of the story then, Mr DeSanquez?' she demanded bitterly. 'Two months after the event, who was going to believe that I was near-as-damn-it raped?'

His stark expression gave her the answer, and Annie grimaced bitterly. 'So the sweet Angel Lacey fell swiftly from grace,' she concluded, 'and I became the notorious Annie Lacey instead—fit to be used for anyone's convenience—including yours.'

He flinched; she accepted it as her due. 'Now, if you don't mind,' she said more calmly, 'I would like to leave here as soon as it's possible.' With that she turned to walk away.

But he stopped her, not by touch but with words. 'Susie,' he bit out grimly. 'Why does Susie not know about your true relationship with Hanson? They have lived together—shared the same bed for six months! Surely some kind of trust should have evolved in that time?'

'You would think so, wouldn't you?' Annie smiled a tight little smile. 'But then, she's always harboured an unnatural hatred of me. Now I know why, of course—' she shrugged '—her being connected with you lot.' It wasn't said nicely and wasn't meant to be. 'But in openly despising me she got Todd's back up.'

Slowly she turned to look coolly at him. 'You see, if any good came out of the Alvarez scandal, then it was the way it brought Todd and me much closer together. He believed my version, you see, Mr DeSanquez. Against all the evidence your family and so-called friends stacked against me, he believed me, stood by me and tried his best to shield me from the worst of the flak the Press wanted to throw at me.

'You could say we found each other,' she likened whimsically. 'And, in so doing, woe betide anyone who tries to come between us, because it will be at their peril—warn Susie,' she added as a mere mocking aside.

'You say you and Susie only share the eyes,' she went on. 'But you don't. You share ruthlessly manipulative natures too. Like you she was willing to go to any lengths to get what she wanted,' she explained, without acknowledging the sudden, angry flash in his eyes at that last insult. 'But the day she challenged Todd to choose between me and herself she lost him.

'He may love her,' she conceded, 'but he also despises her for trying that. Now, when I tell him about this little— charade she fixed up for me,' she pointed out, 'he'll cut her right out of his life. And don't take that statement lightly,' she warned when scepticism lightened his eyes, 'because just as you and Susie bear similar genes so does Todd to his father. He'll do it for my sake, just as his father did it to me for his wife's sake.'

'And you?' César questioned. 'Do you possess that same streak in you?'

Do I? Annie paused to think about it. 'I don't know,' she was forced to admit in the end. 'It hasn't been put to the test yet.'

'Then maybe it is time that it was,' he murmured. 'The way I hear you, Hanson means all the world to you. Will you—cut him right out of your life for his own sake?' he challenged silkily.

Annie frowned. 'I don't see the connection.'

He thrust his hands into the pockets of his loose-fitting

trousers. 'I still hold the final card, Angelica,' he reminded her carefully. 'And, bearing in mind your analysis of my character just now, it will do you well to remember my ability to use it. Nothing has changed, except, maybe, my opinion of you as a person,' he allowed. 'But the success of *Cliché* still hangs on the promise of my collaboration.'

An icy shiver slid down Annie's spine. 'I still don't see what you're getting at,' she said warily.

His eyes were hard now, his expression grim. 'You either keep to your side of our deal,' he softly spelled out for her, 'or I will withdraw my support at the eleventh hour, giving Hanson no chance to put something else in my place.'

Annie took a stunned step back. 'You would still do that?' she choked. 'After everything I've just told you?'

His expression was bleak but firm. 'Susie needs time to mend her relationship with Hanson,' he stated grimly. 'I promised her that time. That promise cannot be forfeited simply because you have pointed out to me what I already knew—that my family can be quite ruthless when they need to be.' Narrowly his green gaze watched her. 'The rise or decline of Hanson Publications remains firmly in your hands, Angelica. You stay here with me and everything runs smoothly. You insist on leaving and it all falls the other way.'

'You bastard,' she breathed. He was no better than his thankless family! Like them he was prepared to sacrifice her feelings as if they didn't matter! 'Last night counts for nothing—nothing at all to you!'

His eyes seemed to go black, the green blanked out by an emotion that Annie was too hurt and angry to interpret. 'It counts,' he granted roughly. 'And indeed alters things slightly…' His pause was deliberate and chilling. 'I did not use protection last night, Angelica. And with hindsight I must presume that neither did you.'

Not slow at getting his meaning, she went so white that her eyes looked like huge dark pools in her horror-pinched face.

A nerve twitched in his jaw as he watched her, but his mouth remained firm with resolve. 'Which leaves us with another—problem we may yet have to face,' he went on. 'Which is whether you are pregnant with my child and, if you are, what we are going to do about it.'

It was all too much. Shock upon shock over the last twenty-four hours, plus the added emotional wrench of her own recent trauma in allowing herself to open up to this man, had Annie swaying, the beauty of the new day fading around its edges until it encompassed only his grimly watchful face.

Pregnant? She shook her head on a laugh that came very close to hysteria. No, she would not so much as allow herself to consider that as a possibility. Fate would not be that cruel to her, surely?

'It has to be acknowledged, Angelica,' he murmured, as though her thoughts were written across her face for his exclusive benefit. 'Children are not made in heaven, as I suspect you would prefer to believe. They are made by the ejaculation of male sperm into the female womb—a process we well and truly carried out last night.'

She flinched, his blunt, clinical description making her hands clutch at her stomach on a shudder of revulsion—an action that made a nerve twitch in his jaw again.

'So what are you asking of me now?' she demanded finally, the very quiver in her voice mirrored in the reactionary tremor of her body. 'Visitation rights when this other farce with Todd is over? Or perhaps you want even more than that,' she added bitterly, fingers lifting to comb her hair agitatedly away from her paste-white face. 'Maybe you prefer to rip the thing from my damned womb before it can cause any more trouble for you!'

At that it was his turn to flinch, but if she gained any satisfaction from it she wasn't aware. Her whole world seemed to have gone topsy-turvy, and she didn't know what she was feeling any more.

'Neither of those things,' he denied. 'I was, actually, about to suggest the *only* option I see open to us. Marriage,' he announced. 'I think you and I should get married, Angelica, and as soon as it can be arranged.'

CHAPTER SEVEN

HYSTERIA did take over now. Annie felt it rise like a lift out of a control from the very base of her feet until it burst free somewhere hot between the ears.

'I don't believe you're real!' she gasped out shrilly. 'I really don't believe you come from this planet at all!' Her blue eyes stared at him through a glaze of utter incredulity. 'I wouldn't marry you if you got down on your knees and begged me to!' she seared at him. 'I wouldn't even be standing here giving you this much of my time if you hadn't incarcerated me on this bloody island of yours!

'My God!' she choked, a hand flying haphazardly up in the air then landing bewilderedly on the top of her head. 'You're sick, do you know that? You ought to see a doctor—the kind who looks inside your head to see what the hell went wrong with it to make you what you are! Or, better still,' she rattled on furiously, 'refer him to me and I'll tell him exactly what's wrong with you, César DeSanquez! You are the result of too much interbreeding from your vengeful Spanish side, that's what you are!

'Marriage? Babies?' she shrieked. 'I would rather rip this hypothetical child out of my womb myself than be party to bringing another of your kind into this w—!'

The stinging slap issued to the side of her face silenced her. The hands suddenly gripping her shoulders and pulling her hard against him made her gasp. The eyes, when she managed to focus on them, were aflash with rage. He looked bigger, darker, more alien than he'd ever managed to look before. And he was throbbing with enough barely leashed violence to knock her down to the ground if she so much as provoked him a fraction of an inch further.

'You will take that back,' he breathed furiously. 'Every word of it. Every filthy, bitter word!'

'You go to hell,' she whispered, shaking with a wild combination of fear and fury.

'I am already there,' he rasped, and dropped his mouth down onto hers.

And she couldn't believe it but it was there—that strong and that quick!—a volcanic eruption of all those feelings that he had so brutally set free the night before!

With a whimpered groan of surrender she weakened at the knees, that tidal heat of wild pleasure sending her melting helplessly against him, jaw slackening, lips parting to allow him angry entry into her mouth.

When he stopped being angry and became aroused himself she wasn't sure. But the kiss did change, turning to something deep and intense, his tongue coiling sensually with her own while his hands slackened their grip enough to slide caressingly beneath her top, shrouding her in fine, pleasurable shivers as he stroked with excruciating lightness across her fine white skin.

She groaned again, her body arching instinctively, and he encouraged her with the deep, drugging urgency of his kiss. Then one hand was moving to her behind, splaying and pressing, drawing her into the braced arch of his thighs where the pulsing evidence of his arousal throbbed through the thin covering of her shorts, shocking and exciting her with the blatant power of his need.

Then suddenly he was breaking the kiss on a fierce intake of air, whistling it in through his teeth as he threw his dark head back in an effort to snatch back control, muttering tight words in Spanish to himself while his hands maintained that pressure against his pulsing thighs.

'No,' he gritted tensely while she waited, panting, frightened, weirdly excited by this effect that she seemed to have on him. 'No,' he said again, sounding hoarse with desperation, then lowered his head and opened his eyes.

They were eyes she found herself drowning in—eyes the same colour as the glittering jade water further out in the bay, eyes that yearned and hated and fought a battle that held her in absolute thrall.

'I will take you now, here on this rock in broad daylight, if I have to,' he enunciated rawly through the trauma of emotion running rife within him. 'And I will go on taking you until you agree to marry me, Angelica Lacey. Marry me and let me lock you away where you can never harm a child of mine. Do you understand?'

Understand? 'And how do you think your wonderful family would react to that?' she flashed bitterly back at him. 'Their gallant knight marrying the enemy!' She made a sound of scorn. 'My God, your sister would die at the horror of it and Susie would expire with chagrin!'

'And what do you think it will do to you if we do not marry?' he flashed right back. 'Or don't you care that carrying a child without a wedding ring will only help to confirm the notorious Annie Lacey's whoring ways?'

She went white, her hand snaking up to make vicious contact with his face—only it never made it. He caught her wrist in a manacle-like grip and held it suspended two inches from his cheek.

'They see what they want to see,' he quoted back at her quite ruthlessly. 'And they will see a woman who eats, sleeps and lives for sex. They will probably decide that you could not even give the father a name!'

'I could,' she spat at him. 'Yours! That wonderful genius Adamas, no less!'

'And the moment you use my name I will slap a court

order on you demanding all rights to my child on the grounds that you are not a fit person to take care of it!' he vowed. 'Who do you think will win in a court of law, Angelica?' he challenged brutally. 'The whore or the genius with the blameless past?'

'My God—' She swallowed tensely on the hot ball of fury blocking her throat. 'Luis Alvarez has nothing on you, does he?'

That hit him on the raw, tightening that arrogant face until the tanned skin lay stretched taut across his lean cheeks. 'I want your agreement,' he bit out.

Annie gave a sound of angry bewilderment. 'There may not even be a child!' she cried. 'So why the hell are we having this crazy confrontation?'

'Because if there is,' he clipped, 'I want to be sure— damned sure—that no one will have cause to question its parentage. And with your track record—true or otherwise,' he put in at the bitter flash from her eyes, 'the poor child is destined to grow up being known only as Annie Lacey's bastard! Is that what you want?'

She flinched, sickened to her very depths because no matter how she tried to refute that insult she could not and knew she could not. Annie Lacey's reputation was set.

The tension she was maintaining in her captured wrist died along with the rest of her ability to fight, and her head lowered, the slow burn of wretched, self-contemptuous tears pressing against the backs of her eyes.

'We could at least wait a couple of weeks to find out if it's worth all of this grief!' she choked out wretchedly.

But he was already shaking his dark head. 'I want this child's hapless beginnings to be blameless, Angelica,' he stated grimly. 'And if that means us taking a risk and marrying now then we will do it. For the child's sake,' he punctuated forcefully. 'Not our own.'

'Oh, God. I hate you,' she whispered thickly. 'I hate you so much!'

'But you now see the sense in what I am saying,' he insisted. The hand still holding her wrist aloft tightened its grip in a demand for the right reply.

She gave it anguishedly. 'Yes—yes!'

His big, bronzed chest, gleaming in the sunshine beneath the loose fall of his open shirt, lifted and fell. 'I will arrange for us to be married tomorrow on Pelican Island,' he decided, 'which is only a short flight away. Then we will come back here until we know for sure either way.' Slowly he lowered her wrist to her side and released it.

'Then?' she prompted thickly. 'What then?'

He shrugged, his beautiful broad shoulders shifting tensely beneath the thinnest cotton. 'That decision will have to wait until we know the answer,' he said, then turned and simply walked away.

The journey to Pelican Island was achieved in near silence. Annie sat quietly beside César as he played the controls, their sunglasses in place to protect their eyes from the bright sun.

They had barely spoken a word to each other during the last twenty-four hours. He hadn't been around to talk to! Because a few minutes after he'd walked away from her on the beach he'd left the island, bringing the helicopter rising above the house then speeding off into the clear blue sky.

He had returned late, just as the sun had been dying out of a rich vermilion sky.

'It is all arranged,' he'd informed her when she'd eventually forced herself to go downstairs and face him over the dinner that Margarita had so carefully prepared. 'We marry tomorrow afternoon on Pelican Island.'

'I thought Pelican Island was private,' she'd murmured, recognising the island's name as a famous retreat for the rich and stressed-out.

'It is leased,' he'd corrected, 'as my own island is. But because it possesses a hotel it is licensed to perform marriage services.'

Which had left her with nothing else to say. So they'd done their best to compliment Margarita's delicious dinner of goujons of chicken followed by freshly caught snapper fish on a bed of fluffy aromatic rice.

During his absence she'd explored Hook-nose Bay, scrambling over rocks and soft silver sand, swimming for hours in the calm waters. That evening her skin had borne the healthy glow of a day's unremitting sunshine—the high-factor lotion she'd found in the bathroom having protected her from the worst of the sun's rays.

By dinnertime she had been tired—tired enough not to care what he thought of her silence or the fact that, other than by that one short burst of conversation, she had barely acknowledged his presence.

He wanted all of this, not her. She needed to make no effort to pretend otherwise, and oddly he had seemed to accept that, his green gaze straying occasionally to her closed face but without attempting to intrude on the self-absorbed shell that she had withdrawn behind.

He waited until they were almost due to land before doing that. 'I have reserved a beach cottage for us at the hotel.' His shaded eyes glanced at her quietly composed features. 'I thought you might appreciate the—privacy until the ceremony is due to take place.'

She said nothing, but her fingers curled slightly in tense reaction where they rested on her lap.

'I have also arranged for something—appropriate for you to wear,' he added casually.

That brought her gaze to him. 'What I'm wearing is more than suitable,' she insisted, adding cynically, 'it isn't as though it's going to be the wedding of the year, after all.'

'I never implied it was,' he agreed almost soothingly. 'And you would look beautiful in whatever you chose to wear, be it sackcloth or that blue linen you have on now. But…' He paused to make a slight adjustment to their flight, his movements deft with confidence as he realigned the helicopter with the bulk of land that she could see looming towards them. 'This will not be a hole-and-corner wedding, Angelica,' he said grimly. 'It is important that it appears the happiest day in both our lives.'

Grin and bear it, in other words, she noted. Well, she was a professional, wasn't she? An absolute expert at make-believe? 'I won't let you down.'

'I know you won't,' he murmured quietly. But the tension between them was beginning to fizz again, and after a moment he sighed. 'Angelica, I want you to believe me when I say I mean you no harm! I do this for your own sake. Your reputation will not stand another scandal!' His eyes flicked to hers. 'I am sorry if that offends you, but it is the truth and I think that you know it!'

'Ah, I see.' The first bubbles of anger began to ferment in the calm interior she had been so carefully maintaining. 'So this is just another case of César DeSanquez being the gallant knight in action. How very altruistic of you,' she said waspishly. 'Remind me to thank you for it some time.'

'I don't look for your thanks,' he snapped, but from the way his lean profile clenched she knew that she'd managed to hit him on the raw. 'I am simply trying to tell you that you can trust me!'

'Trust?' She made a hard sound of scorn. 'Don't talk to me about trust,' she derided. 'I will never trust another human being again.'

No answer to that. Annie waited, seething in silence, for him to pile the blame back on her, as he had so competently done with everything else, but nothing came. He just tightened his mouth and increased their speed, and let the animosity that she was determinedly generating try its best to choke the very air around them.

They landed beside a row of low palm trees that formed a line of shelter from the fiercest heat of the sun along the inevitable crescent-shaped beach.

Annie waited patiently while César shut down the engine then jumped down to come around and help her alight. As they ran clear of the steadily slowing blades Annie noticed the scattering of pretty, red-roofed bungalows almost hidden from view amongst a rich mixture of tropical shrubs and trees.

A man, tall and tanned and leanly built, met them with a welcoming smile and a warm shake of their hands. He was American, and older than he looked at first glance. It was obvious that he knew César well because after the initial introductions, and—she supposed—the expected congratulations, he fell into warm conversation with César as he led them along a path towards one of the bungalows.

Annie didn't bother to listen. She had, in fact, effectively switched off—something she had learned to do early on in her career, when time had dragged heavily during long, tedious waits between short, hurried shoots.

The inside of the bungalow revealed a surprisingly large sitting room furnished in prettily covered rattan. A pair of plate-glass sliding doors stood open on a view that drew her attention, and she walked over to gaze out at it while the two men finished their conversation.

Then a door closed quietly and there was silence behind her—the kind of silence that began to shred her nerve-ends as she tried to pick out just where César was without her having to turn to find out.

She felt a real reluctance to look him fully in the face. She hadn't done so, she realised—not voluntarily, any-way—since the night they'd shared a bed.

The chink of ice on glass told her that he was over by the little bar she had spied as she'd come in. And her nerves shredded a bit more when he came to stand directly behind her, a bronzed forearm lightly covered with silky, black hair appearing in her vision. He was holding a tall glass filled with something clear and refreshing, tiny bubbles swirling up from the chunks of ice settled at its base.

'Nothing too alcoholic,' he said. 'Mostly tonic, a splash of lime and the smallest tot of gin.'

'I don't drink spirits,' she informed him coolly, refusing to accept the glass.

'I have noticed,' he drawled, refusing to withdraw it. 'Another lesson taught by Alvarez?' he asked. 'I believe you were very drunk when you were seen being led into the bedroom that night.'

'Your bedroom,' she punctuated tightly.

'Yes.' He sighed. 'I'm sorry I ever said that but yes, it was mine.'

She swallowed on whatever was thickening her throat. His bedroom—his apartment. His bedroom—his island. It was as if he had to be connected with all the real traumas in her life.

'I sold the apartment, Angelica,' he inserted quietly. 'I never stepped foot in it again after that night. I could not cope with the vision of the woman I wanted for myself lying in the arms of another man. Any man,' he extended roughly. 'The fact that it happened to be Alvarez only helped to generate my contempt of him—not my contempt of you.'

'You can say that now, with hindsight.' She smiled sceptically.

'It is the truth,' he stated. 'You were drunk. Everyone who saw you allowed you that much at least. So did I.'

Yes, she had been drunk. Giddy, hiding all her hurts from the world behind a screen of careless gaiety. 'I suppose you are now making the assumption that, being drunk, I probably encouraged him to do what he did.' She didn't want it to, but her voice sounded husky with hurt.

He sighed again, reaching around her with his other hand so that his body had to make a glancing contact with her own as he firmly took hold of her hand and lifted it, pushing the glass into her palm.

'I am learning,' he murmured while she stood breathlessly cocooned in the circle of his arms, 'to make no assumptions about you, Angelica. And no,' he added, 'I do not believe you encouraged him—because you tell me it was not so. And, although you may not have noticed, I have believed every word you've ever said to me without needing corroboration. The truth, you see, tends to glow like a challenge in your beautiful, defiant eyes.

'So take the glass,' he urged. 'Drink to quench your thirst, and maybe to steady your nerves a little for what is to come.'

Her fingers tightened around the glass.

'Thank you,' he murmured, as though she had just conceded some obscure but precious point, while Annie had to fight a new battle with the tears that wanted to fall from her eyes.

Then he was stepping back and she found that she could breathe again, but the glass chattered against her teeth as she lifted it to her quivering mouth.

'Now.' With distance between them, he sounded more like his normal, arrogant self. 'Over to your left there is an *en suite* bedroom set aside for your exclusive use. I have a matching one to your right. You have just under an hour, Angelica, to turn yourself into the beautiful bride I expect to see when I meet you back here.' With that he turned and walked away.

A beautiful bride.

Annie stared at herself in the full-length mirror and wanted to throw something at it to smash to smithereens the person she saw looking back at her.

Professional training gave her the expected bridal look, the equipment to do it having been provided by a man hell-bent, it seemed to her, on causing her everlasting pain.

The gown she'd found waiting for her was white, frothy, lacy, unashamedly romantic, with flamboyant off-the-shoulder sleeves edged with a deep ruffle of the finest hand-stitched lace—the same lace that floated around the low scooped neck of the fitted bodice and was sewn into the hem of its full, ballerina-length skirt.

The whole confection was about as far away from what anyone would expect Annie Lacey to wear for her wedding as a gown could get. Shy, frivolous, sweet—virginal.

And she felt a bigger fraud than ever.

A light tap at her door had her turning to face it just as César let himself into the room. Her breath caught on a silent gasp, her blue eyes darkening in surprise at how he looked.

He was dressed almost entirely in white himself. White trousers of the finest, finest cotton. White cotton overshirt with a mandarin collar fastened from tanned throat to waist by what looked like sapphire studs—the genuine article, she assumed, knowing who he was. No tie—the shirt did not warrant a tie. It was as he turned slightly to close the door

behind him that she saw the white silk ribbon holding his
jet-black hair in place.

'The accepted dress of a Venezuelan,' he answered her
curious look. 'It is called a *Liqui-Liqui*.'

Strange man, she found herself thinking achingly. An
unconventional man. A man with such conflicting sides to
his character that she found it impossible to work him out.
Sometimes proud, coldly conventional, sometimes so
avant-garde that he shocked her—like now.

My God, she thought hectically. He's really a complete
stranger to me. And I'm about to marry him!

A shudder ran through her—of horror or fear or excitement she wasn't sure, because he had her so confused that
she really could not be sure of anything any more.

He had come to a standstill one long stride into the room,
his green gaze narrowed on her as it travelled slowly from
the dainty white satin shoes on her feet to the top of her
golden head. Annie waited in mute defiance for him to
make some remark about the distinct lack of decoration on
her head.

Sheer habit had made her dress her hair to suit the garment she was wearing; the long hair had been caught up
in a silky twist at her crown, then she'd teased fine silken
strands to fall around her face so that they accentuated the
delicate line of her long, slender neck, but she'd drawn the
line at adding the lace veil with its circlet of blue rose-
buds—a crowning hypocrisy she refused to comply with.

'You look beautiful,' he said gruffly.

She didn't bother to answer. She was Annie Lacey, after
all—professional model. She knew how good she looked.

So a short silence followed, one which oddly caught at
the tiny muscles in her stomach and tied them into knots.
This should not be happening, she told herself wretchedly.
Neither of us wants it. None of it is real.

'Here.' He broke the silence, walking towards her with a flat velvet box in his hand.

Annie instantly recognised it for what it was, and snapped her hands behind her back. 'No, I won't wear whatever it is,' she refused.

'Why not?' A sleek black brow rose in question.

She gave a stubborn shake of her head. 'I don't need your jewels, Mr Adamas,' she used the name bitingly. 'Only your real name for appearance's sake.'

'Still fighting me, Annie?' He smiled. But it wasn't the teasing note in his voice that made her quiver, it was the use of her pet name falling for the first time from his beautifully sculptured lips that did it.

She struggled for breath. 'I think I've been remarkably compliant, if you must know,' she told him. 'But I draw the line at looking as if you bought me with—those.' Her eyes flicked a contemptuous glance at the unopened box. 'Keep them for your next wife,' she suggested tartly. 'Since this one is already praying for deliverance before the rest of this month is out.'

He should have got angry. She'd certainly intended provoking him into it. But he didn't; his green gaze studied her stiff face for a moment before he said quite gently, 'Five million dollars is a lot to pay for a wife, Angelica.' And as her mouth dropped open in stunned disbelief he tossed the velvet case onto the bed behind her. 'But I am willing to pay it for just one kiss from your *sweet* lips.'

She was still too busy struggling with the cost of whatever was in the box to realise his intentions. So when his mouth closed gently over her own she found herself returning the kiss without really being aware that she was doing it.

'You just earned your prize,' he murmured gruffly as he

lifted his head. Then he added tauntingly, 'Or were you too busy counting dollar signs to notice?'

She blinked up at him, taking a moment or two to realise just what he was getting at. Then her blue eyes flared on a surge of anger and she spun around, lurching to grab at the velvet case then twisting to thrust it right back at the arrogant swine.

But he was already over by the door. 'Five minutes,' he warned. 'Wear them or not. I really do not care. They now belong to you.'

'But I don't want them!' she shouted at his disappearing back.

'And neither, *querida*, do I.'

She wore them in the end. Out of sheer cussedness or because she had the oddest feeling that she'd managed to offend him over the dratted things, she wasn't sure. But it was certainly with a grudging defiance that she eventually opened the box and found herself staring at the most beautiful necklace she had ever seen in her life.

Sapphires—exquisite dark blue sapphire hearts circled by tiny diamonds and linked together by the finest white gold, each setting a perfect match to the next—and the next and the next! There were over a dozen of them in all, fashioned to balance the larger central stone that quite literally took her breath away.

But that wasn't all. Nestled in the sensual curve of each sapphire heart sat a diamond—heart-shaped again, and seeming to flash a message at her that she refused to read. It had to be her imagination, she told herself breathlessly, because the white gold claw grips which held the two jewels together took on the shape of fingers to her mesmerised eyes, as though each pair of hearts rested in the palm of a delicate hand.

She couldn't wear these! She couldn't!

Yet, when a warning knock sounded at her door, she found herself tremulously fixing the necklace round her throat before she hurried from the room.

'Thank you,' he murmured when she eventually joined him, and once again she gained the impression that her compliance had actually managed to move him.

Feeling tense and nervous, she reacted with bad grace. 'Well,' she snapped, 'where is this charade supposed to take place?'

A small nerve twitched in the corner of his straight mouth. 'Here,' he answered quietly. 'Right here.' And indicated with an outstretched hand the open glass doors.

'Outside?' she questioned in surprise.

'It is traditional.' He nodded gravely.

A frisson of something frighteningly close to yearning shivered through her. No. She swallowed tensely. She couldn't go through with it. Not like this. Not with all the—

'Come, Angelica.' His hand closed gently around her slender waist.

'N-no,' she whispered. 'I can't do this. It isn't right. I feel a fraud. I...'

César turned her fully to face him, a hand coming up to cup her chin gently. 'Don't lose courage now,' he entreated softly. 'Everything will be fine, you'll see. Trust me.'

Trust him. He kept on telling her to trust him, but how could she when he had done nothing but trick and deceive her from the first moment they'd met?

'Please,' he murmured deeply, as if he could read her thoughts as his own. 'Please?'

His eyes held onto hers, dark green and probing, seeming to reach right inside her to some tiny, frightened point of need and soothe it gently. Her body quivered on a shaky little sigh, her mind going fluffy as it began to lose its grasp on reason.

A flash bulb popped.

'Are we ready?' a soft voice intruded.

Annie turned her head, seeing what her dazed mind interpreted as an angel standing in the open doorway to the room—a small, dark-skinned angel with snowy white hair, white flowing robes and a beautiful smile.

She blinked in an effort to clear her head, glanced hazily back at César, who had not moved his gaze from her face.

She felt trapped suddenly, lost, drowning in the compelling expression in his eyes. So much so that she didn't see the second flash bulb pop, did not even notice the photographer who was capturing in full Technicolour Annie Lacey decked out in white lace and sapphires, gazing into the eyes of the man she was about to marry.

CHAPTER EIGHT

IT WAS over. And the moment they found themselves alone again Annie seemed to lose complete grip on reality.

Strain, she told herself in some vague corner of her mind. You've cracked beneath the strain, and dropped weakly down into a nearby chair.

César had disappeared into his own room. He had murmured a reason for going at her but she hadn't absorbed the words. Her mind seemed to have completely shut down. Nothing going in—nothing much coming out. It was a strange, lost, floaty feeling that kind of buffeted her gently from the inside, holding her slack-limbed and still.

Coming back from his bedroom, César stopped dead, his gaze homing in on her frail white figure, looking more lost and vulnerable than he had seen her to date. A moment's anguish passed across his face, forcing his hands into two tense fists before he grimly relaxed them; then he was moving forwards to go and squat down beside her.

Carefully he reached for her hands. They were cold, and gently he began chafing them between his own. 'Surely it was not quite this bad an ordeal?' he mocked, infusing a teasing lightness into his tone.

She turned her head to look at him, her eyes like two huge sapphires in her lovely white face. 'Why the photographer?' she asked.

His shrug was careless. 'He came with the package,' he said. 'Why, did he bother you?'

'No.' Nothing bothered her. Not any more. She looked away again, her eyes drifting sightlessly back to the open windows where a soft, warm breeze disturbed the curtains pulled back by thickly plaited ties.

A knock came at the door; César laid her hands back on her lap before standing up and moving away. Annie looked down at them, stretching out the fingers where two new rings glinted in the light—one a hand-crafted, intricately woven band of the richest, purest gold, the other a beautiful sapphire and diamond ring designed to match the necklace at her throat. When César had slipped it on her finger directly after he had slid the gold band there she'd been too surprised to protest.

Now she just stared at it and wanted to weep.

A movement in front of her brought her unblinking gaze upwards. César was standing over her, a cup of something steaming hot in his hands. Silently he handed it to her. Annie caught the scent of a good old-fashioned cup of tea, and sipped gratefully at it until she felt life begin to return to her body at last.

'Thank you,' she murmured finally. 'That was thoughtful of you.' Then, because he was just standing there watching her with a concerned frown marring his attractive face, she added wryly, 'I'm sorry. I seemed to lose contact with myself for a few minutes there.'

'But you feel better now?'

'Yes.' She flexed one of her hands and watched the colour seep back into the bloodless skin. 'Odd—to have such a reaction to something that is, after all, only a sham.'

He didn't answer, something vaguely disturbing in his still, quiet stance. Then, before she could try to work out what was troubling him, he made a move that was rather like a gesture of contempt.

'You're right,' he agreed. 'The whole thing was an absolute farce. With hindsight I cannot think of a more flippant way to make such solemn vows.' He sounded harsh and bitter. Annie glanced at him in surprise, but he was already turning away. 'Take your time. Enjoy your tea,' he invited as he strode tightly towards his own room. 'Then get changed and we will get out of here. The quicker we can be alone, the quicker we can put all of this from our minds!'

'Regretting it already, César?' she drawled.

He stopped. 'Maybe,' he said grimly without turning around. 'Maybe I am regretting the whole damned thing!'

So, what did you expect? she mocked herself starkly as he shut himself away. Protests? Reassurance? Avowals of undying love? Tears spread across her vision but she blinked them angrily away.

You're beginning to believe your own press, she told herself angrily. Annie Lacey gets married so therefore she must be in love.

But you're not in love with him, are you? Are you?

And he is certainly not in love with you!

They had another row before leaving the bungalow, this particular one ending up with them both shouting because this time Annie was determined to win—no matter how scathing he became.

'Will you take them back?' she insisted, thrusting the velvet case into the rigid wall of his chest. They were both safely in the case—the necklace and the beautiful sapphire ring. 'I don't want them!'

'Well, neither do I,' he countered, refusing to take hold of it. 'They're yours. I gave them to you, and if there was an ounce of good manners in you you would accept them graciously as most women would do!'

'I am not *most women*,' she snapped, taking offence at even that basically innocent remark. 'I do not accept ridiculously expensive gifts—even from the man who was my first lover!' she flashed at him before he could flash the

remark at her, and she was sure that he would have done—
she could see the threat of it glinting in his angry green
eyes. 'Or because he happens to be my first husband, come
to that,' she added for good measure.

'And your last if you don't stop this!' he countered impatiently.

'But why do you want me to have them?' she cried in
honest, angry bewilderment. 'Why—why—why?'

To her absolute surprise dark colour spread across his
high cheeks, a sudden discomfited look forcing him to hood
his eyes. 'I made them for you,' he muttered, so gruffly
that she barely caught the words.

'What?' she prompted doubtfully. 'What did you say?
You made them—for me? Is that what you said?'

'Yes,' he hissed, as though the confirmation were
wrenched forcibly from him. 'They were designed for
you—made—made exclusively for you, OK?'

For the first time he sounded truly American. Usually he
sounded a rather attractive mix of two cultures, but that
forced admission, with its accompanying flail of one angry,
defensive, very threatening hand that was warning her not
to push the subject further, had been pure American bull-
ishness all the way through.

She blinked, silenced. And with a harsh sigh he thrust
his fists into the pockets of his casual camel-coloured trousers. 'If you don't want them,' he gritted, 'then sell them,
chuck them—give them away. But don't try giving them
back to me because I just don't want them.'

'But this is crazy!' she whispered when eventually she
found her voice again, unable to leave the subject even with
the threat he had issued still pulsing in the air between
them. 'Why should you design something as beautiful as
these for someone like me?'

Another sigh. His shoulders hunched, and for a long,

tense moment Annie thought that he was going to refuse to answer. 'They match the colour of your eyes,' he said at last, in a tight dismissive tone that was supposed to make her say, Oh! That's why! with relief, when he had to know that that excuse had to be the most laughable he could have offered. These beautiful pieces had been conceived and made long before he'd ever met her, at a time when he'd despised her for everything she was.

'No,' she said. 'It isn't enough that the sapphires happen to match my eyes. Half the world's population has blue eyes! So you're either trying to fob me off with just about the weakest excuse you've come up with for anything to date or this is what I suspected it to be from the beginning—a gift of conscience. And, as such, I refuse to accept it—unequivocally.'

Their eyes locked on each other's, hers in challenge, his in a kind of defiance that she found strangely exhilarating. But as they continued to stand there warring silently other elements began to join in the battle. Her senses began to stir, tiny muscles deep down inside her beginning to pump to a rhythm that set her whole body pulsing.

He had to be feeling it too, because she watched his green eyes darken, his mouth slacken from angry tension into a heart-contracting sensuality.

No. She denied it as the air around them seemed to grow hot and heavy, the ability to breathe it in more difficult with each shallow breath. No. But she couldn't seem to find the will to break the disturbing contact.

Sex—she named it contemptuously as the whole cacophony of sensation grew into a pounding throb. He wants me, and, God help me, I'm responding! Fingers tingled with the need to touch; breasts stung with a need to feel his mouth closed around them. Warmth flooded the sweet, burning liquid of desire into her shaking limbs.

No. She denied it again. No! And in an act of sheer desperation she broke the mood by stretching out an arm and with a defiant sideways flick sent the velvet case slewing onto a nearby table.

It landed with a thud and a slither. César did not so much as bat an eyelid, but at least the hunger died out of his eyes.

He turned abruptly, placing his tense back with its ridiculous pony-tail towards her, and—damn it—she suddenly wanted to grab hold of that lock of hair, wrench at it, hurt him, launch herself at him and beat her fists against the ungiving wall of his back in an effort to relieve this—this crazy sense of bitter frustration throbbing in her blood!

Sexual frustration! she told herself angrily. And it's all his fault! He's done this to me! Made me aware, know, want—desire!

'Shall we go, then?' he said, and moved arrogantly off towards the door.

Instantly the feelings running rife inside her flipped over to become something else entirely, her gaze flicking to the discarded jewel-case then back to him again.

He didn't mean it, she told herself nervously. He was calling her bluff. No man just walked away and left what amounted to a five-million-dollar tip for the maid!

He was standing by the bungalow door with his hand curled around the handle, waiting for her to join him. Mutinously Annie walked forward, cold sweat beginning to trickle down her spine the closer she got to him, and still he made no move to retrieve the case. Unable to stop herself, she glanced back at it, black velvet askew on a polished tabletop. Her mouth was dry, her fingers twitching at her sides as she turned back to him.

'Don't,' she pleaded.

'Your choice,' he returned with ruthless indifference. And he calmly opened the door and stepped through it.

Annie hovered between a stubborn desire to defy him to the last and a real horror of what it would mean if neither gave in. Then with a growl of angry defeat she darted back to pick up the case.

Her eyes were hard as she walked back to him. To be fair, César made no remark whatsoever—either by word or gesture. He simply waited until she was out of the room then drew the door shut, his manner grimly aloof as he led the way back through the garden to the waiting helicopter.

It did not augur well for the journey back to his island. Annie was too busy drowning in a sea of her own resentment, and he seemed to have drawn himself behind a wall of impenetrable calm.

Still clutching the case, the moment they were back at the villa she made a bid for escape, stalking off towards the stairs with her spine and shoulders stiff.

'Annie.'

Her spine stiffened even more. For some unknown reason he had suddenly taken to calling her Annie, instead of Angelica in that crisp, tight way he used to use. She didn't like it. Didn't like what it did to her. It hinted at care and affection—an intimacy that touched tender places inside.

'What?' she bit out ungraciously, pausing but refusing to turn. If he had something to say then she was determined that he was going to say it to her back!

'Come swimming with me.'

Of all the things she might have expected him to say at that point that had never been in the running! The invitation stunned her—and the way he'd said it, with such wary uncertainty, shook her poise enough to make her spin around.

He was standing framed by sunlight in the open door, filling it, consuming the light so that she could not see his face. She slid her fingers absently over the velvet case while she tried to search out the catch in the invitation. He remained silent, watching her, waiting, tense—she could sense his tension even with the full length of the huge hall between them.

'Why?' she demanded finally.

'The bay has some wondrous sights to offer,' he answered quietly. 'I think you would enjoy discovering them with me.'

'I could make those discoveries just as pleasurably on my own,' she pointed out churlishly. 'Especially when you think I have two whole weeks to do little else but explore the bay.'

'But to do it with someone who knows it well will be much more rewarding,' he pointed out. 'And I would—enjoy sharing the experience with you.'

She was tempted; despite all the animosity darting around them she had to admit that she was tempted. It was hot, and she was fed-up, restless, eager to be using up some of the energy pounding like a frustrated rubber ball inside her. But swim with him? Display yet another climb-down from frosty aloofness to him?

'All right,' she heard herself say reluctantly, yet felt better for saying it, some of the tension easing out of her achingly taut frame. Then with a flash of inspiration she added slyly, 'I'll come if you'll relieve me of these.' Challengingly she held out the velvet case. 'I'll never get a moment's rest worrying about them otherwise. Lock them away in a safe or something—I presume you do have a safe here, considering who and what you are?'

Surprisingly he nodded, moving into action, that lean, muscled body sheer poetry in motion as he covered the distance between them. Without a word he took the case from her. With his face in the same shade she occupied she could now read his expression. Ruefully conceding seemed to describe it best.

He was giving her back what she had just given him—
a climb-down. It helped to warm her frozen feelings a little.

'I will promise to guard them well for you.'

Not so big a climb-down, Annie acknowledged. But now
she'd relaxed she couldn't seem to find the strength to start
battling once again.

'Ten minutes?' he asked, seeming suddenly vitally alive
as he walked off towards a door to the right of the vast
hallway. 'On the beach,' he added. 'I'll bring the snorkelling gear.'

He was already waiting for her when she walked down
from the house towards the small, sandy beach. He was
dressed in nothing more than a pair of black swimming
shorts, and her eyes flickered reluctantly over his long,
tanned legs with their coating of crisp, dark hair that curled
all the way up to the bulging apex at his thighs.

She swallowed, feeling that warm rush of awareness ex-
plode inside her. For a few dragging moments it held her
helpless and distraught. Then she managed to close her
eyes, shut out the pulsing cry of her awakened body, shut
out the sight of the man who had incited it all to life.

'Ready?'

He sounded strange, as though something was constrict-
ing his throat. Glancing at him again, she felt a fine sweat
break out on her skin at the expression on his dark, chiselled features as his eyes ran over her skimpy sugar-pink
one-piece then came burning back to her face.

He knew. He knew why she had stopped walking and
what was happening to her. He knew because she could
see that the same thing was happening to him.

And it's getting worse, she accepted starkly. Stronger.

He looked away with a sharp, jerky gesture of denial,
his solid jaw tightening, his big chest heaving, his hands
clenching into two tight fists at his sides. Then he seemed

to get a hold of himself. 'I thought we would borrow Pedro's boat,' he said. 'He keeps it in the next bay.' A hand lifted to indicate across the headland covered in lush tropical undergrowth. 'We can take it out and anchor it over the reef. That way we will see more.'

He didn't wait for an answer but bent to snatch up the snorkelling gear piled by his feet and strode off, back rigid, that black silky tail of hair covering the tension in his spine.

Her own inclination was to turn and run in the opposite direction. But, shaken and disturbed as she was by the power of need he had awoken inside her, she was also tensely aware that his needs were just as strong, and she had a horrible suspicion that if she did turn and run he would follow, and, as sure as hell, the eruption she could feel building steadily between them would happen. She could feel its threat to her bubbling fretfully beneath the thin surface of her self-control.

So she began to follow him, reluctant but aware that at least this way they both had time to pull themselves together.

She was right—well, half right—she noted wryly several tense minutes later as they emerged from a narrow pathway that led over the top of the rocky headland and through the lush undergrowth to a tiny circle of sand, where she could see a small boat with an outboard motor lying lopsidedly just above the tide line.

They were fine so long as they did not make eye contact with each other. And the fact that César was of the same mind made it easier to remain calm as he threw the snorkelling gear into the bottom of the boat then began dragging it, his muscles rippling in the sunlight, into the water before inviting her to get in.

'Pedro uses this for fishing,' he explained, once the motor had sprung into life and they were moving slowly across the top of the clear, calm sea. 'He catches something fresh and different every day.'

'They live very quietly here,' Annie remarked, her eyes fixed on the cut and swell of water around the boat. 'Don't they get lonely with no other company than their own?'

'They visit their family on the mainland quite often,' he told her. 'I have a launch anchored at Union Island. It is at their disposal whenever they feel the need to make use of it.'

'But no phone.' Annie frowned. 'How do they let anyone know what they want without some line of communication?'

'Been searching for a way to cry for help, Angelica?' he drawled.

Her cheeks flushed, because that was exactly what she had done yesterday after he'd left her alone. She'd wanted to ring Lissa—not Todd but Lissa—and beg her to find a way out of this mess without involving Todd.

Todd. Even white teeth buried themselves anxiously into her lower lip. If Todd found out what had been going on here there would be hell to pay. She was sure of it.

'There is a radio,' César inserted smoothly, 'linked directly with my head office in Caracas. But, other than that, they are, I assure you, content with their lot or they would not stay.'

'What kind of office?' she asked him, reluctantly curious about this man she had married. 'I mean,' she continued mockingly, 'what do you do when you're not being Adamas?'

He smiled at the way she had put that last bit. 'Actually, my fascination for precious stones and metal is really just a hobby.' He shrugged, as though a billion-dollar hobby was peanuts to him.

'But as DeSanquez—' wryly he used that mockery she'd

used on himself '—I head the DeSanquez Organisation—oil, a couple of diamond and gold mines, a beef ranch or two, several other business interests which bring in a good revenue. All this I inherited from my father,' he informed her. 'But my mother was the family artist. From her I learned to develop my skill with precious metal and stones. From my father I learned to succeed in big business.'

The double persona. Annie had always known it was there in him. 'And the hair?' she asked, because it was the hair that first had made her suspect that he was two people. 'Do you wear it so long because of some DeSanquez tradition? Or—?'

His laughter was warm and resonant, and it shimmered through Annie like a heatwave. 'Nothing so—romantic,' he replied, still smiling. 'I simply—like it this way. Call it the artist in me, if you like, needing to make a stand against the businessman.' he cocked a quizzical eyebrow at her. 'Does it bother you?' he asked curiously. 'Would you rather I had my hair cut in a more conventional style?'

'No!' she denied impulsively, then flushed as his green eyes began to gleam. 'It—it doesn't bother me one way or the other,' she said offhandedly.

'Doesn't it?' he murmured softly. And she had to look away from those dark, knowing eyes, wishing that she hadn't mentioned his ridiculous hair!

She went quiet after that. And César turned his attention to guiding the little boat out of the shelter of the tiny cove and towards the mouth of Hook-nose Bay, where he stopped the engine and tossed the small anchor out onto the reef.

'Have you snorkelled before?' he asked.

Annie nodded and so did he. 'Good. So you know what to do with these.' He handed her a pair of flippers and a snorkelling mask. 'Give me a minute to get into the water and I'll help you out of the boat.'

Surprisingly it turned out to be an enjoyable hour. With César leading the way they snorkelled over the tip of and between narrow canyons of coral, treading water regularly when one or the other saw something interesting beneath them.

They saw brightly coloured cardinals and butterfly fish and spotted drums. Pretty blue parrot-fish swam in and out of the coral, and a couple of big groupers hurried away when they saw them coming. At one point César grabbed urgently at her hand, demanding her attention then pointing over to a deeper point on the coral where she could see a long, sleek silver fish with a pike-like face. Barracuda! she recognised instantly, and tried to turn and swim back to the boat.

But César stopped her, holding onto her arm and grinning at her through his mask. Firmly he pulled her off in the other direction, where they found an octopus sitting on a rock, his bulbous body swaying to and fro in the lazy current.

Then a dark brown moray eel slid its ugly face out from between two rocks and Annie decided with a shudder that she'd had enough. She turned swiftly before César could stop her and swam quickly back to the boat.

'Yuk!' she exclaimed as they both bobbed up beside the boat. 'Did you see that moray? He has to be about the ugliest creature alive in the sea!'

'Don't let Mrs Moray hear you saying that,' César warned teasingly. 'She may take offence and bite off your toes.'

The fact that Annie had just removed her flippers and thrown them into the bottom of the boat, leaving her toes very vulnerable, meant that his remark was well timed. She shrieked, and made a lurching dive for safety, almost managing to drown them both as she landed in a flail of arms and legs against his big, strong chest.

One of his arms closed instinctively round her while the other hand grabbed at the side of the boat, his amused laughter filling the air.

Then he wasn't laughing, and Annie had gone perfectly still because it had happened, just like that. Quick, strong and undeniable. Awareness—hot and stifling. Skin sliding wetly against skin. Bodies remembering—recognising the pleasurable potency of the other.

His arm was tight around her slender waist, his eyes burning fiercely into the wide, shocked depths of hers.

'Please, César, no,' she pleaded when she saw his gaze drop to her mouth.

'Why not?' he murmured huskily. 'Why not, when you know it is what we both want?'

'No.' She shook her wet head, fingers curling tensely into the rigid muscles in his shoulders.

'A kiss. Just a kiss.'

'No.' But she felt the muscles deep in her body tighten in sweet expectancy.

'Yes,' he countered, his eyes darkening languorously, his mouth taking on a soft, sensual curve. 'Yes, dammit, yes.' And he moved to angle his lips against her own.

Annie shied away, twisting her head and stretching her body as she made a desperate grab for the boat with both hands. The action set the little boat rocking precariously, and for a moment she hung there helplessly, because César did not immediately concede defeat and let her go, his arm remaining a possessive clamp around her slender waist. Her heart began to pump, tension in the muscles around it making each heavy thump painful. She closed her eyes, wet lashes spiked and trembling against the soft skin covering her high cheek-bones.

If he pulls me back…she thought tensely. If he pulls me back I'll give in to him. I know I will!

Then the arm was slackening, and instead of imprisoning it became two hands on her waist, helping to lever her into the boat.

She didn't look at him as he joined her there, and though she felt his eyes on her she let the tense silence grow. The afternoon was spoiled now anyway, the brief period of easy pleasure they had found in each other's company ruined by a torment that simply refused to go away.

César must have been thinking along similar lines, because instead of getting them under way he sat back and let loose a heavy sigh. 'Refusing to acknowledge it will not make it easier,' he said gravely. 'It simply makes it worse. Believe me, I know.'

'The voice of experience?' she flashed at him bitterly.

He grimaced then shrugged. 'Yes,' he admitted, though she suspected that he didn't want to.

'You are a complete stranger to me.' Grimly she stared at the gold band encircling her finger. 'A week ago I didn't know of your existence. Three days ago we met and parted without my even learning your name. Forty-eight hours ago…' Almost exactly, she then added as a bitter, silent adjoiner as her gaze drifted out to the steadily dying day. 'You were throwing insults and threats at me and vowing to ruin my life!'

'And two hours after that you were lying in my arms,' he added, 'getting to know me as intimately as a woman can. What does that tell you, Annie,' he prompted gently, 'about the insults and threats that preceded the passion?'

It told her that they were a front to what had really been erupting between them. Memories crowded in—hot, turbulent memories that darkened her eyes and thickened her breath. Then came the shudder of shame—the shame of knowing how easily and thoroughly she had surrendered to the morass of desires raging through her that night.

'Instant physical attraction is not uncommon between the sexes, Angelica,' César inserted quietly. 'It happens all the time.'

Not to me it doesn't, she thought. 'You are still a stranger,' she said. 'A man who set out to trap and manipulate me from the first moment we met.'

'I'm sorry.' He heaved an impatient sigh. 'I have learned to regret my original intentions. What else can I say?' His green eyes glinted at her in helpless appeal.

'Nothing,' she mumbled, and made a play of straightening the wet snorkelling gear littering the bottom of the boat.

César watched her for a while, his face tight and grim. Then he sighed again, and turned his attention to pulling up the anchor.

They chugged back to the little cove in sober silence, sitting close in the tight confines of the small boat, yet with a thick wall erected between them. With a deft cut of the motor at just the right moment he eased the nose of the boat up onto the beach on the crest of an incoming wave. Then he was jumping out and wading forwards to help Annie clamber out.

The feel of his hand on her arm made her flesh tingle, and she couldn't stop the revealing shiver that feathered her slender frame.

His grip tightened fractionally in response. 'It won't go away,' he repeated roughly from just behind her. 'We've lit the flame, Annie. Now it's hungry for more.'

She didn't answer, but pulled free of him and walked away on legs weak and trembling in reaction, because she knew that he was right. And, far from going away, it was getting stronger. Worse. Desperate almost.

Dinner that evening was an ordeal. To be fair to César he tried to keep the mood light and casual, but she could hardly look at him without feeling her senses catch light.

It frightened her—the intensity of her awareness of him. Her mind refused to stop replaying to her how his silken, tight skin, hidden beneath the conventional white shirt he was wearing, felt to the touch, or reminding her how those long, blunt-ended fingers he used to pick up his glass or lift his fork to his mouth could draw such clamorous pleasure from her. His mouth, sipping intermittently at wine, was saying words she did not hear, because she was too lost in the memory of how they had felt tasting her—

'More wine?'

'What?' She started, her eyes focusing on the sardonic expression in his. He knew, and she flushed, looking quickly down and away. 'No—thank you,' she refused, and jerked to her feet. 'I'm—t-tired,' she stammered nervously. 'I think I'll go to bed.'

She didn't wait for him to answer, didn't look at him again, but she was fiercely aware of his sardonic gaze following her hurried journey across the room, and felt as if she was ready to crack in two under the tension inside her as she left him with a flurry of nervous limbs.

CHAPTER NINE

THE moon set early in the Caribbean, leaving it to the myriad stars hanging in the satin-dark sky to provide what light there was filtering into Annie's bedroom. It was enough, or at least enough to save the room from a total blackout. She could just make out the mirror hanging on the opposite wall, for instance, and the dark shapes of furniture scattered about the room.

Wide awake, even though it had to be way past midnight, she traced the shapes lazily with her eyes, her body very still beneath the white cotton sheet that she had drawn up beneath her arms. But inside she was restless, troubled—disturbed by what was bothering her and what she could not seem to control unless she lay very still like this and breathed very carefully, and centred her whole concentration on keeping it all severely banked down.

Is this what it feels like, she wondered, to want what you shouldn't want? To desire what you should not desire? To need it so badly that it actually became the driving force for your life's blood?

Sighing shakily, she lifted a hand to rest it beneath her cool cheek, settling against it as though it would offer some comfort, some relief.

It didn't, and the fingers on the other hand began to tap a restless dance against the graceful curve of her long thigh beneath the sheet. Her gaze lowered to watch them, her mind acknowledging that the restlessness was beginning to break out. Perhaps she should get up and take a walk along the beach? she mused. Do something—anything to take her mind off what she knew was trying to break through all her restraints.

Sex. You've tasted the elixir, Annie, and now you're hungry for more.

She smiled at her own mockery, then stopped smiling, the fingers stopping their tapping when her gaze caught the washed-out glint of gold encircling the third finger on her left hand.

Married to a man who made you a millionairess within minutes of putting that ring there. She frowned. What had made him do it? No man in his right mind gave a woman he hardly knew a gift like that!

There again, no man who saw that woman as little better than a whore took her to bed and ravished her. Not a man of César's calibre, anyway.

He was a strange man—a complicated man. A man who contrarily confused, infuriated and fascinated her with his quick-fire changes in character. One minute arrogant, insufferably domineering—bullish. The next, soft, caring, gentle, considerate—dynamically charming when she least expected it.

Dangerous too, she added to her growing list. Dangerous because he had managed to do what no man before him had ever done, and had got beneath the protective skin she wore so thickly around herself. Dangerous because he wanted her with a hunger that burned constantly behind whatever else they were doing, whether that was slinging insults at each other or just trying—trying—to be civilised towards each other.

And what about yourself? she then countered grimly. Your behaviour is no less contrary than his! You profess to hate and despise him for what he's done, but you also want him with the same unforgivable hunger.

Every time you look at him you torture yourself with

memories of how his lips felt against your own, or how frighteningly superb he looked naked and aroused, or what it felt like to have him deep inside you! If he so much as touches you your skin leaps into vibrant, burning life, your stomach muscles knot and your thighs throb.

Hell, even lying here just thinking of him and it's all beginning to happen!

Restlessly she moved again, flipping over to lie curled on her side, half considering getting up, going for that walk along the beach that she had suggested to herself, when her bedroom door came open, and all thoughts of any kind were suspended as the disturbingly dark bulk of a man seemed to fill the whole room.

He paused for a moment. She stopped breathing, her very bones tingling as if they'd just received an electric shock.

Then he was stepping inwards and closing the door behind him. Her heart took up an unsteady hammer. Eyes huge, throat locking, she watched him walk slowly towards the bed where she lay.

He was wearing a thin black cotton robe and nothing else as far as she could tell. And she could almost feel the tension in his body as he came closer, bringing with him the scent of male heat and the tantalising freshness of a spicy male soap.

As he came to a standstill right beside where she lay she lifted her eyes to let them clash with his; hers were wary, questioning what this unexpected visit meant when really she knew exactly what it meant. The reality of it was already turning the very tissue of her being to a warm, sensual liquid because his eyes were hiding nothing—nothing.

Yet in silence he waited. Breathlessly she waited. Eyes locked. The tension between them was so fraught that she could almost taste it, even ran her tongue around parched lips as if to do just that.

When long moments passed and she had said not a word he bent down towards her, braced his hands on the pillow either side of her head and murmured softly, 'Invite me to stay.'

Her senses quivered. 'I...' The sound came out frail and breathless—hardly a sound at all really as she found herself caught by the beauty of his sensually moulded mouth hovering a bare inch away from her own.

'Please.' He closed the gap and kissed her. It was nothing more than the gentlest touch of his mouth against her own, but her own lips clung as he drew away again.

'Please,' he repeated softly. 'Please...'

At last she breathed, her breasts lifting and falling on the small, constricted action. But other than that she couldn't manage another single thing. Yet...

Had she answered? she found herself wondering dizzily. She was vaguely certain that she hadn't said yes, but was also sure that she hadn't said no.

But whatever she did do César took it as an affirmative, because after a moment he whispered, 'Thank you.' Then he was straightening again, holding her gaze with his own darkly burning one as he unknotted and stripped off his robe, paused for a moment as if to give her a final opportunity to make a protest, jaw clenched, the rigid walls of his stomach clenched, his body already wearing the evidence of desire.

Then he lifted the edge of the thin sheet and in one fluid, graceful movement came to lie down beside her.

His fingers were trembling a little as he gently stroked them across her cheek and slid them beneath the heavy fall of her hair. Then he was drawing her towards him, turning her, moulding her, and slowly—oh, so slowly that her senses began to vibrate, her lips to pulse, part, gasp out a

single shaky breath—he closed the gap between their
mouths.

His lips were as full and pulsing as her own, both so hot
that they seemed to fuse, the shock of it sending one of her
hands jerking up to press against his chest.

He shuddered. It ran through him like a tidal wave, drawing a groan from him; then he was pushing her gently onto
her back and coming with her, his upper body crushing her
into the soft mattress as it pressed lightly down.

For a moment her courage failed, memories of that other
hot violent eruption of passion making her gasp in shaky
fear.

But he soothed her with a caressing hand. 'No,' he murmured, as if he knew exactly what had frightened her. 'This
is passion I am feeling for you, not angry desire. It runs
through my blood like a fire, but it is not destructive. Some
fires cleanse, Angelica,' he told her softly. 'I want to
cleanse that other experience from your mind.'

Then he was kissing her again, and any hope of forming
a conscious decision for herself was lost in the slow, deep
sensuality of it.

It went on and on, not even breaking when he began to
caress her, his hand sliding against the smooth silk of her
nightdress in a long, sweeping motion that followed the
delicacy of her ribcage, the flatness of her stomach and
finally the length of her thighs where the nightdress ended
and satin-smooth flesh began.

She must have moved restlessly because he instantly
soothed her again, bringing his other hand out from beneath
her head to lay it gently against her cheek.

And still the beautiful kiss did not break. Nor did it when
he spent an age seemingly content to stroke her like that.
He didn't touch her intimately, didn't even try to remove
her nightdress, but simply played a kind of magic with her

flesh, coaxing, gently coaxing the fine, light tremors to overtake her, and eventually her muscles to begin expanding and contracting to the sensual rhythm he induced.

In the end she couldn't stand it, and dragged her mouth away from his with a sharp, helpless gasp for air. He let her go, his eyes almost sombre as they studied her, his hand pausing against the quivering flesh of her stomach.

'What?' he whispered. 'What?'

She closed her eyes in confusion. Even his softly spoken voice was having the most overwhelming effect on her. 'I don't know,' she breathed, panting a little in an effort to control what was happening inside her.

'Then don't try to think,' he advised. 'Just follow me. Trust me, Annie. And between us we will make this the most beautiful experience of our lives.'

Trust him. Follow him. She really did not have any choice. From the moment his mouth captured hers again she was lost—lost in the dark, sensual beauty of the man. Lost in what he could make her feel, and lost in the wonder of what she could do to him.

It was slow and it was rich and it went very deep, each touch, each caress, each accidental brush of their skin heightening an awareness inside them that seemed to encapsulate the two of them in a hot, dark world of their own.

His touch became more intimate, knowing, sending her boneless so she lay there in helpless thrall. The caress of his tongue on her eager skin drew soft gasps of pleasure from her, the silk-like thrust of his throbbing manhood nudging against her thigh filling her with a sense of power that made her bold.

When she began caressing him he fell heavily onto his back, to lie blatant in his desire for more, eyes closed, mouth parted, his gasps of pleasure urging her on. His skin felt like tightly padded satin, the muscles beneath it rigid then rippling in response to her touch. She kissed his damp throat then his shoulder, then, unable to resist it, tasted his sweat on her tongue, trailing it over his chest until she found and began to suck on his tight male nipple.

His hands jerked up to grasp her head tightly, holding her there while he seemed to stop breathing, to go motionless as the sensations she was causing inside him took hold.

Then her hand glided tentatively over his stomach, and he jolted into life like a man shot, startling her as he reared upwards and over her, his hand whipping down to imprison hers as his husky growl revealed the extent of his arousal before he was kissing her hungrily again, stopping her from thinking again, taking control again, slowing things down, drawing it out until she really believed that she was going to die if he didn't do something to ease the unbearable pressure building deep down inside her.

Her hand jerked to his hair, fingers curling, tightening, tugging with unknown violence, dragging the thin ribbon free so that the black satiny mass slid like a curtain all around her. She sighed against his mouth, restlessly urgent. Someone was groaning and whimpering, and she knew that someone was herself. Her senses were in ferment, rushing in a panicked stampede through her body in an effort to crowd where the tension grew.

He must have understood because he moved then, sliding between her thighs where his fingers still played their magic, keeping up that sensual rhythm until the very moment when he joined them in a single mind-blowing thrust.

Annie arched like a bow, arms flying out and upwards in total abandonment. He arched too, like a giant wolf about to howl its mournful song, his long back, his dark head in a taut arch of pleasure, and for a space out of time neither were of this earth, neither aware of the other as sensation washed their brains of all else.

Then she felt the tug of her own muscles, felt them draw him in deeper, felt him grow and throb and fill her; then desperate fingers were reaching for him even as he came down towards her.

Afterwards she lay wrapped tightly in his arms, his body curled round her as though she were in need of protection and he was determined to give it. They didn't speak, hadn't found the words to cover what had just taken place. All Annie knew was that in the moment when he'd entered her César had become her; she'd felt that right down to the very roots of her being. Whether he'd experienced the same thing she didn't know, but by the way he'd held her and kept on holding her, even long after he had fallen into a deep sleep, she had to believe that he had.

He woke her once more before morning, bringing her swimming up from sleep to the pleasure of his suckling lazily on one of her breasts. His caresses were already wreaking their magic on her body, filling her with a sweet, moist heat that made her stretch sensuously then sink on a shivery sigh into the rapture he was creating.

It was slow and it was relaxed and it was sleepy, and it seemed to draw a much deeper response from both of them which left them clinging to each other in a lead-weighted aftermath filled with nothing but a silent awe.

The next morning she awoke to find him still sleeping beside her, the sheet pushed down low over his thighs. He was lying on his side and facing her, an arm thrown heavily across her waist, his hair flowing over one satiny bronze shoulder, lying almost lovingly in that warm, moist hollow that formed the muscular ridge of his neck.

He looked different in sleep—more relaxed, more attractive while those sharp green eyes were hidden from view.

His mouth still had that fatally sensual shape to it, but then, she acknowledged, it always did—whether he was tense or angry or just behaving normally. It was his mouth that had first ignited her senses and it had been wreaking its devastation ever since.

Feeling the stirring of excitement take root inside her at this near voyeuristic pleasure she was taking in just looking at him, she blushed and looked away.

Moving carefully so that she would not waken him, she slid out from beneath his arm and moved stealthily up and off the bed. Her body was stiff and aching, and she smiled wryly to herself as she made her way to the bathroom. They said sex was the best exercise for toning the body. She believed it. She felt as though she'd spent last night tied to a toning bed, except—a shiver of something incredibly sexy quivered through her—no toning bed left your senses feeling like this!

The shower was warm and refreshing, and she stood beneath it with her head tilted back, eyes closed while the water gushed over breasts still full and aching. Her nipples were tight and sharply sensitive, and seemed to have forgotten how to retract. She released a soft sigh as the water began to soothe them, though the ache between her thighs remained a dull, pulsing throb.

Was it always like this after a long night of loving? she wondered. This acute awareness of her own femininity? And was this strange yet pleasant feeling that she had been totally invaded all part of the allure that kept the desire to experience it again and again so strong?

'Good morning. You started without me, I see.'

The sound of that deep, pleasant voice accompanied a pair of long-fingered hands sliding around her wet ribcage.

She let out a startled gasp, her eyes flicking open as a warm mouth bent to nuzzle that susceptible point between her shoulder and throat. Her hands snapped up to cover his where they rested just beneath the heavy swell of her breasts. And she couldn't control the expressive way that her shoulder lifted, her throat arching to the erotic suck of his mouth.

'Mmm,' he murmured, drawing her backward against his warm body. 'You taste of clean water and that delicious flavour called Annie. I am addicted,' he confessed. 'I shall now require the taste of her several times a day.'

She quivered at his provocatively teasing banter, but had no equally provocative answer ready to offer him. This kind of situation was so new to her that she was quite frankly at a loss as to what to do or say.

Then his hands shifted upwards, and she arched convulsively on a sharp, indrawn rasp of air. 'Don't touch!' she gasped.

He went still for a moment, then turned her to face him, water gushing over her shoulders to splash onto the whorls of dark hair on his chest as he searched her anxious eyes, then her blushing cheeks, then finally the way her bent arms braced against his chest in an effort to keep his body away from her wet, silky breasts. 'Ah,' he said, then surprised her with the smuggest, most sensually triumphant grin that she had ever seen.

'It isn't funny!' she flashed out indignantly. 'They hurt!'

'Poor Annie,' he murmured in sympathy, but his grin widened, the man in him annoyingly proud that his loving could have such a lingering effect.

Then he swooped, taking one engorged nipple into his mouth and sucking so ruthlessly that she cried out, then gasped, then quivered as pain became a piercing pleasure.

If she'd worried about how she was going to face him this morning then that worry became swallowed up by what happened next.

It was as erotic as it was unconventional to her untutored soul. What with the warm water gushing, ignored, over both of them and his hands sliding down her supple spine to gather her against the rhythmic probing thrust of his hips, he ignited her desire for him so quickly that the night before might not have taken place.

His mouth lifted to capture her own, and, hungry, searching, they strained against each other while his loose hair received the full flood of warm water, plastering the satin pelt to both their faces, water running in rivulets down their noses and circling their joined mouths.

He broke the contact to drag in a harsh breath, his big chest lifting and falling in a tortured rasp. Then he was taking hold of her arms and urging them around his neck before he clasped her just below her buttocks, forcing her legs apart and around his tight waist as he lifted her up against him. His smooth, slick entry literally took her breath away.

Then the shower snapped off, and this latest variation on the act of love was achieved in a cubicle engulfed in warm, sensual steam...

For days they carried on like that—long, lazy, sensual days when they seemed to become so absorbed in each other that they could put the rest of the world right away.

The ate together, they slept together, they played in the sea or simply lazed beneath the shade of one of the big flame-trees together, supposedly content to read a novel each, but really it was usually just another way of enjoying the sexual tension always, always present between them. Her fingers trailed delicately over the fine, crisp hairs on his arm as she read; his hands lightly caressed her sun-kissed thigh as he did the same.

And, of course, they made love all the time—any time.

His appetite seemed utterly insatiable, and hers rose greedily to meet his with little encouragement.

But that didn't mean she didn't have moments when she allowed her thoughts to drift towards the blunt reality of why they were here at all. But if she so much as mentioned home or work or, more importantly, the obligation they both had to Todd and *Cliché*, he would simply shut her up in the most effective way he could find.

Sex. But she did allow herself to wonder, during those few brief moments before he made her lose touch with the sensible part of her mind, if these were deliberate manoeuvres applied to stall her for some deep, dark reason of his own.

The trouble was that she *wanted* to be manoeuvred. She *wanted* to think of nothing else but this and him and— God—make believe it all really meant something.

Why? she asked herself frowningly one morning when she sat modestly covered by her bathrobe in front of her mirror, rubbing at her damp hair with a towel.

And she was almost bowled over by the power of the answer which suddenly erupted inside her. Her hand went still, she looked up and focused on the new, helplessly vulnerable expression now colouring her blue eyes.

No. She shook her head, glanced away, refused to accept it. She could not be falling in love with him as well!

As well as what? she asked herself tautly.

As well as being so sexually obsessed by him that she could barely look at him without wanting him badly!

'Damn,' she muttered shakily, glad that he was still in the bathroom and therefore not there to witness this revealing bit of self-analysis taking place.

Love. She tried tasting the word carefully.

Had she become one of those poor, wretched creatures— a woman in love?

God. Yes, she admitted, and covered those knowing eyes with a decidedly shaky hand.

She was in love with him. Of course she was in love with him, or why else had she let herself become such a slave to all of this?

And it isn't even real! She pulled her head away from her hand to take that blunt realisation full in the face. This—all of this had begun as one huge set-up!

A week ago he was committed to hurting you, Annie! she told herself. And, despite what happened in between, a few days ago he was still using blackmail to force you to bend to his will!

And what about Todd? Did he still intend using his power as Adamas to make Todd bend to his will?

She knew by experience that he could be downright ruthless with that power. Susie meant a lot to him—he had said as much during their fight down on the beach the other day.

But—now? After all of—this? Was he still intent on forcing a split between herself and Todd simply for his cousin's sake?

César used that moment to walk into the room, arrogant in his nakedness. Annie—in breathless silence, via the mirror—watched him saunter towards her, bend to brace himself with his hands against the dressing table, either side of her body, smile a heart-achingly tender smile into her wary eyes then lower his head to taste her throat, his damp hair swinging in a slick, heavy pelt to one side.

Could this man who could smile at her like that still want to put his cousin's feelings before her own?

'César…' she murmured hesitantly, her blue eyes anxious as they watched him nuzzle her throat.

'Hmm?' She quivered as the soft sound vibrated across her skin. He felt the response and did it again. Only the 'hmm' this time was an expression of pleasure.

Annie closed her eyes and tried very hard to concentrate—not on him but on the question she wanted to ask.

'Todd,' she said. 'What are you going to do about Todd and the *Cliché* launch?'

He went still for a moment, his mouth warm where it rested against her softly throbbing pulse. Then, 'This is no longer your problem,' he dismissed, returning his attention to her throat.

'But of course it's my problem!' she insisted, trying to arch away from his seeking lips. 'I'm worried about the *Cliché* launch!'

'Worry about me instead,' he said huskily, and sucked the small fleshy lobe of her ear into his mouth.

She quivered, lips parting on a soft gasp of stinging pleasure. 'Stop it!' she said, determinedly pulling away. 'We need to talk.'

There was another moment's silence when she thought he was going to ignore her—once again. His head remained bent, his hands braced either side of her. Then he straightened, and his eyes when they connected with hers via the mirror were suddenly inscrutable.

'So, talk,' he conceded coolly.

Her heart gave a small flutter—cowardice, she recognised, wanting to drop the whole subject before she spoiled what they had going here. But...

'What are you going to do about me?' she said. 'And Todd and his magazine launch?'

'You forgot to add Susie into that equation,' he inserted, turning away.

'Susie?' Twisting around on the stool, she stared up at him. 'But I don't understand.' She frowned. 'Everything's changed now! Surely you aren't still intending to—?'

'And what has changed exactly?' he drawled as he

moved with a lithe, arrogant grace back across the bed-room.

Her heart took up a slow, heavy pumping as she watched him go, the rear view almost as excruciatingly desirable as the front view. The man had muscles where muscles ought not to be!

'Y-you know I'm no threat to Susie's personal relation-ship with Todd,' she reminded him huskily, having to strug-gle to subdue the feelings that were threatening to divert her from the subject in hand. 'But our business relationship is different! I won that contract fair and square, César. And neither you nor Susie can have any justification in wanting to take it away from me now!'

'You still want to keep it?' Reaching around the open bathroom door, he hooked a clean towel from the rail inside while holding her gaze with a cool, questioning look.

She frowned. 'Of course I want to keep it.'

'Why?'

'Why should I not want to?' she countered.

'Maybe because I am asking you not to,' he suggested quietly, wrapping the towel around his lean hips.

Annie came stiffly to her feet, not sure whether the sud-den movement was brought on by the discomfiting subject matter of this conversation or because of the blatant sen-suality with which this man did everything—even held this damned conversation!

'And why should *you* want to do that?' she demanded.

'Because this particular contract is just one job among many jobs to you,' he replied, with a dismissive shrug of one taut, bronzed shoulder. 'But to Susie it would be the making of her career. Oh,' he continued when Annie opened her mouth to speak, 'I know she's good. But she's not in your league, Angelica. You can survive without the big boost the *Cliché* launch will give your career, whereas

Susie's career will probably never really recover from losing that contract to you in the first place.'

Her eyes widened at this cool business assessment he made of both herself and Susie. 'So you want me to give it all up for Susie's sake?' she choked in blank disbelief.

'Would that be such a very big hardship to you?'

Was that a question or a not very subtle statement of command? she wondered. Then sat down again slowly—very slowly because it suddenly occurred to her that it didn't matter whether it was a question or not. The very fact that he was making the sounds at all was enough to make her legs tremble so badly that she had a fear that they would collapse if she did not keep them under strict control.

Betrayed, she realised painfully. She was feeling betrayed on every level. Betrayed by the subterfuge he had used to get her here to this island in the first place. Betrayed by his later remorse and apparent desire to put things right once he'd realised his mistake, and betrayed by the depth of intimacy he had used to bring her oh, so cunningly to this moment of truth.

And all of it—all of it done in Susie Frazer's name. Blow his own sister! Blow Luis Alvarez! This—everything that had taken place over the last week—had simply been manoeuvre and counter-manoeuvre on his part, with this one goal in mind!

To make Annie Lacey malleable enough to do anything for him that he asked of her.

What a bloody fool she had been. Now she felt sick.

'What are you thinking?' His voice seemed to reach her from down a long, dark tunnel.

'I'm thinking you're a bastard,' she whispered thickly.

Silence.

Her eyelashes flickered, then lifted to allow her eyes to focus on him. He was standing there across the room like some—some noble Apache chief! she likened wretchedly. Wearing that skimpy white towel like a loincloth that left too much naked, bronzed muscle on show! His hair was hanging sleek and straight to the proud set of his shoulders while those crazy green eyes of his looked down that long, arrogant nose at her as if he couldn't believe that this *woman* could dare to insult him like that!

Then he sighed and moved in a grim gesture of impatience. 'Dammit, but you are my wife now, Angelica!' he exclaimed, with what she saw as an appalling confirmation of his arrogance. 'You do not need to do that kind of work any more! Whereas Susie—'

'Wife?' From somewhere—she didn't know where—anger took over from nausea and shot her furiously back to her feet. 'And when exactly did I become your wife, César?' she demanded with a withering scorn. 'From the moment you realised that your and Susie's plans were no longer justified, so you had to find another way to keep me here incarcerated on this island?'

'Don't be stupid!' he snapped, beginning to stride towards her. 'I told you I had no intention of harming you! Why can't you show me a little trust?'

Trust. There was that rotten word again.

'What is there to trust?' she demanded bitterly. 'Your word—when you've done nothing but break it since I met you?'

'Just because I asked for a little common charity does not mean I am about to break my word to you!' he rasped as he reached her.

'No? Well, my answer is a clear-cut, unequivocal no. I won't hand over the *Cliché* job to Susie.' Her blue eyes lifted to challenge him with a look of fierce contempt. 'So where do we go form here? César—hmm?' she taunted dangerously. 'Where...?'

CHAPTER TEN

To HELL, apparently. They went to hell, Annie decided later as she lay in the middle of the rumpled bed that César had just stalked angrily away from—after taking her to hell by the most exciting route he could find.

And now she lay devastated, maybe suffering from shock—she wasn't sure. All she did know was that that one small question had exploded into a blistering row and from the blistering row had come the blistering sex.

But, worse, she had not been dragged down into the fiery depths of that hell protesting. No, she'd gone willingly—eagerly!

'Oh, God,' she groaned, rolling onto her side so that she could bury her shame in the snowy white pillow.

His pillow. A pillow that held the scent of him. And almost instantly she was assailed with the kind of thoughts and feelings that cruelly mocked the sense of shame.

It wasn't as if she could even comfort herself with the knowledge that she'd tried to fight him off! Because she hadn't.

From the moment his hands had reached out to take hold of her she had lost all sense of reason. Pure sexual exhilaration had fizzed up from the centre of her fury to coil in a hot, pulsing constriction around the muscles of her womanhood, and she'd gone, kicking, scratching, biting, into the fiery vats of passion with him, giving him back kiss for savage kiss, caress for ravaging caress until the whole wild battle had finally converged in a soul-destroying climax which had left her dead-limbed, mind-blown and spent, and him punching the pillow with a white-knuckled fist as he fought to regain control of his shattered emotions.

Then, 'Damn you,' he'd muttered to her as he'd climbed off the bed. 'Damn you to bloody hell for making me behave like that!'

If he'd called her Annie the super-tramp he could not have hurt her more than that angry damning did.

Then she heard it, and her head picked up, ears tensed and listening to the faint, deep whooshing sound that took a few moments to register in her sluggish brain.

No, she thought hectically. She refused to believe it—not after what had just taken place on this bed! No!

Suddenly she was jackknifing to her feet, fingers scrambling, body trembling in her haste as she dragged the rumpled sheet with her and began draping the fine cloth around her body even as she ran out of the open French windows and onto the upper balcony.

The sun was high, blinding as it hit her eyes, and she almost lost the sheet altogether when she instinctively lifted a hand to shade out the brightness. Then she saw it, hovering just twenty feet from the ground, the powerful whir of blades shattering the still air with its blunt, cruel statement.

'No, César,' she whispered, tripping over the trailing sheet as she staggered to the balcony rail. 'Don't you dare. Don't you dare!'

But he did dare, apparently. And it felt as if everything living inside her took a swooping dive to her stomach as the helicopter slowly turned until it was facing out to sea, then shot forward, leaving her leaning there against the balcony rail, watching it go, while hot tears of bitter helplessness ran unchecked down her cheeks.

It hurt. His cruel desertion of her hurt. The fact that he could leave her here like this after what had just taken place in the bedroom behind her—hurt.

Where was he going? Why was he going? Was he going to find Susie to explain that he couldn't make Annie Lacey bend totally to his will?

A whole week she was left alone to stew in her own bitterness, seven long frustrating days and nights when all she did was consolidate every bad thought that she had ever had about him. It was a week in which she barely left the villa and had Margarita fussing around her like a worried hen as her moods swung from anger to hurt and from hurt to wretched tears and from tears to a cold, dark depression that refused to lift no matter how often she told herself that none of it was worth this much grief.

On the eighth day she was sitting in the coral-coloured sitting room when the familiar sounds of helicopter blades heralded his return.

Her heart skipped a couple of beats, but other than that she didn't move, did not lift her eyes from the paperback that she was supposed to be reading. For the space of thirty long, taut seconds she showed no visible sign at all that his return interested her in the slightest…

Then smoothly, coolly, calmly she got up, walked out of the room and up the stairs to her bedroom.

She was methodically folding clothes into her suitcase when he appeared in the doorway. She felt his arrival, felt his sudden stillness when he saw what she was doing, felt his eyes home sharply in on her—and didn't even grace him with a glance.

'What are you doing?' he demanded finally.

She didn't bother to answer the obvious either, her hands

remaining steady as they settled soft, silky underwear in the suitcase lying open on the stand by the bathroom door.

'I'll be ready to leave in a few minutes,' she informed him instead.

Silence. A silence so taut that it made her ears begin to tingle and her chest grow tight. Then, 'Don't be foolish!' he said roughly, striding further into the room to throw something onto the nearby tabletop. 'You are not going anywhere. OK, so you are angry with me,' he allowed magnanimously. 'I acknowledge it.'

Big of you, she thought, and continued back to the dressing table to begin emptying the next drawer.

His eyes followed her in pulsing frustration. 'Angelica…' he sighed, reaching out with a hand to stop her as she went to walk past him.

She turned on him like a rattlesnake. Then wished to God that she hadn't when she felt herself hit by the full, stinging blast of his grim, dark attraction.

Why do you do this to me? she screamed out in silent anguish as her senses caught alight and began crackling like a flash-fire through her blood.

He was standing there in the immaculate clothes of a businessman. Plain grey tie worn over a crisp white shirt. Plain grey twill trousers sitting perfectly on the top of polished black shoes. The epitome of convention in fact. While that hair of his, so arrogantly contained in is slender black ribbon, shrieked 'Rogue' at her! 'Scoundrel! For God's sake watch out!'

'Don't you touch me!' she spat at him in sheer reaction. 'Don't you—' disgustedly she wiped his hand from her arm '—dare touch me!'

His chin went up, his eyes alight with the green, green glow of affronted pride, his chiselled mouth pulling into a straight, flat line that did nothing—nothing to spoil its innate sex appeal! While she just stood here, breasts heaving, eyes defying him, waiting with her senses on full alert to see how he was going to react to that little bit of ego-squashing.

'Look…' he muttered after another tense pause. 'This is crazy.'

Her word, Annie thought possessively. Crazy. Her whole existence had been crazy from the moment she'd first set eyes on him!

'What do you want me to say, Angelica? That I am sorry? That I should not have left here the way that I did? I know it,' he accepted. 'You know it! But I had to leave. I did not like what we were doing to each other. I needed to be alone—to think—to try to find a—'

'Well, at least you had the *choice* whether to go or stay!'

There was another short silence while he took on board the full import of that last remark. Then he gave another heavy sigh, and the muscles in her chest began to throb. She wasn't sure why. They just did, holding her tense and still and so utterly miserable that she wanted to weep.

'I just want to leave here,' she repeated thickly. 'Now—as soon as it can be arranged.'

'We have to talk.'

She shook her head. 'What is there left to talk about?' she asked. 'The *Cliché* launch?' Her mouth took on a bitter twist that mocked the whole subject. 'I'm no longer interested in discussing that with you,' she announced. 'Not any of it.'

'And why not?' he asked grimly. 'It meant all the world to you a week ago.'

'A week ago I was still living in cloud-cuckoo-land,' she derided. 'Since then, and while you've been off having your lonely think, I've been having mine. And I want out. Out of this house and this island, out of any commitment I may have to you so I can go and deal with my own commitments myself.'

Take that, you arrogant devil, she thought, and turned stiffly away.

'You said you'd wait until we knew if there was a child or not.'

She paused half a stride back to her suitcase, her eyes closing on a moment's frozen stillness. When they opened again the blue was empty—as empty as she was feeling inside right now.

'There isn't going to be a child,' she told him huskily, and continued jerkily on her way. 'So that's it,' she went on in a tone that said she didn't care, when really she had cared. It had come as yet another devastating blow to find out how much she had cared about carrying his baby. 'All promises to you fulfilled,' she stated. 'Now I want you to fulfil your promise to me and let me go.'

'You could be lying...' he drawled, his eyes narrowing in suspicion at her carefully controlled voice.

'You expected me to preserve the evidence?' she mocked with crude sarcasm.

He didn't like to hear it from her. The sudden black flash of disapproval in his eyes told her that he didn't like it. 'Don't talk like that,' he said grimly. 'It degrades you.'

She swung round. 'And you think it isn't degrading to have my word questioned as you just did?' she threw back.

His mouth closed tight, his face with it. 'So you want to leave,' he said quietly after a moment.

She nodded. Mute. Determined.

He let out a short sigh. 'We have something good going

for us here, Angelica, if you could try to show me a little trust.'

Trust. There was that word again—trust.

'And what is there to trust exactly?' she derided. 'When none of this has been real?'

'It's been real enough!' he countered. 'This is real!' Stepping forward, he reached out to grab hold of her hand and tugged it out in front of them both so that the band of gold on her finger glinted in the sunlight. 'We made solemn vows to each other and signed a legal document to make it real!'

'I'm not talking legally, I'm talking personally!' Angrily she snatched back the hand, clenching her fingers over the ring that was to her only a sham, like the vows they shared and the document they'd signed. 'You—me—actually meaning those vows we said to each other! That wasn't real!' Her tight mouth quivered. 'Yet we both had the gall to behave as if they were.'

'We like making love to each other,' he pointed out.

She sighed, but didn't deny it. He was right, after all—they did like making love. Revelled in each other, in fact. Drowned in each other.

'We like being with each other. We like talking together and laughing together—or even fighting together as we are doing now!'

'I'm not the one fighting here!' she denied vehemently. 'All I'm trying to do is get packed to go home! I hate all this fighting we do,' she added as a muttered aside.

To her utter annoyance he laughed! 'Liar,' he said. 'You love it. It excites you. Just the same as it excites me to fight with you.'

'Is that supposed to be some kind of joke?' she gasped in choking indignation.

'I am not joking,' he denied. 'I tell you—' His hands slapped a brazen gesture on the top of his thighs. 'No joke,' he claimed, drawing her angry eyes downwards.

And dark heat rumbled into her face when she saw what was happening to him. 'You're disgusting,' she snapped, looking angrily away.

'I am a man,' he replied, as if that made everything acceptable.

'And an arrogant one.'

'I do not deny it.' He shrugged. 'But then,' he added silkily, 'I am not the one denying anything here.'

'Why don't you go to hell?' she flashed, for want of a better answer to that.

'What—again?'

Her insides jumped, blue eyes flickering warily upwards to catch the way that those sleek black brows of his had arched in a gesture of mocking knowledge. So he too had seen that last sexual battle they'd fought as a visit to hell, she realised with a sudden flutter of alarm as he began to walk towards her.

'How nice of you to offer,' he went on silkily. 'Thank you, I think I will...'

And she began backing. 'Don't you come near me!' she choked, her heart pumping dangerously fast, hands held out in front of her as if to ward off the devil.

He reached the hands; they flattened against his rock-solid chest. Eyes narrowed and glinting bright green with intention, he herded her backwards like a piece of cattle until her back made thudding contact with the wall. And still he kept on coming, until her braced arms buckled beneath the strain and his body was making full and dangerous contact with her own. In all her life she had never felt so intimidated—or so exhilarated!

'No!' she gasped out breathlessly. 'Please, César! Don't!'

Too late, his dark head was already lowering, his mouth hot as it made contact with hers. She could feel his heart pumping beneath her spread palms, could feel the warmth of his body, the powerful muscles, felt his tongue run in a moist, sensual slide across her tightly clamped lips.

And in seconds she could feel herself surrendering, her mouth wanting to part, her tongue to join with his, her fingers trembling with a desperate need to rip open his shirt and bury themselves in the crisp, dark hair covering his chest—the whole lot threatening to fling her screaming with delight into that wild, hot well of passion.

Oh, God, she thought dizzily. But she wished that she could hate him! She knew that she *should* hate him! She *wanted* to hate him! But she didn't. She loved him!

With a sob of anguish she tried to thrust him away. He growled something impatient, brought his hands snaking up to rake roughly through her hair—cupping her head—arching it backwards—long thumbs sliding across her heated cheeks to hold her face up to his—enthralling her with the urgency with which he forced her lips apart and hungrily deepened the kiss.

And in an act of sheer self-preservation she gave a violent push at his shoulders and managed to wrench her throbbing mouth to one side. It stopped him. His dark head came up, his big chest heaving, his own cheeks flushed with desire, and his eyes barely focused as they stared at her.

'If you've quite finished,' she heard herself say with unbelievable cool, 'then I would now like to get packed and leave.'

He was suddenly very still, the new silence beating like a hundred war drums inside her head as she stood there defying him with her eyes. Ever since she'd met him—all along the line!—she'd given in to him. But this time—this time she was determined to win.

And at last and finally he must have realised it, because his eyes went black with anger then cold as pale green ice. He took a step back from her, severing all body contact like a scalpel slicing through flesh.

'OK, Angelica,' he said grimly. 'If that is what you want. You win.'

With that he turned and walked out of the room.

'You win', she repeated dully to herself as she wilted against the wall behind her, eyes closing, heart hurting at the prize that she had just managed to win for herself.

Freedom, she supposed you'd call it. She'd just won the freedom to choose to leave here at last.

So why did she feel as if she'd just lost the biggest prize of her life?

No, that's weak thinking, Annie, she told herself grimly. He doesn't love you. He wants you, she conceded bitterly. He desires your body like crazy, and he's possessive and territorial about it. But that isn't love.

A man in love doesn't lie and cheat and connive to trap. He doesn't blackmail and bully and seduce and—Oh, shut up! she told her hectic brain. Shut up! Stop rubbing it in!

Eyes flying open with a flash of pained anger, she thrust herself away from the wall—

It was then that she saw it—a brown paper package lying askew on the pale wood tabletop. Her mind did a flashback of César tossing it there.

Slowly, uncertainly she began to walk towards it. Drawn there. Unable to resist.

It was an envelope, she realised. A special kind of envelope. Big, rectangular, card-backed. Her mouth went dry, clammy sweat breaking out all over her as she recognised it instantly for what it had to be.

The kind of envelope a photographer put prints in.

Her flesh began to tingle with a new guilt-ridden fear, and she knew why. She was going to look inside it—knew she couldn't stop herself. Even though she knew with a cold sense of anguish just what she was going to see.

Susie decked out for the *Cliché* launch.

It had to be. What else could it be?

Fingers trembling, heart hammering, she slipped open the flap and slowly slid the contents onto the shiny tabletop.

For a dozen heart-stunning moments she was completely unmoving. Didn't breathe, didn't blink, didn't function at all on any human level.

Because they were not photographs of Susie.

Tears blurred her eyes, hot and burning, catching as a sob in her throat.

They were not even photographs in the true sense.

They were mock-ups of the front and centre-fold pages of a magazine—'CLICHÉ' superimposed in red across a beautiful Caribbean blue sky.

'Oh, God,' she whispered as she stared at them, a hand jerking up to cover her trembling mouth.

There was an old saying about cameras never lying. But, being a professional model, Annie knew this to be an utter untruth. Cameras could and did lie—all the time.

But this camera wasn't lying. The camera that took these pictures was so glaringly obviously telling the truth that no one—no one who looked at these images in front of her could even begin to doubt that what was being shown was the truth.

Two people about to marry each other.

Two people decked out in white and gazing into each

other's eyes with such a bitter-sweet intensity that it was as clear and clean and spiritual as the smile on the minister's face in the background that these two people were madly, blindly in love.

'But I didn't even know then,' she whispered to herself in thickened dismay.

'I did.'

With a shaken gasp she spun around to find César leaning in the open doorway to the balcony.

Dark colour flooded into her cheeks then drained away again, leaving her pale and shocked by what he had just said.

'Why didn't you tell me about these?' she asked shakily.

He had his hands stuck in the pockets of his grey trousers. She couldn't see his face because the sun was right behind him, but she saw a broad shoulder lift and fall in a lazy shrug. 'There never seemed to be an—appropriate moment,' he replied very drily, referring, she presumed, to the fact that they'd started fighting almost from the moment he'd come into the room. 'Do you still want to leave here?' he asked suddenly.

She shook her head, tears blurring out her vision.

'Good,' he replied, but his tone was oddly flat and reserved. It held her back from running to him as she wanted to do. And there was a decided reticence about the slow way he straightened himself then came further into the room.

'Those pictures are the reason I was away so long,' he explained. 'I had to go to London. To see your half-brother. We—talked,' he said, after a small pause which suggested that they'd done a whole lot more than just talk. 'About you, mainly. But also about the *Cliché* launch.' Another pause, and again she received the odd impression that he was telling her all of this with constraint.

Was he still angry because she'd rejected him a few minutes ago? she wondered. Was he waiting for her to apologise, beg forgiveness?

'Hanson had those mock-ups done for his first issue, but if you don't want it splattered all over the world then we won't do it.' Another shrug and he had reached the end of the bed. 'But...'

Ah, Annie thought, and stiffened, the cynical side to her nature recognising that there was usually a big 'but' to most things.

'I had trouble convincing him of a few—provisos of my own before I would give permission.'

'What provisos?' she asked warily. She didn't like this— she didn't like any of it. She had just experienced the absolute beauty of discovering that the man she was in love with loved her too, yet the whole thing was being so thoroughly dampened by his manner that she was already beginning to doubt what her own eyes had told her those photographs claimed!

'There are two envelopes on the table, Angelica,' he pointed out.

'Two?' She glanced back at the table, then made a sound of surprise. He was right, and there were two! She hadn't noticed.

'It has to be sheer fluke that you opened the right one first,' he then said drily. 'Or I don't think you would be standing there eating me with your beautiful eyes as you have been doing.'

Sarcasm, dry and taunting. It hurt.

'Open it,' he commanded.

She shook her head. She didn't want to. There was going

to be something horrible in that other envelope, or why else would he have said what he'd just said?

'This is it, Angelica,' he stated quietly. 'The point where you learn you were right not to trust me. Open it,' he repeated. 'Open it.'

Reluctantly she pulled the other envelope towards her. Lips dry, fingers shaking, she opened the flap then slid the contents out.

No mock-ups this time, she noted on a sickly hot wave of disenchantment, but glossy seven-by-nines. Professional photographs—of Susie. Susie in white, wearing rubies. Susie in gold, wearing emeralds. Susie in black, wearing the most beautiful diamonds... Tears flashed across her eyes as slowly, shakily, with the silence growing thick all around her, she looked at each photograph in turn—a half-dozen of them in all.

'No sapphires,' she murmured finally.

'No,' he confirmed. 'No sapphires.'

Hurt blue eyes flicked around to search out his. 'Why not?'

There wasn't a hint of emotion showing in those steady green eyes. 'They're yours,' he reminded her quietly.

That was all he said, and, swallowing thickly, she looked away from him again. 'Did you ever intend using me for this shoot?'

'No.' Just as quiet, just as lacking in emotion. She flinched.

'You see, I promised Susie years ago that the next time I put a collection together she could show it,' he explained in that same quiet, flat voice. 'It isn't her fault that I decided to use the Adamas name as bait to hook you, Angelica. That was my decision. Those pictures were taken weeks ago—well before Hanson made his decision to use you instead of Susie for his launch. I made that promise to her in good faith and I couldn't, in all fairness, break it simply because I had made the damned thing so complicated.'

Which was why he had tried so hard to talk her round that day before he'd left, Angelica realised. And at last began to understand the full tangle that this web of conspiracy had got into.

'She loves Hanson, dammit!' he suddenly exploded when she showed no sign that any of what he'd said had got through to her. 'And she believed that he loved her! On the strength of that love she'd constructed this great plan where he chose her to launch *Cliché* and she came up with the biggest scoop for his first issue he could possibly hope for! I'd even gone to London specially to be there when she did it!' A sigh rasped harshly from him. 'Have you any idea how deeply he hurt her when he chose you instead of her?'

'Yes,' she whispered, because she was feeling a little of how that hurt felt herself right now. 'Has Todd seen these?' she then asked quietly.

'Yes,' he sighed. 'He's seen them. I took them with me to try to make him see some sense about Susie. He didn't,' he clipped. 'The man is—'

Hurt, Annie put in silently when César cut the rest of the sentence off. Not that 'hurt' was what César had been going to say, she noted from the angry look on his face.

'Anyway,' he went on, 'I've offered him a deal whereby he can launch *Cliché* with our wedding—hence the mockups—' he indicated them with his hand. 'So long as he fronts Susie and the Adamas collection in his second issue.'

She said nothing, her blonde head bowed over the two different sets of photographs scattered on the table.

'I'm sorry if you feel I have forfeited your feelings with

this decision,' he went on heavily after a moment. 'But, being faced with the dilemma I had made for myself, I saw no other way out without hurting someone, and…'

My feelings were easier to hurt than Susie's, she silently finished for him when he stopped, shrugging eloquently instead.

'And Todd agreed?' she asked.

'No,' he said. 'He is considering my offer as we speak and is due here in a couple of days with his decision.' Another sigh, and the atmosphere in the sunny room thickened a little more. 'He already had a fair idea of what has been going on here, Angelica,' he informed her. 'We were caught by a Press photographer in that tight embrace when I poured the champagne over you the first night we met. The picture appeared in the paper the next morning.'

More bad publicity, she thought, and shuddered.

'Hanson recognised me as the same man who had let him discover the Adamas identity that same night,' he went on. 'Almost immediately my real name DeSanquez struck a chord in his brain, connecting me with the Alvarez affair, and since then he has been tearing his hair out trying to trace where you'd been taken. He was worried about you,' he huskily confessed. 'Frightened because he had to suspect me of planning the whole thing for the purposes of revenge and…' His expressive shrug acknowledged how accurately Todd had put the full picture together. 'So I had to do some quick thinking if I was going to stop him from guessing the rest.'

'And said—what?' she asked, turning coolly to face him.

He was half leaning, half sitting on the edge of the dressing table, outwardly perfectly relaxed—if you didn't notice the tell-tale nerve working in his jaw.

But his eyes were studiedly impassive as he continued.

'I told him the truth,' he answered simply, then almost immediately qualified that remark. 'Or the truth as far as it was necessary, anyway.' And the smile that played briefly around his mouth hinted at just which part he had left out. The big love scene—their big love scene. The one that had ripped a gaping hole in the Annie Lacey persona. 'Then I showed him the pictures of our wedding day and let them speak for me.'

'And did they?'

'Oh, yes.' He smiled. 'They speak loud and clear to anyone who looks at them, don't you think?'

She refused to take him up on that one; there was still too much left to be said. 'And Susie?' she prompted. 'What did you tell him about Susie's involvement in it all?'

'I told him that Susie knew nothing of what I had planned for you here,' he stated flatly.

But her sceptical look made him sigh with impatience.

'It's the truth,' he insisted. 'Susie knew nothing! Which is why it is so unfair for her to pay the price for my sins. She loves Hanson!' he declared. 'And whatever slant you want to put on it your relationship with him did look suspect! She had a right to feel jealous, used, unfairly treated!

'And, yes,' he added before Angelica could say it herself, 'she hated you for being what she saw as the woman who was wrecking her life on both personal and professional counts. But her hatred stopped short of plotting with me against you. I didn't need her help to plot,' he then said drily. 'I am cunning enough to manage without the need of an accomplice.'

'You threw that champagne over me deliberately,' she pointed out.

His wry half-nod acknowledged it.

'It was Susie who took great delight in telling Todd all

about the embrace which followed,' she added. 'She knew exactly who you were.'

'And that part, I concede, was a set-up. But only in as far as I promised to get you out of the way so she could talk to Hanson. As to the rest—she was then and still is totally in the dark!'

Did she believe him? Annie shifted restlessly. She wanted to believe him. It was easier on her pride to believe that Susie knew nothing of what had been planned on this island for her arch-rival Annie Lacey.

'So, why are you telling me all of this?' she asked carefully.

'Because,' he said quietly, 'I need your support when Hanson gets here. I need you to help convince him that Susie is the innocent party in all of this, and that you really don't mind that Susie has taken the Adamas scoop from you.

'It's important to her, Angelica,' he added roughly, when her cool face gave him no hint at all as to what she was thinking. 'It is important to Hanson that he is offered a way to—give a little where she is concerned! He is in love with Susie, but, as you once told me yourself, he is capable of never forgiving her if he truly believes she collaborated with me against you.

'Please,' he appealed, 'in the face of what those mock-ups tell us, show a little compassion for someone less fortunate in love than yourself and back me up in all of this.'

She moved at long last, shifting out of her cool, still stance to turn back to the array of photo work littered across the table. Her fingers flittered across those of Susie and settled on one of César and herself. It was one in which the photographer had captured the moment when César had slid the rings onto her finger. His dark head was bent, his lean profile taut, his mouth straight and flat and grim. But the eyes were alive—looking at her while she looked at the rings—alive with a burning, helpless—

'No…' she whispered, beginning to gather up with trembling fingers every mock-up lying there. 'I d-don't care what you do with the Adamas thing. Susie can keep it. It doesn't matter a jot to me. But—' she turned, clutching the mock-ups possessively to her chest '—I won't allow you to publish these, César. I won't,' she warned him defiantly. 'I won't let you make a public spectacle out of these!'

CHAPTER ELEVEN

'"A SPECTACLE"?' César's lean body came out of its casual resting position to shoot stiffly to its full, impressive height in affront. 'What do you mean, "a spectacle"?' he demanded. Then he added icily, 'Are you saying that you look on our marriage as a joke?'

'No!' she sighed, wondering how a man with all his arrogance could be so damned touchy sometimes! 'But look at these, César!' she pleaded, her hand coming out shakily to offer the mock-ups. 'Look how beautiful they are. How—special!' she cried. 'Too special to have them made a public mockery of!'

'A mockery?' His frown was dark, his face an angry map of puzzled indignity as he looked from her anxious face to the mock-ups then back again. 'I don't understand. Why should anyone want to mock them?'

'Because out there I am still Annie Lacey the notorious man-eater!' She spelled it out rawly. 'And they'll be shocked that you of all people would marry me!'

'Who?' he demanded. 'Who, in your estimation, is that crass-minded?'

Her eyes closed briefly on a tense, tight sigh. 'The Press,' she said. 'They can be so vicious when they get their teeth into someone—you know that! They'll slay you the moment they see these photographs!' Her chest heaved on a wretched indrawn breath.

'Then they'll dredge it all up again, replay the whole Luis Alvarez nightmare again. They'll mock Todd for printing the wedding pictures of his long-term on-and-off lover—and you for being stupid enough to take me on! Th-then they'll mention your sister,' she concluded thickly, 'and wonder how you could marry the woman who wrecked your own sister's marriage!'

'So you would prefer to hide our marriage away like some dark secret rather than face the world with what those pictures show as the truth?' Sighing tightly, he came to take the mock-ups from her and tossed them contemptuously aside. 'Is this your novel way of telling me I have misread our whole relationship?' he said in a clipped voice.

'No!' She groaned at the interpretation that he had put on her words. 'Our marriage was a very special moment in my life! Those pictures make it special because they say so much to both of us!' Her eyes burned into him with a dark blue appeal. 'You're special to me,' she told him achingly. 'I'm thinking of you! I want to protect you! Not myself,' she dismissed. 'I couldn't care less about what they want to throw at me. But—'

He laughed! He was scornful, but he actually laughed. 'Do you mean,' he enunciated in choking disbelief, 'that you're making all this fuss—for my sake?' His hand snaked out, capturing hers so that he could tug her up against him. 'Look at me, Angelica,' he commanded grimly. 'Look into this face and tell me what you see.'

She looked, her eyes pained with love and bright with the unshed tears of her own uncertainties.

'Does this look like the face of a man who worries about what other people say or think about him?' he demanded. 'Does it?'

No, it did not. It looked like the face of a man hewn from the hardest, smoothest rock—a man as invincible as his Adamas trade-name implied him to be. The Spanish conquistador. The Apache chief. The face of arrogance personified.

The man she loved.

'But your sister isn't hewn from the same invulnerable mould as you, is she?' she pointed out wretchedly.

'Cristina?' He frowned, then bit out, 'To hell with Cristina. I've already spoken to her—told her the truth. She accepted it—painfully,' he acknowledged on a small, tight grimace that said that the truth had not been easy to take. 'But Cristina will be no problem to us. Unless,' he then added with a sudden sparkling wry humour, 'you allow for the way her guilty conscience will probably have her hounding you for the rest of her life—looking for her own redemption.'

'You're sure?' she murmured uncertainly.

'I am very sure,' he huskily confirmed.

Her soft mouth quivered. 'Then let go of my hand.'

'Why?' He frowned.

'I need something.'

Reluctantly he let go. Instantly she stepped closer, her fingers sliding over his muscled shoulder and around his strong neck, searching for, finding and curling around his tail of hair, then she buried her face in his warm throat and sighed as if she'd just been saved from drowning.

He muttered something and gathered her possessively in. 'What made you suddenly do that?' he asked tensely.

'Do what you like with the pictures,' she whispered into his taut throat. 'Give them to Todd—don't give them to Todd.' Her lips slid a sensual caress across his skin. 'I don't care,' she said. 'You're Adamas. Invincible. My rock. I'm marooning myself.'

'Ah,' he said, relaxing as he caught on. 'So you are relinquishing all responsibility to me?'

'That's right.' Her lips moved on to taste his chin. He needed a shave, so she stopped caressing and bit sensuously instead. 'You say you don't care what they throw at you, so—prove it. Publish and be damned, Mr Adamas,' she challenged. 'Let them throw the lot at you—you can take it.

'I can just see the world headlines—SUPERMODEL ANNIE LACEY LANDS VENEZUELAN OIL BARON IN GRENADINE LOVE COUP!' she quoted. '"The price for exclusive rights to her body, a five-million-dollar sapphire and diamond-encrusted necklace from the Adamas collection, no less!"'

'Oh, please,' he drawled, the sound deep and sensually amused. 'GREAT GENIUS ADAMAS! I will not be upstaged by your supermodel status.'

She grinned, then stopped grinning to look seriously into his warmly laughing eyes. 'You're sure you don't mind?' she asked softly. 'That they're going to have a field-day with all of this?'

'Do I look as though I mind?' he murmured lazily.

'No,' she pouted. 'You look—'

She didn't manage to finish that sentence because the look was transformed into action—an action that had them tumbling onto the bed and into a wild, hot, passionate morass of sensual rediscovery.

'You were very rough on him,' Annie remarked a few days later as they stood together on the lower veranda, watching the helicopter that had brought Todd to the island that morning take him away again.

Todd had arrived in a belligerent mood, still unforgiving of Susie and determined to get the exclusive on Annie's marriage to César—without having Susie wearing the Adamas collection included in the deal.

He'd gone away conceding everything to a tough-talking, utterly immovable César—still belligerent, still feeling as if he had been manipulated by both César and Susie, but with his good business-sense winning over bruised ego in the end.

And the only consolation that he had gained from the whole episode was a total reassurance that Annie was exactly where she wanted to be.

'This whole business has been rough on everybody,' was César's unsympathetic reply to her now. 'I don't see why your half-brother should come out of it any less battle-scarred than the rest of us. Susie looked like a whipped dog that day he announced you were going to front his launch into Europe,' he added grimly. 'I don't know how I kept my hands off his cruel throat.'

'Poor Susie,' Annie sighed, turning to watch the helicopter fly out of sight. 'Do you think they'll manage to sort out their personal problems after this?' she asked worriedly.

'We have given them the means by which to keep communications open with the Adamas deal. The rest,' he said grimly, 'is up to them. But, you know, with a bit of trust on his side, Angelica, things need not have become as bad as they did for him and Susie.'

He was right, and she didn't argue with him. In fact, she had always tried to get Todd to tell Susie the truth about their own relationship, because she had known that it was causing unnecessary problems for both of them. If he had done, then maybe none of this would have happened.

Which was a bit of a double-edged sword, really, she mused wryly, because then she would not have been standing where she was standing right now—in the arms of the man she loved!

'And anyway,' César concluded with a shrug, 'I have no wish to dwell on their love-life any more than I have done already. My own love-life is complicated enough without taking on board their problems as well.'

'I am not complicated at all!' she denied, turning in the

crook of his arm to glare at him. 'In fact—' she pouted '—I bet you've never had such an easy conquest as me! How long did it take?' she demanded. 'Twenty-four hours from meeting to getting me into your bed?'

He smiled with his mouth, but his eyes didn't; they darkened into a breathtaking seriousness. 'Four years,' he corrected. 'I spent four years aching for you. You tormented my mind, my heart, my empty soul...'

Sighing, he pulled her closer. 'I don't think I will ever come to terms with what one urgent phone call did to the next four years of my life,' he murmured heavily. 'I had it all set up—the party at my London apartment, the contact who would bring you to it. Then there was the teeth-gritting, electric anticipation of actually getting to meet you in the flesh at last. Then the call that forced me away that night.' His mouth tightened. 'And everything just seemed to fall apart around me. I hated Alvarez for doing that to me.'

'And hated me for letting him come near me,' she added hollowly.

'No!' He denied that. 'I hated you for ruining any hope I had of ever approaching you. Anyone else, Angelica,' he muttered painfully. 'Anyone else and it wouldn't have mattered. I am no prude! But my own sister's husband?' His sigh was tense. 'It left me with nothing—nothing to cling on to, you understand?'

'Don't,' she whispered, settling her trembling fingers against the grim tension of his mouth.

He kissed the fingers, but also dislodged them with a small, grim shake of his head. 'Then suddenly there you were again,' he continued, his eyes dark green with emotion. 'Being thrust into my life again, this time threatening Susie's happiness!'

'But—'

'Shush.' He silenced her. 'I will finish. Mistakes are mistakes, Angelica. All of us have had to acknowledge that one way or another over these last two weeks. But before the mistakes were exposed I had spent four years seeing you as the kind of woman I could never care for—*should* never care for,' he qualified.

Then he smiled very ruefully. 'It did not stop me from wanting you, though,' he admitted, dropping a kiss on her tender mouth. 'It simply turned that want into a frustrated kind of ache that gnawed at me every time I saw your face on a billboard or in a magazine or—' He stopped and sighed.

'Then the Susie thing came up,' he went on. 'And, I have to admit it, I was quite ready to pay you back for four years of hell. I called it revenge for myself.'

He kissed her again before she could say anything. 'And I knew it the moment I saw you in the flesh that night—it was the first time I had actually been in the same company as you, did you know that?' His expression was wry. 'Four years lusting after one special woman, and I hadn't even met her!'

'Fantasising gone mad.' She smiled.

He laughed, but it wasn't with any humour. 'A lot of things gone mad,' he agreed. 'But I learned one very dangerous thing on that first meeting. And it was that holding you in my arms was like having all that madness turning into sanity. It felt right,' he said softly. 'It felt good! And, even more dangerous, I knew you too were shocked by how good it felt.

'After that,' he claimed with more his usual arrogance, 'you really did not stand a chance. I may have used all kinds of excuses for bringing you here, but I knew deep down inside that I was bringing you here for myself. I wanted you for myself. Susie no longer mattered. The

Alvarez thing no longer mattered. From then on the only mistakes being made were because of the lies entangling both of us. I thought I was dealing with a very spirited, very tough, very experienced woman.' If it was possible, his eyes darkened even further. 'So I made love to the woman I believed you to be, and found I had defiled an angel—'

'No,' she protested. 'Don't call me that! It's not true and I always hated it. It was just another lie I lived with, can't you see that?' Her breasts moved against his chest with a small heave of pain. 'Most of my life has been spent playing a lie. First with my mother's help.' The hurt that memory could still cause shot across her blue eyes. 'Then as a silly character created to sell breakfast cereal, for goodness' sake!'

'Don't cry,' he muttered when a film of tears washed across her eyes.

'I'm not!' she denied, but the denial was thick with tears too, and with a shaky sigh he captured her trembling mouth.

It was a now familiar kiss—the one that caught fire at her lips and burned its way to every corner of her body, cleansing all the bitterness and hurt right out of her as it went. She sighed as she gave in to it, her soft lips parting, her tongue searching, finding, and she gave another pleasurable sigh as her hands went up around his neck and found that shank of hair that she loved to hold onto in moments like these.

It was wonderful—like coming home through the storm and finding warmth and comfort waiting for her. He pressed her against him and she melted into the embrace, loving the feel of her breasts cushioning against the solid warmth of his chest, loving the feel of his body alive and pulsing against her own.

He muttered something in Spanish as he drew away, his

eyes burning like angry green flames as they delved into her own. 'You understand that I love you whoever you are, whatever you are?'

'I understand,' she smiled softly.

He nodded, always arrogant, no matter what other emotions were running rife through him. 'Angelica DeSanquez,' he muttered, then added tersely, 'Remember how I said that! For Angelica Lacey no longer exists!'

'Did I tell you I'm madly in love with you?' she heard herself say, and actually cried out in alarm as he took her mouth again in a volcanic eruption of emotion that threatened to consume them both.

'You unman me,' he muttered hoarsely as his dark head dipped lower so that he could taste her silken throat. 'You always do. But then,' he added ruefully, 'I think you enjoy doing it.'

'You don't feel unmanned to me,' she remarked provocatively, nudging her hips against his swollen body.

His sigh was oddly shaken. 'Let go of my hair,' he ordered. 'You're hurting.'

'No.' Her grip only tightened as her mouth went in search of his ear to taste it. 'I like it,' she whispered. 'It's sexy.'

With a husky growl he bent and scooped her up into his arms.

'Where are we going?' she enquired innocently.

César sent her a glaring glance. 'Guess,' he mocked as he strode with grim intention into the coolness of the house.

Annie let go of the hair so she could trail a tender fingertip down his taut cheek. 'I love you, César,' she told him again. 'Thank you for loving me too.'

'Oh, hell,' he gritted as his firm stride faltered. 'If you don't stop saying things like that I'll take you right here on the stairs!'

'Sorry,' she said, her blue eyes alight with pure female mischief, her white teeth pressing into the sensual fullness of her bottom lip. 'I just wanted to say it, that's all.'

'*Santa María!*' he rasped out explosively as he entered the bedroom and toppled them both onto the bed. 'I have never known a woman affect me as badly as you do!' he muttered complainingly.

'Good,' she said. 'Keep it that way. Or I'll make like Delilah and cut off your sexy hair.'

'No need to worry about it,' he said grimly as he began dragging clothes off both of them. 'I don't even exist when I am not with you.'

'You're with me now,' she murmured consolingly.

'No, I am not,' he denied, then came over her and entered her. 'Now I am with you,' he grunted in rough satisfaction.

'If this isn't real,' she groaned as she flexed to take him in further, 'I don't ever want to wake up.'

'It's real,' he assured her. 'Feel it.' He gave a thrust of his tight hips. 'Real.'

'I belong to you, don't I?'

'Of course. What kind of statement do you think I am making here?'

Tears filled her eyes, turning summer into midnight. 'I've never belonged to anyone before,' she whispered confidingly.

The real Annie Lacey, he saw, with a pain that cut deep into his breast. Like a child, she looked helplessly, vulnerably exposed. His big chest moved on a wave of fierce emotion.

'You belong,' he avowed. 'Mine.' It was hot. It was gruff and it was possessive. 'Now take hold of my hair,' he instructed tensely.

'Why?' she asked, momentarily thrown by the command.

'Because it's sexy! All right?'

She smiled, and suddenly she was no longer Annie the vulnerable child, but Annie the sensual woman, exalting in her own power. Her fingers fixed around his hair then pulled fiercely, smothering his groan of pleasurable pain as she brought his hot mouth down onto her own.

A moment later and the ribbon fell away, allowing black silk to enclose them as they lost themselves in each other.

Yes, I belong. This is real, was Annie's last coherent thought. This is wonderfully, exquisitely real.

Anne Mather began writing when she was a child, progressing through torrid teenage romances to the kind of adult romances she likes to read. She's married, with two children, and she lives in the north of England. After writing, she enjoys reading, driving and travelling to different places to find settings for new novels. She considers herself very lucky to do something that she not only enjoys, but also gets paid for.

A WOMAN OF PASSION
by
ANNE MATHER

CHAPTER ONE

THE man was there again. Helen could see him striding away along the shoreline, the creamy waves lapping the soles of his canvas boots. It was almost impossible to make out any distinguishing features from this distance, but he was tall and dark-haired, and the way he walked made her think he was not seeking recognition. On the contrary, if she was an imaginative female—which she'd always assured herself she wasn't—she'd have speculated that he took his walk so early to avoid meeting anyone.

She had no idea who he was. And doubted that if she'd observed him at any other time of the day he'd have aroused any interest at all. But for the past three mornings—ever since her arrival, in fact—she had seen him walking the beach at six a.m. Always alone, and always too far away for her to identify him.

Of course, if she herself had not been suffering the effects of the time-change between London and Barbados, she probably wouldn't have been awake at six a.m. But, as yet, her metabolism hadn't adapted to a five-hour time-lag, and each morning she'd found herself leaning on her balcony rail, waiting for the sun to make its appearance.

And it was probably just as well that the man chose to walk along the shoreline, she reflected ruefully. Standing here, in only the thin cotton shift she wore to sleep in, she would not have liked to think herself observed. At this hour of the morning, when no one else in the villa was awake, she could enjoy the beauty of her surroundings unhindered. Once the children were awake—and Tricia—her time was no longer her own.

Yet she shouldn't complain, she told herself severely.

5

Without Tricia's help, she had no idea what she'd have done. A young woman of twenty-two, with no particular skills or talents, was anathema. Would-be employers wanted written qualifications, not heartfelt assurances that she could do the job they had to offer.

Of course, until her father's untimely death, she hadn't given a lot of thought to earning her own living. She'd been reasonably well educated, though she'd be the first to admit she was no academic. Nevertheless, she had attended an exclusive girls' school and an equally exclusive finishing-school in Switzerland, and she'd considered herself admirably suited to maintain her role in life.

Which had been what? She pulled a wry face now. Well, to find a man like her father, she supposed—or like the man she had thought her father to be—and get married, raise a family, and repeat the process with her own children.

She sighed. Only it wasn't to be. She wondered if her father had given any thought to her dilemma when he'd taken his yacht out for the last time. Had he really jumped, or had he only fallen? With the sea calm and the yacht found drifting, unmanned, ten miles south of the Needles, it was hard not to think the worst.

Naturally, she had been distraught when they brought her the news. She couldn't believe that her father, who had been an excellent yachtsman, could actually have drowned. And the fact that they'd not found his body had kept her hopes alive. Whatever the coastguards said, he wasn't dead.

But he was. His body had been found a couple of days later, and the realisation that she was alone now had been numbing. Even at the funeral she'd half expected James Gregory to come striding into the chapel. It was strange how that had sustained her through all the interminable expressions of grief.

Afterwards, however, while the guests were making a rather unsympathetic attack on the splendid buffet the housekeeper had provided, Max Thomas, her father's solicitor, had drawn her aside. And in a few short words he had swept the ground from under her feet. Her father, it appeared, had been destitute. For years he'd been living on borrowed time, and now that time had run out.

Incredibly, considering the affluent lifestyle they had enjoyed, James Gregory had been in serious financial difficulties. The estate he'd inherited from his father—and which had supported successive generations of Gregorys—was bankrupt. In spite of the pleas of his tenants for an injection of capital, no help had been offered. And, although a couple of years ago he had had the idea of opening the house and grounds to the public, that too had proved unsuccessful without the proper investment.

Remembering all those holidays in the Caribbean, the winters spent in Gstaad, the summers in the South of France, Helen had had no doubt as to how her father had spent his money. And he'd never betrayed his anxieties to her. She'd always had everything she'd ever wanted.

Maybe if her mother had still been around things would have been different. There was no doubt that Fleur Gregory's departure, when Helen had been barely four years old, had had a salutary effect on her father. Until then he'd seemed quite content to live in the country. But her mother had found country life boring, and she'd eventually run off with a wealthy polo-player from Florida she'd met at a party in town.

That was when James Gregory had bought the London apartment, but, from Helen's point of view, living in London had seemed rather boring at first. She had missed her friends, and she had missed the horses, and although they continued to spend holidays at Conyers it had never been quite the same.

Of course as she'd got older and started school her attitudes had changed. Her friends had been in London then. They had been young people from a similar background. And the boyfriends she'd eventually collected had all been as fun-loving as her father.

But her father had only been what she had made him,

she reflected sadly, remembering how devastated she'd been to learn that her father had been borrowing money on the strength of securities he no longer owned. The estate had not one, but three mortgages hanging over it, and with the interest that was owing and death duties, there'd been precious little left.

The following months had been harrowing. Coming to terms with her father's death would have been bad enough; coming to terms with the fact of his probable suicide had been infinitely worse.

Everything had had to be sold, even her car and the little jewellery she'd owned, and because her father's only living relative was an elderly aunt, who'd disowned him long ago, Helen had had to deal with all the awful details herself. Max Thomas had helped, but even he had had no idea how distressing it had been. People who had once professed themselves her father's friends had cut her dead in the street. Young men who'd phoned her constantly had suddenly been out of reach.

Not that Helen had particularly cared about her sudden loss of status. The hardest thing to bear was the absence of the one person she had really loved. She didn't blame her father for what he'd done, but she did miss him. And she wished he had confided in her before taking that final step.

She could have contacted her mother's sister, she supposed. Aunt Iris must have read about what had happened in the newspapers, but she hadn't been in touch. Besides, Helen had shied away from the idea of asking for charity from the Warners. She and her father had had nothing to do with them in recent years, and it would have been hypocritical to ask for help now.

Nevertheless, things had been fairly desperate when she'd run into Tricia Sheridan in Marks & Spencer's. In the four months since her father died she hadn't been able to find a job, and although she had only been living in a bed-sitter, the rent had still to be paid. Office managers, store managers—all wanted more than the paltry qualifications she had to offer. The only position that had been open to her was a forecourt attendant at a petrol station, and she had been seriously thinking of taking it when Tricia came along.

Tricia, whose husband worked for the Foreign Office, had been living in Singapore for the past two years. She was older than Helen; she had been a prefect when Helen was still in middle school, but because of her prowess at sports all the younger girls had admired her.

She had singled Helen out for attention because Helen's father had presented the school with a new gymnasium. A gymnasium he couldn't afford, Helen reflected sadly now. But at the time she'd been so proud of his generosity.

Tricia had quickly discerned Helen's situation. And had been quick to offer assistance. Why didn't Helen come to work for her? she'd suggested. She needed a nanny, and she was sure Helen could cope.

It had all happened so quickly that Helen hadn't really stopped to ask herself why—if five-year-old Henry and four-year-old Sophie were such poppets—Tricia didn't have a nanny already. The other woman's explanation that as they had been out of the country for some time they were out of touch with current agencies, hadn't really held water, when she'd had time to think about it. She'd simply been so relieved to be offered a job that she'd agreed to her terms without question.

She supposed she'd had some naïve idea that there were still people in the world who did do things out of the kindness of their hearts. Even after all the awful experiences she'd had, she'd actually been prepared to take Tricia's offer at face value. She needed a job; Tricia was offering one. And the salary was considerably larger than any she'd been offered thus far.

In addition to which she would not have to pay the rent on the bed-sitter. Naturally, Tricia had declared, she must live in. Nannies always lived in, she'd said. It was one of the advantages of the job.

Helen wondered now whether she would have stuck it as long as she had if she had not given up her bed-sit. In a short time she'd discovered that, far from being out of touch with the agencies, Tricia had, in fact, tried several before offering the post to her. Unfortunately, her requirements did not jell with most modern-day nannies. They were either too old, or too flighty, or they couldn't follow orders, she'd declared, when Helen had mentioned her findings. But Helen had a theory that they simply refused to be treated as servants.

In any event, beggars couldn't be choosers, and in the three months since she'd been working for the Sheridans, Helen had discovered it wasn't all bad. Tricia was selfish and demanding, and she did expect the younger woman to turn her hand to anything if required. But, when their mother wasn't around to encourage them, Henry and Sophie were fun to be with, and Andrew Sheridan was really rather nice.

Not that he was around much, Helen conceded, cupping her chin on her hand and watching the man who had started her introspection disappear into the belt of palms that fringed the far end of the beach. His work took him away a lot, which might have some bearing on Tricia's uncertain temper. That, and the fact that he never seemed to take her seriously. As easy-going as he was, Helen could quite see how frustrating it must be to try and sustain his attention.

For herself, she imagined a lot of people would consider her position a sinecure. After all, she had her own room, she was fed and watered regularly, and the salary she was earning meant she could put a considerable amount each month into her savings account. If her hours were long, and a little erratic, she had nothing else to do. And at least Tricia didn't feel sorry for her, even if she could be a little patronising at times.

Still, she wouldn't be here if it wasn't for Tricia, she reminded herself firmly, lifting her face to the first silvery rays of sunlight that swept along the shoreline. The fine sand, which until then had had an opalescent sheen, now warmed to palest amber, and the ocean's depths glinted with a fragile turquoise light. Colours that had been muted lightened, and a breeze brushed her calves beneath her muslin hem.

It was all incredibly beautiful, and the temptation was to linger, and enjoy the strengthening warmth of the sun. Helen felt as if she could watch the constant movement of the waves forever. There was a timelessness about them that soothed her nerves and renewed her sense of worth.

But she had spent quite long enough thinking about the past, she decided. Turning back into her bedroom, she viewed her tumbled bed with some remorse. It would have been so easy to crawl back into its comfort. Why was it she felt sleepy now, when an hour ago she couldn't rest?

The room, like all the rooms in the villa Tricia had rented, was simply furnished: a bed, a couple of rattan chairs, a chest of drawers. There was a fitted wardrobe between this room and its adjoining bathroom, and louvred shutters on the windows to keep it cool. The bedrooms weren't air-conditioned, even though Tricia had kicked up something of a fuss when she'd discovered this. However, the maid who looked after the villa had remained impassive. There was nothing she could do about it, she said. Perhaps the lady would prefer to stay at the hotel?

Tricia hadn't preferred. It was far too convenient to have their own place with their own kitchen, where Henry and Sophie could take their meals without constant supervision. In addition to which, the place belonged to a business friend of Andrew's. And he would not be amenable to them transferring to an hotel.

As she took her shower—tepid water, but refreshing—Helen remembered that Tricia's husband was joining them today. He hadn't accompanied them out to the Caribbean. Tricia had explained that there were meetings he had to attend, but Helen suspected Andrew had simply wanted to avoid such a long journey with two demanding children.

As it was, she had had to spend most of the flight playing card games with Henry. Tricia and Sophie had fallen asleep, but Henry had refused to close his eyes.

Still, they were here now, and for the next four weeks surely she could relax and enjoy the sun. She'd already discovered that it was easier entertaining her young charges when the beach was on their doorstep. So long as Tricia didn't get bored, and insist on giving parties every night.

The shower left her feeling refreshed and decidedly more optimistic, and after straightening the sheets on the bed she pulled on cotton shorts, which were all she wore over her bikini. It had been Tricia's suggestion that she dress like one of the family. Any attempt to dress formally here would have seemed foolish.

It was only a little after half-past six when Helen emerged from the villa and crossed the terrace. Her feet were bare, and she took care not to stand on any of the prostrate beetles, lying on their backs on the tiles. These flying beetles mostly appeared at night, attracted by the artificial light, and, although she knew they were harmless, Helen had still to get used to their size and speed of movement. She had a horror of finding one in her bed, and she was always glad when Maria, the maid, brought out her broom and swept them away.

Beyond the terrace, a stretch of grass and a low stone wall was all that separated the grounds of the villa from the beach. Although she would have liked to go for a walk along the beach herself, Helen knew the children would be getting up soon and demanding her attention. It was no use expecting Maria to keep an eye on them when she arrived to prepare breakfast. Likeable though she was, she was also lazy, and looking after infants was not her job.

Perching on the wall, Helen drew one leg up to her chin and wrapped her arms around it. The sun was definitely gaining in strength, and she could feel its heat upon her bare shoulders. Although her skin seldom burned, she had taken to wearing a screening cream this holiday. The sun

had a definite edge to it these days, and she had no wish
to risk its dangers.

All the same, it was amazing to think that the temperature in England was barely above freezing. When they had
left London three days ago, it had actually been snowing.
But February here was one of the nicest months of the year.
There was little of the humidity that built up later on.

The water beyond the beach was dazzling. It was tinged
with gold now, its blue-green brilliance reflective as it
surged towards the shore. Helen had already found that its
power could sweep an unwary bather from her feet. Its
smoothness was deceptive, and she had learned to be wary.

Fortunately, there was a shallow pool in the grounds of
the villa where the youngsters could practise their strokes.
They'd both learned to swim while they were living in
Singapore, and although their skills were limited they could
safely stay afloat. Helen had spent most of yesterday morning playing with them in the pool. Tricia had gone into
Bridgetown, to look up some old friends.

'Helen!'

Henry's distinctive call interrupted her reverie, and, turning her head, she saw both children standing on the veranda, waving at her. They were still in their pyjamas, and
she got resignedly to her feet. Until it was time for their
afternoon nap, Tricia expected her to take control.

'Have you been for a swim?' asked Sophie resentfully,
as Helen walked along the veranda to their room. She
pointed at the damp braid of streaked blonde hair that lay
over one shoulder. 'You should've waked us. We could
have come with you.'

'Woken us,' said Helen automatically, realising as she
did so how quickly she had fallen into the role of nursemaid. 'And, no. I haven't been for a swim, as it happens.'
She shooed them back into their bedroom. 'I had a shower,
that's all. That's why my hair is wet.'

'Why didn't you dry it?' began Sophie, then Henry
turned on his little sister.

'For God's sake,' he exclaimed, 'give it a rest, can't you?' He flushed at Helen's reproving stare. 'Well—she's such a stupid girl.'

'I'm not stupid!'

Sophie responded loudly enough, but her eyes had filled with tears. She always came off worst in any argument with her brother, and although she tried to be his equal she usually lost the battle.

'I don't think this conversation is getting us anywhere, do you?' declared Helen smoothly. 'And, Henry—if you want to make a statement, kindly do so without taking God's name in vain.'

'Mummy does,' he muttered, though he'd expected Helen's reproof. 'In any case, I'm hungry. Has Maria started breakfast?'

'I doubt it.' Helen started the shower as the two children began to unbutton their pyjamas. 'She hasn't arrived yet, as far as I know.'

'Not arrived?' Henry sounded horrified. 'But I want something to eat.'

'Then we'll have to see what she's left in the fridge,' said Helen calmly. 'Now, come on, Sophie. You're first.'

By the time the children were bathed and dressed, Helen had already refereed a dozen arguments. Anyone who thought having children of a similar age automatically meant they would be company for one another couldn't be more wrong, Helen reflected drily. In some circumstances it might work, and she was prepared to accept that there must be exceptions, but Henry and Sophie were in constant competition, and it didn't make for amiable dispositions.

To her relief, Maria had arrived and was making the morning's batch of rolls, when they arrived in the kitchen in search of breakfast. 'Morning, Miss Gregory,' she greeted Helen with a smile. 'You're up and about very early.'

'I guess it's because I still haven't got used to the fact that it's not lunchtime already,' replied Helen. She rubbed her flat stomach with a rueful hand. 'It's the hunger that does it. We're all ravenous!'

'Well, sit down, sit down. I've a batch of rolls in the oven that's almost ready. Why don't you have some orange juice, while you're waiting? Or there's some grapefruit in the fridge, if you'd prefer it.'

'I don't want grapefruit,' said Sophie, wrinkling her nose, but Henry only looked at her with contempt.

'I do,' he declared, though Helen knew he didn't like it. 'You're just a baby. You still drink milk.'

'I drink milk, too,' said Helen firmly, before it could deteriorate into another argument. 'Would you like orange juice, Sophie? That's what I'm going to have.'

'Mmm,' Sophie was off-hand, until she saw her brother's face when Helen put half a grapefruit in front of him. Then she gave him a mocking smirk, and sipped her juice with exaggerated enjoyment.

Helen was helping herself to a second cup of coffee when Tricia appeared in the kitchen doorway. She wasn't dressed yet. She was wearing a trailing chiffon négligé, and her reddish hair hadn't been combed and stood out around her head. A tall woman, whose adolescent athleticism hadn't continued into adulthood, Tricia had a constant battle to remain slim. It was a fact that she resented and which caused her some irritation. She regarded the little group around the table now without liking, and when Sophie would have slid off her chair and run to greet her mother she waved her back.

'D'you have any aspirin, Maria?' she asked, with a weary tilt of her head. 'I've got the most God-awful headache. It must have been that seafood you served us last night. Are you sure it was fresh?'

It was hardly the way to gain Maria's sympathy, and before the woman could make any comment, Helen pushed back her chair. 'I've got some paracetamol,' she offered. 'It's good for headaches.' Particularly hangovers, she added silently, recalling how Tricia had drunk the best part of two bottles of wine the night before.

'Oh, have you?' Tricia turned to her with some relief. 'D'you think you could bring them to my room? I think I'll stay in bed this morning.'

'But you said you'd take us into town this morning,' Henry protested, not yet old enough to know when to keep his mouth shut, and his mother turned on him angrily.

'What a selfish boy you are!' she exclaimed. 'Always thinking of yourself. Perhaps you'd like to spend the morning in bed as well. It might make you realise I'm not doing it for fun.'

'Oh, Mummy—'

'I don't think Henry meant to upset you,' put in Helen hurriedly, earning a grateful look from her young charge. 'Why don't you go back to bed, as you say, Tricia? I'll get the paracetamol, and then bring your breakfast on a tray. I'm sure you could manage a croissant, and Maria's brought some mango jelly and it's delicious.'

'Well...' Tricia adopted a petulant air. 'That does sound nice, Helen, but I don't know if I'll be able to eat anything. My head's throbbing, and I'm sure I'm running a temperature. I may have to call the doctor if it doesn't let up soon.'

'I'm sorry.'

Helen could sympathise with her. Having a headache in a hot climate always seemed so much worse. The light was so bright, for one thing, and there seemed no escape from the heat.

Tricia sighed. 'Perhaps if you brought me some coffee?' she suggested. 'And a little orange juice to wash the tablets down. Oh—and maybe a lightly boiled egg, hmm? And do you think you could find a slice of toast?'

'Leave it to me.'

Helen ushered the other woman out of the room, before she could remember the threat she'd made to Henry. Then, when Tricia was safely installed in her bedroom, she returned to the kitchen to find Maria grinning broadly.

'Just a lightly boiled egg,' she declared wryly. 'And some coffee and some orange juice and some toast…' She paused to give Helen a wink. 'Did I miss something?'

Helen wouldn't let herself be drawn. All the same, it wasn't the first time Tricia had spent the morning in bed. When they were in London, she had seldom seen her employer before lunchtime. If Tricia wasn't attending some function or other, she rarely got up before noon.

When the tray was prepared, she collected the paracetamol from her room and delivered it in person. Tricia was lying back against the pillows, shading her eyes with a languid wrist, which she removed when Helen came into the room.

'Oh, there you are,' she said. 'What have you been doing? I've been waiting ages.'

'Just five minutes,' Helen assured her, depositing the legs of the tray across her knees. 'Now, if you want me, I'll be on the beach. I'm going to take the children to search for shells.'

Tricia shuffled into a sitting position, and reached for the orange juice. 'Well, don't be long,' she said, swallowing the tablets Helen had given her with a mouthful of the juice. 'You're going to have to go and pick Drew up from the airport. I can't possibly do it. His plane is due in just after two.'

Helen stared at her. 'But that's this afternoon. You'll probably be feeling perfectly all right by then.'

'I won't. I never feel all right until the evening,' replied Tricia firmly. 'And driving all that way in these conditions—well, it's simply out of the question.'

Helen took a breath. 'He'll be expecting you to pick him up,' she said carefully.

'Then he'll be disappointed, won't he?' Tricia regarded her testily. 'My God, you're almost as bad as Henry. Does no one care that I've got a migraine? I can't help it if I'm not well.'

'No.' Helen moistened her lips. She'd already learned

that there was no point in arguing with Tricia when she was in this mood. 'Well—will you take care of Sophie and Henry, then? I don't think Maria is willing—'

'Can't they go with you?'

Tricia stared at her impatiently, and Helen realised she wasn't being given a choice. She couldn't leave the children to look after themselves. But it was almost an hour to the airport, and Sophie, particularly, didn't travel well.

'Can we leave it until nearer lunchtime?' she suggested, hoping against hope that Tricia might have changed her mind by then. She'd have thought her employer would have been keen to see her husband again. It was several days since they'd come away.

'I expect you to go and meet Drew,' Tricia informed her inflexibly, and Helen couldn't help thinking that there was no sign of the frail invalid they had encountered earlier. 'Must I remind you that if it wasn't for me you might not have a job? Let alone a well-paid one in enviable surroundings.'

'No.' Helen felt her colour deepen. 'I mean—yes. Yes, I do appreciate it.' She turned towards the door. 'I'll—tell the children.'

'Good.' Tricia attacked her egg with evident enthusiasm. 'Just so long as we understand one another, Helen. I don't like pulling rank here, but it really had to be said.'

CHAPTER TWO

MATTHEW AITKEN lounged behind the wheel of the dust-smeared Range Rover, waiting for his assistant, Lucas Cord, to emerge from the arrivals hall. He was getting impatient. The plane from New York had landed more than twenty minutes ago, and as Fleur had been booked into a first-class seat her luggage should have been cleared some time ago.

It was hot where he was sitting. There was little shade at this time of day and, despite the air-conditioning in the vehicle, which had been working fairly adequately on the journey to the airport, a prolonged period of waiting was causing the heat to rise. The annoying thing was that he wouldn't have been here at all if his phone hadn't been out of order. He'd discovered that when he'd tried to call New York that morning, and as he needed to speak to his publisher rather urgently he'd had no choice but to try elsewhere.

In consequence, it had made sense to continue on to the airport. Lucas had offered to make the call for him, but he'd wanted to speak to Marilyn himself. It was so much easier to deal with the matter personally. And the delay in the completion of the manuscript was his problem.

All the same, he disliked giving Fleur the impression that he had nothing better to do than come and meet her. It wasn't as if he was even eager to have her here. But she was still his sister-in-law, even if his brother was no longer around. Chase's death at the age of forty-two had been such a bitter blow.

Which, of course, was why the latest manuscript hadn't been completed. Although it was eight weeks now since

Chase's fall, he was finding it hard to work. Dammit, he
thought irritably, what had Chase been thinking of to attack
his opponent so recklessly? It wasn't as if he was an amateur. He'd been playing polo for almost thirty years.

Fleur, of course, had been devastated. When he'd seen
her at the funeral, he hadn't doubted that it was a blow to
her, too. She had been dressed all in black and oozing tears,
and he'd had to feel sympathy for her. For the first time in
his life, he'd pitied her. He couldn't believe even she could
have wanted Chase dead.

But as he sat there in the Range Rover, with sweat dampening the shirt on his back and his bare thighs sticking to
the leather seat, he couldn't help remembering that he
hadn't always felt so charitably towards her. He'd been
only sixteen when his brother had brought Fleur to live with
them. The fact that she had still been married to her first
husband at that time hadn't sat too happily with their father
either, but Chase had been mad about her, and somehow
they'd all settled down.

It was just as well his own mother hadn't been around,
Matthew reflected drily. Emily Aitken had died of a rare
form of cancer when he was ten, and until Fleur had come
to live at the ranch their housekeeper, Rosa Cortez, had
been both wife and mother to the three men.

Fleur had changed all that. In no time at all she was
giving Rosa orders, telling his father what to do, and bullying Chase into doing whatever she wanted. His father
hadn't liked it but he was a mild man, more at home with
temperamental horses than temperamental women, and at
least he could escape into the stables whenever he felt like
it.

Of course, the horses their father bred were what had
enabled Chase to become the successful sportsman he had
been. The Aitken Stud was famous throughout the United
States, and enthusiasts came from as far afield as Argentina
and Europe to buy the spirited stallions he produced. It was
a lucrative business, and for all Matthew had been so

young, he had had no doubt that Chase's wealth had been a goodly part of his allure. Fleur had liked spending his money too much to have been attracted to a poor man, and he'd sometimes wondered what her first husband must have been like, and whether he had been wealthy, too.

Fortunately, during the early years of their marriage, he, Matthew, had spent most of his time away. College, and then university, had enabled him to avoid the image of his big brother being turned from a laughing, confident man into a grovelling supplicant. Whatever Fleur had, Chase had certainly been hooked on it, and Matthew had preferred to stay out of their way whenever he was at home.

He had been twenty-two when Fleur tried to seduce him. He remembered the occasion vividly. Chase had been away, playing a match in Buenos Aires, and his father had been attending the horse sales in Kentucky. Matthew wouldn't have been there at all had it not been for the fact that he was attending an interview the following day in Tallahassee. The editor of the *Tallahassee Chronicle* was looking for a junior reporter, and Matthew had been hoping to get the job.

At first he hadn't believed what was happening. When Fleur had come to his room, he'd assumed there really must be something wrong. It was when she had complained of being so lonely and started to shed her satin wrap that he'd comprehended. And, although his hot young body had been burning, he'd succeeded in throwing her out.

However, he hadn't been able to hide the fact that she'd aroused him, and Fleur had seen his weakness as a challenge. At every opportunity she'd let him see how willing she was to be with him, touching him with clinging hands, bestowing longing looks.

Matthew had been sickened by it. It wasn't as if there had been any shortage of women his own age, ready and willing to satisfy his every need. But not his brother's wife, he'd assured himself disgustedly. Dear God, he'd thought, if he ever got that desperate, he'd go out and buy a gun.

Not that his attitude had deterred Fleur. On the contrary, she'd seemed to find his resistance very appealing. It became a point of honour with her to succeed, and not until he threatened to tell Chase did her provocation cease.

Of course, that was a dozen years ago now, and Matthew had long stopped worrying about his brother. His own career—first as a newspaper columnist, and then as an overseas reporter working for an agency based in New York—had broadened his mind, and he was no longer surprised by anything people did. Working in war-torn Lebanon and South-east Asia, he'd become inured to man's inhumanities to man. The problem of a sex-hungry sister-in-law seemed small indeed, when compared to the struggle between life and death.

Besides, in his absence, Fleur and Chase had appeared to reconcile any differences they might have had. They had both grown older, for one thing, and Matthew's different lifestyle had reinforced the barriers between them.

Then, five years ago, Matthew had written his first novel. A lot of it had been based on his own experiences in Beirut, and, to his amazement, it had been an immediate success. Film rights had been optioned; in paperback it sold almost five million copies. He'd become an overnight celebrity— and he'd found he didn't like it.

That was when he had had the notion of moving out of the United States. He'd always liked the islands of the Caribbean, and the casual lifestyle of Barbados suited him far better than the hectic social round of living in New York had ever done. When his second book was completed, he had it written into the contract that he was not available for subsequent publicity. He preferred his anonymity. He didn't want to become a media hack.

But, to his astonishment, like Fleur when he'd rejected her, his public found his detachment as intriguing as she had done. Avoiding talk-shows and signing sessions made no difference to his sales. His books apparently sold themselves, and curiosity about his lifestyle was rife.

All the same, it was a lot harder to reach him at Dragon Bay. The villa, which he had had erected on the ruins of an old plantation house, had excellent security features, and Lucas Cord—once his sound technician, but now his secretary-cum-assistant—made sure he wasn't bothered by any unwelcome guests. Matthew supposed he'd become something of a recluse, only visiting New York when he needed stimulation. He seldom invited women to Dragon Bay. He wasn't married, and he had no desire to be so.

Which was probably something else he could lay at Fleur's door, he reflected cynically, watching as a dusty estate car skidded into the parking area and a girl and two young children tumbled out. For all his brother's marriage had lasted until his death, he doubted Chase had really been happy. He'd lived his life constantly placating a woman who'd tried to cheat him at every turn.

'Henry—wait!'

The girl—or was she a young woman? Matthew was never quite sure of the distinction—yelled desperately after the small boy, who had darted recklessly between the parked cars. She seemed hung up with the other child, who appeared to be doubled up with pain, and Matthew could see an accident in the making if the boy gained the busy area where the taxis were waiting.

Without giving himself time to think about the pros and cons of what he was about to do, Matthew thrust open his door and vaulted out of the Range Rover. His long legs swiftly overtook the boy's, and his hand descended on the child's shoulder seconds before he reached the open road.

'Ouch.' The boy—Henry?—looked up at him indignantly. 'Let go of me! I'm going to meet my daddy.'

'Not without your mother, you're not,' returned Matthew smoothly, turning to look back towards the cars. 'Come along. I'll take you back. Did no one ever tell you it's dangerous to play in traffic?'

Henry looked up at him mutinously. 'I wasn't playing.'

'Nor are the drivers,' said Matthew drily, feeling the

boy's resistance in every step they took. He was aware that
his action had drawn some unwelcome attention, and he
hoped that no one imagined he was enjoying himself.

The child's mother was hurrying towards them now, and
Matthew regarded her with some impatience. With her
waist-length braid and narrow body, she hardly looked old
enough to have two children, albeit of pre-school age. But
she had the casual elegance of many English holidaymakers
at this time of year, women who knew nothing about caring
for their own children, and he felt a surge of anger at her
obvious lack of control.

'Oh, Henry!' she exclaimed when she reached them,
bending down to grab the boy's hand with evident relief.
'Don't you ever—ever—go dashing off like that again. If—
if—' she cast a swift glance up at Matthew '—this gentleman hadn't caught you, you could easily have been
knocked down!'

'Perhaps if you'd held on to his hand sooner, he wouldn't
have had the chance to run away,' observed Matthew
shortly, aware that it was really no concern of his. It wasn't
his place to tell her how to look after her children, and the
deepening colour in her cheeks caused him as much discomfort as herself.

The trouble was, he realised, she had annoyed him. Driving into the car park like a mad thing, allowing the boy to
put his life in danger. People like her shouldn't be allowed
to have children, he thought unreasonably. Though why he
felt so strongly about it, he really couldn't say.

'Yes,' she said stiffly now, facing him with eyes that
were an indeterminate shade of grey. 'I know it was remiss
of me to let Henry run off like that. But—' she cast her
gaze down at the younger child, who Matthew could see
was looking quite green '—Sophie was feeling sick again,
and it all happened rather fast.'

It was a valid explanation, and Matthew knew it, but for
some reason he couldn't let it go. Was it that her colouring
reminded him rather too strongly of the woman he'd been

forced to invite here? Or was it some lingering sense of resentment that he'd had to get involved at all? Whatever the solution, he knew that she disturbed him. And he resented that intensely.

'Wouldn't it have been more sensible, then, to leave the child at home?' he countered, and her eyes widened in obvious disbelief. He was getting in too deep, and he knew it. All it needed was for her husband to appear and he'd be totally out of his depth.

'Mr—?'

'There's Daddy!'

Before she could finish what she had been about to say, the little boy started pulling at her arm. A tall man in a business suit, trailed by a porter wheeling a suitcase on his barrow, had just emerged from the airport buildings, and Matthew's frustration hardened as the little girl set up a similar cry.

'Daddy, Daddy,' she called, her nausea obviously forgotten. 'Daddy, we're here!' She tugged at her mother's hand. 'Let me go. Let me go. I want to go and meet him.'

The young woman cast Matthew one further studied look, and then released both children as the man got near enough to hold out his arms towards them. 'Perhaps you'd like to tell their father what a hopeless case I am?' she invited coldly. 'I'd introduce you myself, but I didn't catch your name.'

Matthew's jaw compressed. 'Forget it,' he said shortly, turning away, but before he could put a sufficient distance between them the children's father came up, carrying both his offspring. He looked quizzically at his wife, and then turned his attention to Matthew.

'Do you two know one another?' he asked. Then, loosening his collar, 'God, it's bloody hot, isn't it? I can't wait to get this suit off.'

'Henry ran away,' said Sophie, before anyone else could say anything, and Henry made an effort to punch her behind his father's back. 'He did,' she added, when she'd regained her father's attention. 'He would have been run over if this man hadn't brought him back.'

'He *might* have been run over,' amended her mother evenly, refusing to meet Matthew's eyes, but her husband set both children down and held out his hand.

'Thanks a lot,' he said, shaking Matthew's hand vigorously. 'I know Henry can be quite a handful. I'm Andrew Sheridan, by the way. And I'll see he doesn't do it again.'

'Aitken,' said Matthew unwillingly, banking on the fact that it wasn't such an uncommon name, and obviously neither of them had recognised him from the jackets of his books. 'Um—actually, your wife wasn't to blame for what happened. Your little girl was sick, and—'

'I'm not—'

'Thanks, anyway.' Before his wife could complete her sentence, Andrew Sheridan intervened. He gave her a mischievous look, and then continued pleasantly, 'You'll have to come and have a drink with us some time. Give us a ring. We're renting a villa out at Dragon Point.'

'Really?' Matthew managed not to make any promises, and to his relief, out of the corner of his eye, he saw Lucas striding towards him with Fleur flapping at his heels. 'I've got to go,' he said, his polite tone disguising the dismay he'd felt at discovering they were holidaying a short distance from his estate. 'If you'll excuse me…' He inclined his head curtly, and walked swiftly away.

He heard the young woman exclaim, 'Why did you do that?' and then, almost immediately afterwards, a choking gasp, as if her husband had hit her. It brought Matthew's head round, in spite of himself, but there was no evidence that she'd been abused. On the contrary, she was staring after him, as if he'd done something wrong, her eyes wide with horror and all the colour drained out of her face.

It was crazy, because she meant nothing to him, but he was tempted to go back and ask her what the hell she thought she was doing. He'd got her off the hook, hadn't he? She should be thanking him. Not gazing at him, for God's sake, as if he was the devil incarnate.

With a grunt of impatience, Matthew swung his head round and continued towards his car. Forget it, he told himself fiercely. It was nothing to do with him. But he couldn't deny a sense of anger and irritation—and the unpleasant feeling that he'd been used.

'Who was that you were talking to?' Fleur asked, after the briefest of greetings had been exchanged—reluctant on his part, fervent on hers. She insinuated herself into the seat beside him, despite the fact that Lucas had held the rear door for her, and gazed at him enquiringly. 'A little young for your tastes, isn't she, darling?' she teased. 'Or have you acquired a liking for schoolgirls in my absence?'

'And if I have?' Matthew countered, her accent jarring on him after his exchange with the other woman. His eyes glittered maliciously. 'I'm only following in your footsteps, sister, dear. We both have peculiar tastes, don't we?'

'I'm not your sister,' hissed Fleur, as Lucas climbed good-humouredly into the seat behind them. She cast the other man a tight smile. 'Perhaps I can get some sense from you.'

'I don't know who they are,' declared Lucas ruefully. 'I've never seen them before. They're probably here on holiday. We get a lot of them at this time of the year.'

'On holiday?' Fleur's expression altered. 'Not friends of Matt's, then?'

Lucas met his employer's gaze in the rear-view mirror, and gave an apologetic shrug of his shoulders. 'Not to my knowledge,' he conceded wryly. He pulled a face at Matthew before adding, 'Did you have a good journey?'

Fleur relaxed, and for the first time since her arrival she allowed herself to show a trace of regret. 'It was—lonely,' she said, rummaging in her capacious handbag for a tissue, and using it to dab her eyes. 'I couldn't help remembering that the last time I came here Chase was with me. He loved to spend time with Matt, you know? It's sad that in recent years they spent so little time together.'

Lucas made a polite rejoinder, and Matthew bit down on the urge to tell Fleur that she knew why that was, better than anyone. He had the feeling he'd been wrong to invite Fleur here, however sorry he'd felt for her at the funeral. She hadn't really changed. She was just as ingenious as ever.

'How's Dad?' he asked now, refusing to be drawn in that direction, and Fleur gave a careless shrug.

'So long as he has his damn horses to care about, no one else seems to matter,' she declared bitterly, as Matthew joined the stream of vehicles leaving the airport, and he gave her a brief, scornful glance. They both knew that wasn't true. Ben Aitken had loved his eldest son dearly, and he'd been shattered when he was killed. What she really meant was that the older man had little time for her, and he didn't have to pretend any more now that Chase was dead.

'But he's well?' Matthew persisted, suddenly recognising the vehicle ahead of them. Andrew Sheridan was driving now, but there was no mistaking the young woman seated in the back. He'd have recognised that accusing profile anywhere. She was staring out of the rear window, and he was sure she was looking at him.

'He was. When I left.' Fleur pulled a pack of cigarettes out of her bag and put one between her teeth. 'I spent a couple of days in New York before coming here.' She scanned the dashboard for the automatic lighter. 'Dammit, where is it?'

Matthew didn't reply, and as if becoming aware that his attention had been distracted, Fleur followed the direction of his gaze. 'Oh, God,' she said disgustedly, 'it's the girl again, isn't it? Whatever is she staring at? Someone should teach her some manners.'

'Her husband, perhaps?' suggested Matthew, determinedly avoiding that cool grey gaze.

'Her husband?' Fleur was disbelieving. 'You're not telling me she's married?'

'With two children,' Matthew conceded tersely. Then, to Lucas, 'They're staying at Dragon Point.'

Lucas frowned. 'At the Parrish place?' he asked, and Matthew's brows drew together.

'Yeah, right,' he said thoughtfully, taking advantage of an open piece of road to pass the other vehicle. Then, with his nemesis safely behind him, he felt free to make the connection. 'I thought the place was occupied when I walked past there this morning.'

Fleur gave him a calculating look as she lit her cigarette. 'That man—the man who was driving the car—he was on the flight from New York.'

Matthew cast her a careless glance. 'So?'

'So—one wonders what she's been getting up to, while her husband's been away.' She inhaled, and then blew smoke deliberately into his face. 'Have you been—comforting her in his absence, I wonder?'

Matthew's jaw hardened. 'Wouldn't you like to know?' he countered, refusing to rise to her bait. 'What I do is my business, Fleur,' he added, meeting her angry gaze. 'And if you must smoke, do it in your own car. I can't stand the smell of stale tobacco.'

'You're a prig, do you know that?'

But Fleur stubbed out her cigarette before giving him the benefit of her scowl. Matthew didn't answer. It would have been far too easy to tell her what he thought she was. Besides, she already knew it. Which begged the question of why she was here…

CHAPTER THREE

IT WAS a good hour's drive back to the villa.

It shouldn't have taken so long. For most of the way the new highway meant that the road was extremely good. But Helen had already learned to her cost that traffic moved much less frenetically in Barbados than it did in London. Yet she was glad of the prolonged length of the journey to try to get herself under control. The shock she had had at the airport had left her palms moist, her knees shaking and her heart beating uncomfortably fast. Dear God, had she really seen her mother? Or was it all some incredible co-incidence?

Of course, Andrew thought she was sulking because he had let the Aitken man think she was his wife. She still didn't know why he'd done it, but that embarrassment had been quickly superseded by other events. That man's name—Aitken—had been familiar, but she'd never dreamed that that was who he was. Until Fleur—if it was Fleur—had come sauntering out of the airport. Then the connection had been too much to ignore.

She expelled her breath with a shiver. Had it really been Fleur? Had it really been Chase Aitken? It had looked like Fleur—or, at least, like the pictures she had once unearthed in the attic at Conyers. James Gregory had seldom mentioned her, and he had certainly never encouraged Helen to ask questions. But the woman had been her mother, after all, and she hadn't been able to help her curiosity.

Yet, if the woman had been her mother, then Chase Aitken was evidently much younger than she'd imagined. Was that what had hurt her father so badly? The fact that

30

his wife had left him for a man almost young enough to be his son?

'There's no point in sitting there brooding,' Andrew remarked suddenly, arousing her from her uneasy speculations, and Helen met his accusing gaze with some frustration. As if she didn't have enough to worry about, without Tricia's husband playing some stupid game of his own.

'I'm not brooding,' she replied, which was true. Her thoughts were far less pretty. If her mother was here on the island, what was she going to do about it? Did Fleur know her father was dead, for instance? And if she did, did she care?

'Yes, you are,' Andrew contradicted her flatly. 'What's the matter, Helen? Can't you take a joke?'

'Was that what it was?'

Helen refused to be treated like a fool, and Henry gave his father a doubtful look. 'Why did that man think you and Helen were married?' he piped up curiously, and Helen heard Andrew give an irritated snort.

'How should I know?' he exclaimed, proving he was not as indifferent to his wife's possible reaction as he'd been to Helen's. If the children accused him of perpetuating the mistake, Tricia wouldn't be at all pleased. Particularly as the Aitkens were exactly the kind of people she liked to mix with.

'Well, perhaps you should have corrected him,' Helen observed now, aware that if she wasn't careful she'd be the one blamed for assuming Tricia's identity, and Andrew scowled.

'How was I to know what you'd told him?' he demanded, refusing to let her off the hook. 'I didn't want to embarrass you, that's all. The man might have been a nuisance.'

Helen was always amazed at the lengths some people would go to protect their own positions, and she gazed at the back of Andrew's head now with undisguised contempt.

What had she expected, after all? She was only the nurse-maid. She just hoped Tricia wouldn't imagine she'd done something to warrant the misunderstanding.

'He was nice,' asserted Sophie, apparently deciding she had been quiet long enough. Happily, she was looking better now that she had something else to think about.

'How would you know?' asked Henry at once, seldom allowing his sister to get away with anything. 'He hurt my arm, and he called me a rude name. I'm going to tell Mummy that Helen didn't stop him.'

'You're not going to tell your mother anything,' cut in his father sharply, evidently deciding that it wasn't in his best interests to let Henry carry tales. 'Or I might just have to tell her that without Mr Aitken's intervention you'd have been minced meat.'

Henry hunched his shoulders. 'I wouldn't,' he muttered.

'You would,' said Sophie triumphantly. 'Anyway, I liked him. And I think Helen liked him, too.'

'Heavens, I don't even know the man,' Helen demurred, annoyed to find that the child had achieved what her father couldn't. Hot colour was pouring into her cheeks, and Andrew's expression revealed that he knew it.

'Who is he, anyway?' he asked. 'You never did tell me. What did you find out about him? You seemed to be having quite a conversation as I walked out of the airport buildings.'

'I don't know anything more than you do,' Helen declared, not altogether truthfully, glad that she was flushed now, and therefore in no danger of revealing herself again. 'I didn't even know his name until you asked him.' Which was true. 'He's probably another tourist. The island's full of them.'

'Hmm.' Andrew was thoughtful. 'He didn't look like a tourist to me. Unless he's been here since Christmas. You don't get a tan like that in a couple of weeks.'

'Does it matter?'

Helen didn't particularly want to talk about it, or think

about it, for that matter. The image she had, of a tall dark man with the lean muscled body of an athlete, was not one she wanted to cherish. Chase Aitken, she thought scornfully, polo-player, playboy, and jock. Not to mention adulterer, she added bitterly. She hoped she'd never see him again.

Tricia was up and dressed when they arrived back at the villa. She had shed her trailing wrap in favour of a loose-fitting tunic, and her auburn-tinted hair had been brushed to frame her face. She looked much different from the languid female who had waved them goodbye, and she greeted her husband more warmly than she'd been known to do before.

'Sorry I couldn't meet you, darling,' she said, getting up from the cushioned lounge chair she had been occupying on the terrace. Set in the shade of a huge flame tree, it was an oasis of shadow in the late afternoon heat that still drenched the villa. Only the breeze from the ocean provided a warm draught of air to dry moist skin, but Tricia looked cool and comfortable, and totally relaxed.

'No problem,' said Andrew easily, bending to bestow a kiss on his wife's upturned lips. But his eyes sought Helen's as he offered the salutation, and she had the uneasy feeling that their relationship would never be the same again.

'Can we have some juice?' Henry cried plaintively, bored by his parents' demonstration of marital felicity, and his mother turned to look at him with some impatience.

'You can't be thirsty,' she said. 'I told Helen to get you both a drink at the airport. Heaven knows, you had enough time.' She glanced at her watch. 'I expected you back half an hour ago. The plane was obviously late.'

'She didn't get me a drink—' Henry was beginning indignantly, when his father chose to intervene.

'Actually the plane was on time,' he said, earning a raised eyebrow from his wife. 'But there was some hold-up with the luggage. And Helen had her hands full, because Sophie had been sick.'

'Oh.' Tricia looked somewhat distastefully at her daughter. 'Not again.'

'Yes, again,' went on Andrew evenly. 'We all had our problems, didn't we, Henry?' He gave his son a warning look. 'Now, run along and ask whoever it is your mother said is looking after us—'

'Maria,' supplied Sophie proudly, and her father smiled.

'Very well. You two go and ask Maria if she'd be kind enough to give you a drink.'

'Helen can do it,' protested Tricia, before Henry and Sophie could leave them. She carefully resumed her position on the lounger. 'As they're obviously tired, it would probably be a good idea to give them their supper early and put them to bed.'

'Oh, Mummy—'

'But I want to talk to Daddy—'

The two children both spoke at once, but Tricia just ignored them. 'You can have an early night, too, Helen,' she added, stretching out her hand towards her husband. 'I shan't need you any more today.' She sighed contentedly. 'Drew and I will enjoy a quiet evening together. It's ages since we had any time alone.'

'Helen's not a child, Trish.' Andrew came to her defence, even though she hadn't wanted him to. 'Put the brats to bed by all means, Helen. But then you must join us for supper.'

'Helen may not want to,' Tricia observed tersely, not at all pleased to have her plans overset. 'She might like a quiet evening, too.'

'We are on holiday, Trish,' retorted Andrew, just as Helen was about to agree with her. 'Besides, I'm sure you'll want to hear about the man we met at the airport. He said his name was Aitken, didn't he, Helen?' He turned back to his wife. 'Do we know anyone of that name?'

Tricia stared first at her husband, then at Helen. 'Aitken?' she exclaimed. 'Did you say Aitken?'

'That's what he said,' said Andrew maliciously, enjoying Helen's discomfort. 'The name is familiar, but I can't imagine why.'

'I can,' said Tricia suddenly, and for an awful moment Helen thought she had made the connection between Chase Aitken and her mother. But then, as the other woman began to speak again, she realised how unlikely that was. Her mother had left her father almost twenty years ago.

'Well, you won't know,' Tricia explained patiently. 'It's the name of the man who owns the house beyond the point. I asked Maria who our neighbours were, and she said his name was Aitken.' She clasped her hands together excitedly. 'D'you think it's the same man?'

'I'd say it was highly likely,' said Andrew, frowning. 'Though the chap didn't make any comment when I told him we were staying here. You'd think he'd have mentioned it, wouldn't you, Helen? Unless we offended him, of course.'

'Offended him?' exclaimed Tricia sharply, looking from one to the other of them with suspicious eyes. 'How could you have offended him? For heaven's sake, Helen, what did you say?'

Helen noticed the assumption that she was the one who must have said something to offend him, and she was just about to explain what had happened when Andrew broke in.

'Well, as you know, Sophie had been throwing up all over the car park, and the bloke came over to offer his assistance. We let him think that Helen was my wife, and I don't think he was impressed by our behaviour.'

'You did what?'

Tricia stared at her husband, aghast, as Helen wished the ground would open up and swallow her. But she had nothing but admiration for the way Andrew had turned the tables. Not only had he implicated her in his schemes, but he'd successfully neutralised any flack from Aitken's direction.

'It was just a game,' he said carelessly, draping his jacket over one shoulder and loosening his tie. 'For God's sake, Trish, I doubt if he believed it. Does Helen look like the mother of these two, I ask you? A fool could see she's far too young.'

'She's exactly four years younger than me,' said Tricia through her teeth, and Andrew gave a dismissive shrug in her direction.

'Like I said, far too young,' he remarked, grinning at her frustration. 'I'm going for a shower now. I assume we do have showers in this place?' He sauntered towards the French doors that opened into the villa. 'You can come and show Daddy where Mummy's room is, Henry. And then, while I'm changing, d'you think one of you could get me a beer?'

'Andrew!'

Tricia's temper was simmering, but he was totally undaunted by her infuriated stare. 'Oh, and ask Maria if she'd get my suitcase,' he added. 'Unless someone else would like to oblige.'

Helen spent an uncomfortable evening on her own.

After giving the children their suppers and getting them ready for bed, she'd sent a message, via Maria, to say she had a headache, and would not be joining her employers for the evening meal. Instead she'd made herself a salad, eating it in her room, with the doors and windows securely bolted.

Which was one of the reasons why it was so uncomfortable, although, compared to the other events of the day, the humidity in her room was of little importance. Dear God, what was she going to do? She was almost sure the woman she had seen was her mother. And she was staying just a short distance away. Oh, lord, how could she bear it?

The clipped exchange she had with Tricia, after Andrew had gone for his shower, hadn't helped. It had been useless trying to explain that Andrew hadn't actually *said* she was his wife, that Aitken—she refused to think of him as Chase—had only assumed it. She hadn't even been given the opportunity to relate properly the events which had led up to his introduction, and if she'd hoped that by telling Tricia how he'd spoken to her—how he'd criticised her— the other woman might relent at all, she'd been wrong. Tricia wasn't interested in her feelings. She was only interested in the embarrassment their behaviour might have caused *her*.

'I think you behaved totally irresponsibly,' she had said, pacing up and down the terrace, and Helen had noticed how somehow she had shouldered all the blame. 'Have you seen the house beyond the point? Well, of course you must have. It's huge, Helen, and obviously expensive. The man must be seriously rich!'

'Why?' Helen had sighed. 'He could be renting the place, just as we are.'

'I doubt it.' Tricia had dismissed that idea. 'I'm fairly sure he lives here.' She had frowned. 'I wonder if he's married. I'd like to meet his wife.'

Helen groaned, and ran her hands over her hair now. The prospect of Tricia meeting the Aitkens socially was one she couldn't bear to endure. Although she doubted her mother would recognise her, her name was obviously going to give her identity away. What would Fleur do if she was introduced to her own daughter by a stranger? Would she acknowledge her? Would she care? Or was it all some awful nightmare she'd invented?

Helen was up even earlier the next morning. The ironic thing was that her body was beginning to adjust to the time-change, but the uneasy tenor of her thoughts wouldn't let her sleep. As soon as it was at all light, she crawled wearily out of bed. Perhaps a swim in the ocean might revive her, she thought tiredly. Right now the prospect of facing any of the Sheridans filled her with dismay.

Stripping off her nightgown, she went into the bathroom and cleaned her teeth. One of the ubiquitous flying beetles had committed suicide in the sink, and she removed it to the lavatory with a handful of toilet paper. Then, returning to the bedroom, she pulled a one-piece *maillot* out of the drawer. Its high-cut hipline was rather daring, but she doubted anyone would see her.

In any event it was black and, in spite of the fact that she'd already spent several days in the sun, she looked rather pale this morning. Pale and *un*interesting, she mocked herself ruefully. Still, that was her role here: to avoid being noticed.

Wrapping a towel about her hips, she unlocked the shutters and crossed the balcony. Unlike a summer's morning at home, it didn't really get light here until after six o'clock. Then, like the twilight that lasted so briefly, there was a rapid transference to day. The sun rose swiftly in these semi-tropical islands, and the air was always transparent and sweet.

Tussocky grass grew against the low wall where she'd been sitting musing the previous day. A shallow flight of steps gave way to the beach, and the sand felt quite cool between her toes. It was coral sand, fine and slightly gritty, and here and there a rockpool gave a fleeting glimpse of shade. There were crabs, too, scuttling out of her path, some of them so tiny they looked like shells. And now and then a seabird came down to hunt for food, screaming its objection to her intrusion.

When she reached the water's edge, she couldn't resist turning her head to see the house Tricia had spoken of the night before. It wasn't wholly visible, which was one of the reasons Tricia had been so interested in it. All they could see from this distance was a sprawling roof, shaded by palms, and a coral wall. Evidence, if any was needed, that their neighbour preferred his privacy.

Still, Tricia was right about one thing, Helen reflected ruefully. It did look an enormous place. Compared to the Aitken house, the villa they were renting looked tiny, even if it did have four bedrooms and a parlour, and the swimming-pool in the garden.

The water felt cold when she broached the tiny rivulets edged with foam that creamed about her feet. Of course, she knew it was only the heat of her body that made her think it. Compared to the English Channel, it was like a Turkish bath.

It crossed her mind suddenly that this was the time she had seen the stranger walking along the shoreline from her balcony. And hard on the heels of this thought came the obvious knowledge of who it must be. She'd seen him often enough, and always walking in this direction. It had to be Chase Aitken, and he was bound to think she'd come to intercept him.

The idea of taking a swim instantly lost its appeal. She had no desire to encounter Chase Aitken again, and the realisation of how fine she was cutting it sent her hurrying back the way she had come. Unless he had better things to do—and her stomach hollowed unpleasantly at the thought—he'd be turning the point any moment. All that had saved her was an outcrop of rock, and a brain that was not quite vapid.

'We meet again, Mrs Sheridan.'

The voice—a far too familiar voice in the circumstances—almost scared the life out of her. She'd thought she was alone on the beach—she *had* been alone when she walked down to the water. But somehow, while she was ogling his house, perhaps, or before the coolness of the water had cleared her head, he'd negotiated the outcrop. He was sprawling in her path now, and she'd almost walked all over him.

'I'm—not—Mrs Sheridan,' she said, choosing the least controversial thing she could say. It was disconcerting to have him looking up at her, and she was glad she still had the towel securely round her hips.

'I know.' With a lithe movement he reversed their positions, his superior height making it necessary for Helen to tilt her head now. 'My—housekeeper—knows your maid, Maria. When I described you, she said you were the Sheridans' nanny.'

Helen felt a quiver of annoyance. 'Why should you describe me to your housekeeper?' she demanded. 'I don't think I like the idea of you—gossiping—about me to your staff.'

His dark eyes flickered. 'I don't gossip—Helen, isn't it? I was curious. You seemed far too young to have two children.'

Helen was angry. 'Did I?' She licked her lips. 'Well, that may be so, but I don't recall giving you permission to use my name, *Mr* Aitken,' she declared stiffly.

His mouth turned down. 'I don't know your surname, Miss—?' he mocked her carelessly. 'Why don't you tell me what it is, and I'll see what I can do?'

Helen swallowed, remembering suddenly that she shouldn't—couldn't—give this man her name. 'It doesn't matter,' she said, hoping to end the discussion. But when she moved to go past him, he caught her arm.

She wasn't afraid—although she supposed she should have been. After all, this was the man who had seduced her mother, and he was hardly likely to quibble over a nanny. Even without being aware of the lean body, partially concealed by the laced ties of his sweat-suit, the hand gripping her forearm was hard. There was strength in every finger digging into her skin, and his musky heat enveloped her in its warmth.

'What is it with you?' he asked, his breath cool against her cheek. 'Just because I spoke out of turn yesterday, you're determined to hold it against me? Look—' he released her, as if realising that force wasn't going to aid his cause '—I'll apologise, OK? If the kid's anything like his father, I guess you've got my sympathy.'

Helen caught her breath. 'And that's supposed to be an apology?'

'No.' Aitken shook his head. 'If anyone needs to apologise, it's Sheridan. He didn't correct me when I made an error of judgement. I guess he thought it was amusing. Making fun of the locals.'

Helen told herself she didn't care where he and her mother lived, but she found herself asking the question just the same. 'Are you a local, Mr Aitken? I wouldn't have thought this was quite your style.'

'But you don't know anything about my style,' he countered smoothly. 'And, as it happens, Barbados suits me very well.'

'I'm so glad.'

Helen was sarcastic, but she couldn't help it, and Aitken regarded her with studied eyes. 'So,' he said, 'I'm glad we've cleared up that misconception.' He glanced towards the water. 'Were you about to go for a swim?'

'I—no.' Helen made the decision quickly, even though the reason for her previous prevarication had now been removed.

'Shame,' he remarked. 'I thought I might join you. Swimming alone can be dangerous. Did no one tell you that?'

'Dangerous for whom?' enquired Helen tautly, and then, with a shiver of impatience, she shook her head. 'I have to get back,' she added crisply, aware that it would be fatally easy to be attracted to this man. And, because it had to be said, 'I'm sure your wife will be wondering where you are.'

'My wife!' Chase Aitken stared at her disbelievingly. 'I don't have a wife, dammit. What gave you that idea?'

Helen swallowed, incapable of answering him right away. He hadn't married her mother, then, she thought incredulously. They'd only been living together all these years. No wonder Fleur had greeted him so—so hungrily. She must never be sure he hadn't found someone else.

Helen felt a little sick. The realisation that Chase Aitken had treated her mother with as little respect as Fleur had treated her father should have been reassuring, but it wasn't. Yet Fleur's problems were no concern of hers. She'd forfeited the right to have Helen care about her when she'd ignored her daughter's existence for the past eighteen years. Helen's nausea stemmed from her own unwilling reaction to the news. In spite of all that had happened, it was Chase Aitken's dark disturbing face that had haunted her dreams last night.

'I don't know,' she muttered at last, turning away and suppressing the urge to confront him with all she did know. She wrapped her arms about her waist. 'I'd have thought it was a reasonable assumption, considering the woman was all over you at the airport.' Her lips tightened. 'And now, if you'll excuse me, I've got a job to do.'

CHAPTER FOUR

MATTHEW strode back to Dragon Bay in a foul temper.

It might have been a novelty for him to be put down by a skinny blonde with more mouth than sense, but it didn't amuse him. He didn't even know why he'd bothered to speak to her. It wasn't as if he cared what she thought of him. He'd been civil, that was all, and she'd insulted him. What the hell did she know about his life?

For God's sake, he thought, letting himself into the grounds of his house through the iron gate set into the wall, there were plenty of women around who didn't take offence when he offered advice. Nothing could alter the fact that the boy had got away from her. So what if the other kid was being sick? She hadn't been about to choke, had she?

But it was that crack about Fleur that had really got to him. Bloody cheek, he fumed angrily. What did it have to do with her? It was little consolation to know that she'd been watching him. He'd known that, dammit. He'd seen the accusation in her face.

For once, the gardens surrounding his villa didn't appease him. Almost two acres of green lawns, flowering shrubs and brilliant flame trees provided a fitting setting for the sprawling Spanish-style villa that was his home. Cool, shaded rooms surrounded three sides of a paved courtyard, with a stone fountain in the centre whose rippling pool was edged with lilies.

Through a belt of palms, he could just glimpse the painted roofs of the cabanas, and beyond that the swimming-pool was a smooth slash of aquamarine, glinting in the sun. The way he felt right now, he would have liked to have plunged his sweating body into the cool water. But the thought that Fleur might choose to join him had him opting for a shower.

Dammit, he thought, crossing the patio, where hanging baskets spilling scarlet geraniums provided a startling splash of colour, he couldn't even do what he liked in his own home. Stepping beneath a shadowed balcony, woven with bougainvillaea, he entered a marbled hallway and mounted grimly to his suite of rooms. He'd always enjoyed his morning walks before, but today he felt decidedly out of tune with himself.

He ran the shower hot, then cold, soaping his limbs aggressively as he endeavoured to lighten his mood. Fleur couldn't stay here forever, he thought, deliberately turning his thoughts from the woman on the beach. She'd soon get bored without the social life she'd enjoyed as Chase's wife. Besides, although there were plenty of stores in Bridgetown to suit her needs, Fleur was an avid shopper. She'd spent a small fortune in beauty parlours alone, and she'd had a new wardrobe of clothes every season.

He wondered in passing where she was planning to live, now that Chase was no longer a factor. He doubted she'd stay on at the ranch, even if his father was willing. She'd always been more at home in the capital cities of the world. He couldn't see her vegetating at Ryan's Bend.

He was shaving when his assistant knocked at his door. At his shout, Lucas came into his bedroom, and Matthew paused in the doorway to his bathroom, his razor still in his hand.

'Problems?' he asked, and Lucas pulled a face.

'Your sister-in-law has already asked where you are, if that's what you mean,' he remarked, propping his stocky frame against a chest of drawers. 'She's having breakfast in the dining-room, would you believe? I thought you said she rarely got up before midday.'

'She doesn't—usually,' Matthew replied flatly, turning back to the mirror and expelling a weary breath. He cursed as the razor nicked his jaw. 'Damn, I guess that means she wants something, doesn't it? You may be right. This is not just a social visit.'

Lucas shrugged. 'Has it occurred to you that she may be short of money?'

'Of course it has.' Matthew rinsed his jaw with fresh water and turned back again, drying his face with a towel. 'But I don't see how. Chase always had insurance. And his horses were worth a small fortune, you know that.'

Lucas considered. 'Could he have been in debt?'

'I guess he could.' Matthew frowned. 'But if he was, he never said a word to me. And wouldn't he have discussed it with my father?' He grimaced. 'Perhaps he did. The old man always was as close-mouthed as a shrew.'

A shrew...

Matthew tossed the towel aside, annoyed to find that the connotations of that particular word were not to his liking. It reminded him again of the young woman he had encountered on the beach. The truth was, for all his irritation with her, she had disrupted his morning walk and his equilibrium. And where that disturbance was rooted, he didn't care to consider.

'So, what are you going to do?' Lucas watched as Matthew tossed the towel aside and pulled on a pair of frayed denim shorts and a loose black T-shirt. 'Ask her right out? Or let her make the first move?'

'That depends.' Matthew forced his thoughts back to Fleur, and scanned the bedroom with narrowed eyes. Then, observing that his watch was lying on the cabinet where he had left it, he went to pick it up. 'I don't intend to allow her to stay here indefinitely.'

'So you'll play it by ear,' remarked Lucas, straightening. 'D'you want to look over the manuscript this morning, or shall I concentrate on the accounts?'

Matthew gave him a resigned look. 'What do you think?'

Lucas grinned, his fair features crinkling humorously. 'Accounts it is,' he said. 'And I'll eat breakfast in the kitchen. I'm not sure I'm in the mood for Fleur's particular kind of chat.'

'And I am?' queried Matthew drily, buckling the slim gold Ebel on to his wrist. 'Remind me to thank you for your support some time, won't you? I don't know what I'd do without you in circumstances like this.'

Leaving the spacious, if slightly austere surroundings of Matthew's bedroom behind, both men walked along the wide gallery that connected all the rooms on the upper floor. Open on one side at present, with sculptured arches giving an uninterrupted view of the ocean, there were tight-fitting shutters which could be closed if a tropical storm blew in from the Gulf. In the latter months of the year there was the risk of hurricanes, too, but thankfully they were few and far between. In the main, the weather was fairly temperate, with humidity being the biggest source of complaint.

They descended the shallow staircase Matthew had climbed earlier, where a glistening chandelier hung from a central bracket. The dining-room, where Fleur was having breakfast, opened on to the inner courtyard, and Matthew left Lucas to his own devices while he trod along the cloistered veranda.

The dining-room was far too big for one person. Matthew had always thought so, although its cream and green décor always gave him pleasure. It was spacious and airy, but on lamplit evenings it could be warmly intimate as well. Like every other apartment in the villa, it was aesthetically appealing as well as functional, and those guests who had been invited here had been agreeably impressed.

Even so, Fleur looked mildly intimidated, sitting at the long oak table. Ruth, his housekeeper, had laid two places at the end of its dark polished surface, and his sister-in-law's expression was reflected in the glaze of fragile china and silver tableware. She was picking rather desultorily at the dry toast set in front of her, a cup of black coffee at her elbow indicating that she was still far too anxious about her weight.

But her features warmed considerably when Matthew appeared in the doorway. Her eyes, already carefully outlined with mascara, lit up, and she patted the chair beside her, as if there were anywhere else he was likely to sit.

'Good morning, darling,' she greeted him affectionately. 'I was beginning to wonder if I'd have to eat alone.'

'Eat?' remarked Matthew drily, indicating the dry toast on her plate. 'Didn't Ruth offer you a croissant? She makes them herself, and they're delicious.'

'They're also about five thousand calories,' exclaimed Fleur, exaggerating as usual. She shuddered theatrically. 'They're full of fat, Matt. You really shouldn't eat them. You may not realise it now, but they can shorten your life.'

'So can smoking,' replied Matthew pointedly, and Fleur dropped her handbag back on to the floor. 'So—did you sleep well?'

Fleur grimaced. 'I never sleep well,' she declared. 'Ever since Chase died, I've lain awake for hours, wishing he was there. I'm a physical person, Matt. I need someone to hold me. But there hasn't been anyone to do that for such a long, long time.'

Matthew's lips compressed. 'Chase has only been dead a couple of months.'

'I know that.' Fleur gave him a defensive stare. 'But— Well, you might as well know, Chase and I had been having problems. It's—almost a year since we—we slept together.' She gave Matthew an appealing look. 'You don't know what it was like. He was such a jealous man!'

Matthew's stomach muscles tightened. 'What you mean is, you were screwing him around,' he stated, and she gave a protesting cry.

'No. No, I wasn't,' she exclaimed bitterly. 'I'm not that sort of woman.' And then, as Matthew gave her a scorching look, she added swiftly, 'You—you were the exception. I was lonely. And you always were such a—such an attractive boy—*man*.'

Ruth appeared at that moment, and Matthew was relieved. He doubted he could have responded to Fleur without rancour. His gut was telling him he'd been a fool to invite her here, but with his conscience eating at him there'd seemed nothing else he could do.

'You like some more coffee, Mrs Aitken?' Ruth asked, after taking Matthew's order for scrambled eggs. A Czechoslovakian immigrant, Ruth had first worked for her employer in New York, but she'd been more than happy to accompany him when he relocated to the Caribbean.

'What?' Fleur seemed distracted, and she regarded the plump housekeeper with some impatience. 'Oh—no. No. Nothing else at the moment. And be sure you cook the eggs with sunflower oil. It's better for the digestion.'

'Just do as you normally do,' Matthew put in evenly, as Ruth looked dismayed. He helped himself to some freshly squeezed orange juice and regarded his sister-in-law with some dislike. 'After almost ten years, Ruth knows how I like my eggs. And add a couple of bacon rashers,' he appended, giving the woman a smile.

Ruth departed, looking slightly reassured, and Fleur met Matthew's eyes without remorse. 'All that cholesterol,' she declared. 'You'll regret it when you're older.'

'Like you, you mean?' he suggested, in no mood to be charitable. 'Just give it a rest, will you? I don't need you to run my life.'

Fleur looked longingly at her bag, but something—a desire to placate him, perhaps, Matthew thought wryly—kept her from reaching for her cigarettes. Instead, she pushed her plate aside and folded her arms on the table, giving him an innocent smile, as if butter wouldn't melt.

'So,' she said. 'What are we going to do today?'

'We?' Matthew regarded her over the top of his glass. 'I don't know what you're going to do, but I've got a book to write.' He paused. 'You can swim, or sunbathe, or go shopping if you'd rather. There's a car at your disposal, and Bridgetown has plenty of shops for you to try.'

Fleur wrinkled her nose. 'I know what Bridgetown has,' she said shortly. 'It's not that long since I've been here.' She hesitated. 'I was hoping you might take me sightseeing. When we were here before, Chase hardly left the house.'

Remembering how tired his brother had looked the last time he saw him did not endear his widow to Matthew at this moment. 'You don't really expect me to believe you want to go sightseeing, do you?' he asked harshly. 'When was the last time you visited a museum, or a cathedral, or watched cruise ships unloading at the quay?' He set down his empty glass with careful precision. 'I may be gullible, but I'm not still wet behind the ears, Fleur. Do what you like, with pleasure, but don't include me.'

Fleur gave him a wounded look. 'You'll never forget that one mistake, will you? I let you see how frustrated I was, God knows how many years ago, and you can't accept that I've changed. I loved Chase, Matt, you've got to believe me.' She waited a beat. 'And I don't think he'd appreciate your treating me like a leper.'

Matthew forced himself to calm down. 'All right,' he said. 'If that's what you'd like, I'll have Lucas show you around. There are some flower caves in Saint Lucy that are well worth a visit, and several old plantation houses on your way.'

Fleur looked sulky. 'You're just being unpleasant,' she said. 'You know I don't want Lucas to take me anywhere. When you invited me here, I assumed it was because you wanted my company. I didn't think I was to be given the brush-off because you want to work.'

Matthew expelled a heavy breath. 'You know why I invited you here, Fleur.'

'Do I?'

'You should.' He looked at her with less than sympathetic eyes. 'You want the truth? I felt sorry for you. Good

God, you practically begged me to let you come here. You said you couldn't stand being at the ranch another day.'

Fleur sniffed. 'So? What's changed?'

'Nothing's changed. That's what I'm saying.' Matthew struggled to be patient. 'You're welcome to spend a couple of weeks here. I can guess things were pretty grim for you at Ryan's Bend. As you say, my father has the horses to keep him busy. Until you decide what you're going to do—where you're going to live—it isn't going to be easy.'

Fleur heaved a sigh. 'You don't understand,' she said, running her fingernail round the rim of a spoon. 'I don't know what I'm going to do—how I'm going to manage. Chase left so little money, and I don't have any of my own.'

'Wait a minute.' Matthew felt the first glimmerings of apprehension. 'What do you mean? Chase was broke?'

'Near enough,' she conceded, her fingers curling into her palms. 'I didn't know until—until afterwards. After all those years of competing and winning prizes, I assumed—' She pressed her lips together. 'But your father put me straight on that account. Did you know he even owned all the horses Chase rode?'

Matthew frowned. 'What about the insurance?' He paused. 'I know Chase was insured. He was very particular about that sort of thing.'

Fleur shrugged her narrow shoulders. 'Well—they wouldn't pay out.'

'What?'

Matthew was appalled, and Fleur shifted rather discomfitedly in her seat. 'Don't look at me like that. It wasn't my fault,' she protested. 'He—he'd been drinking before the—before the game when—it happened.'

'Chase?'

'Yes, Chase.' Fleur tilted her head. 'That's why they wouldn't pay. They said he was to blame.'

Matthew pushed back his chair and got up from the table, unable to sit still as the import of what she was saying assaulted his senses. He'd assumed until then that Chase's death had been a terrible accident. Now Fleur was telling him that Chase had broken the rules.

'Why?' he said now, turning to face her, and Fleur gazed at him with uncomprehending eyes.

'Why, what?'

'Why had he been drinking?' snarled Matthew. 'As I recall, Chase didn't even like the stuff. Why would he swallow alcohol when he knew he had to play?'

'Don't ask me.' Fleur gave him an indignant look. 'I wasn't his keeper. Besides, perhaps you didn't know him as well as you thought you did. In recent months, he'd been drinking quite a lot.'

Matthew pushed his hands into the pockets of his shorts, aware of an overwhelming urge to shake Fleur until he got the truth. Oh, he didn't doubt there was some truth in what she was saying. But the reasons for Chase's behaviour had not been explained.

A feeling of regret assailed him. It was true that in recent months he hadn't seen as much of either Chase or his father as he should have. And the ironic thing was, it had been because of Fleur that he'd stayed away from his home. He'd always been conscious of what had happened, however much he'd tried to ignore it. And it had been easier for him to avoid the ranch, and the unpleasant memories it evoked.

'I think—' Fleur started, and even though Matthew gave her a warning look, she pressed on anyway. 'I think he knew his game was failing,' she declared firmly. 'His average was falling, and I know he was worried about staying in the team. You know what polo-players are like: they have this macho image. I think Chase was afraid he was losing it. He was the oldest man on the field.'

Matthew's eyes narrowed. 'How would you know?'

Fleur held his gaze for a defensive moment, and then looked down at her plate. 'I hope you're not implying what I think you're implying,' she said, her voice constricted. 'I told you: I loved your brother, Matt. Whatever you think, I miss him every day.'

Matthew turned away, staring bleakly towards the glistening ocean. He missed Chase, too. More than he could ever have imagined. Dammit, that was why he'd invited Fleur here. To try and assuage the guilt that he still felt.

'If you want me to leave, I will,' Fleur offered in an unsteady voice, and Matthew squashed the uncharitable thought that her words were calculated. But there was no denying her ability to take advantage of a situation, and she must be pretty sure he wouldn't take her up on it, or she'd never have taken the risk.

'Forget it,' he said now, but when Ruth brought his breakfast it was an effort to attack the food. He felt sick even thinking about what Chase might have suffered during the last months of his life. If he had been worrying about his future, why the hell couldn't he have said?

An hour later he was sitting at his desk, wondering if he should call his father, when Lucas buzzed his private line. Lucas monitored all incoming calls from his office, and Matthew seldom took unsolicited calls, unless they were from people he knew.

'You've got a call,' Lucas announced ruefully. 'From Andrew Sheridan. I can tell him that you're out, if you like—or busy. But I thought I'd better clear it with you first.'

Matthew frowned. To say he knew Andrew Sheridan was certainly an exaggeration. And, as Lucas knew nothing about his encounter with Helen on the beach, he knew he thought it was just a formality. But, in spite of himself, Matthew was intrigued. And there were other considerations here that made him say, quite uncharacteristically, 'I'll speak to him.'

'You will?'

Lucas couldn't hide his surprise, and Matthew guessed his assistant thought he was being rather foolish. But, 'Why not?' he said, wondering what else the day could throw at him. 'We can't live like hermits while Fleur's here.'

'If you say so.'

Lucas sounded off-hand, but he connected the call at once and rang off. It was just curiosity, Matthew told himself, determining to be civil. He was curious about Andrew Sheridan's relationship with Helen. It had occurred to him that it might not be as innocent as it seemed.

'Aitken?'

Andrew Sheridan's voice was one of those upper middle class English voices, and it grated on Matthew's nerves this morning. It seemed to imply that he should be glad to hear from him, that as a commonplace colonial he was being honoured.

'Sheridan,' he offered in response, wishing he'd taken Lucas's advice after all and avoided the call. It wasn't as if he was finding it easy to concentrate in any case, and the idea that Helen might be having an affair with her employer was already assuming far too much importance.

'I hope you don't mind me ringing, old man,' Andrew exclaimed jovially. 'My lady wife insisted that I call and put the record straight. The young lady you saw me with yesterday wasn't Mrs Sheridan. She's our nanny, actually. It was all a rather bad joke.'

Matthew didn't make the mistake of admitting his knowledge this time. 'No problem,' he said, unwillingly relieved that Helen apparently hadn't mentioned their encounter on the beach. And then, untruthfully, 'I never gave it another thought. Whoever she was, she seemed to have her hands full.'

'Well, yes.' Andrew sighed. 'I'm afraid Henry and Sophie *are* something of a handful for her. Poor Helen hasn't had a lot of experience. We may have to let her go if something like that happens again.'

Matthew felt unreasonably resentful on her behalf. 'I doubt if anyone could have coped any better,' he declared coolly. 'Perhaps if she hadn't had to bring the children to the airport in the first place, there wouldn't have been a problem.' He paused. 'Is your wife an invalid, Sheridan? I'm just wondering why they didn't stay with her, when the little girl obviously suffers from car sickness.'

Andrew Sheridan was unnaturally silent for a moment, and Matthew hoped that he was offended. He had no desire to get involved with any of the Sheridans, and, despite his instinctive defence of her, the less he saw of their nanny the better.

'So, in your opinion, it was just a chapter of accidents,' Andrew said at last, and Matthew acknowledged that he'd underestimated Sheridan's persistence. 'I'm glad about that. Helen's an engaging creature, isn't she? I wouldn't like to dismiss her, when she's had such a lot of bad luck.'

The desire to ask what bad luck he was talking about was pressing, but Matthew contained himself with difficulty. It had been said for just that reason, to inspire his curiosity, and after this morning's little fiasco he was not about to bite.

'Anyway,' Andrew went on, when it became obvious that Matthew wasn't going to fall for that line, 'I didn't ring to discuss the merits—or otherwise—of the children's nursemaid. No, I'm ringing to ask you and your—well, partner—to have drinks with us tomorrow evening. What do you say?'

'Oh, I—' Matthew was on the point of refusing when the image of an indignant woman, with misty grey eyes and sun-streaked hair, swam before his eyes. In spite of the anger she had aroused in him, he was not averse to giving her a taste of her own medicine. After all, she'd accused him of neglecting his wife, just because she'd seen him with Fleur at the airport. It might be amusing to take Fleur with him, just to see how she responded to that.

'I know you must be a busy man,' Andrew added, obviously aware of Matthew's ambivalence, 'but we would appreciate the chance to make amends. And I know Trish would love to meet you. She's admired your house so often on her walks along the beach.'

Matthew hesitated. 'Well—'

But his mind was already made up. It would amuse Fleur, he knew, and get her off his back for a couple of hours. Besides which, he was in a mood for action. His doubts about Chase's death had only fuelled his sense of guilt…

CHAPTER FIVE

HELEN stood in her bedroom, trying to calm her nerves. Ever since Andrew had told her that Chase Aitken and his 'partner' were coming for drinks this evening, she had been in a state bordering on panic, and it wasn't getting any better.

It was all very well telling herself that her mother hadn't recognised her, and therefore she had no reason for her anxiety— but it didn't work. What if either Tricia or Andrew used her surname? Combined with her age and appearance, wasn't the coincidence just too great?

She felt sick, too, but that was mostly hunger. She'd hardly eaten a thing since lunchtime the previous day. As soon as Andrew had dropped his bombshell her throat had closed up and her appetite had vanished. She was afraid of what might happen, and nothing could alter that.

Yet she had nothing to be ashamed of. She hadn't abandoned her husband and small daughter and taken off with a man who was far too young for her. Oh, she knew there were no hard and fast rules about relationships. She'd even heard of cases where an older woman and a younger man were very happy together. But not at the expense of their families; not when they had children to leave behind...

Damn her, she thought painfully. Damn Fleur, and damn Chase Aitken. Why had it had to be him who came to her assistance at the airport? Why couldn't it have been some stranger, instead of her mother's playboy lover?

Of course, she might be able to avoid them. Tricia hadn't invited her to join them, but that might be because she expected her to do so anyway. In London things had been different. Then Helen had only joined her employer for supper if Andrew Sheridan had been out of town. But since arriving in Barbados there'd been no lines of demarcation, and although the first night Andrew arrived she'd managed to evade their company, last night she hadn't been so lucky.

Privately, she suspected they found an undiluted diet of one another's company boring. They seldom dined alone at home, and when they went out it was always with friends. Tricia said they were sociable animals, but Helen suspected that without diversion their marriage might not survive.

Which didn't help her, she thought now, slapping away one of the annoying sandflies that had found its way into her bedroom. Could she pretend to have another headache? She didn't think Andrew would believe her. But surely Tricia wouldn't care, when she was getting her own way about Chase Aitken.

'Helen…'

A sleepy voice from the doorway alerted her to the fact that Sophie, at least, had not settled down after her day in the sun. The little girl's face was flushed, and Helen guessed she had been taking her hat off again. Neither child liked wearing headgear, but the heat made protection essential.

'What is it?' Helen asked now, thinking how adorable the little girl looked in her frilly baby-doll pyjamas. 'You're supposed to be fast asleep.'

'I'm thirsty,' said Sophie, pleading the perennial excuse of children everywhere. 'And Henry's got Matilda, and he won't give her back.'

'Oh, dear.' Abandoning any thought of dressing for the evening, Helen pulled a baggy T-shirt over her shorts and accompanied the little girl back to the children's bedroom.

Henry was pretending to be asleep, clutching the rag doll that Sophie had had since she was a baby. Matilda, as she called her, was very old now, and a little tatty, but she went everywhere with her, and especially to bed.

Walking into the adjoining bathroom, Helen got Sophie

a glass of water and then approached Henry's bed. The little
boy's eyelids were tightly closed, but their twitching gave
him away. However, it suited her purposes to pretend she
believed him, and, whisking Matilda out of his grasp, she
handed her to Sophie.

Henry's eyes opened at once, but Helen was already
tucking his sister into bed. 'I thought you were asleep,' she
said innocently. 'And you'd forgotten to give back Sophie's
doll. But if you'd like a doll of your own, I'll tell your
mother. I'm sure we could find you one in town.'

Henry's jaw jutted. 'I don't want a doll,' he said sulkily.
'I'm not a baby, like her.'

'No, you're not,' said Helen. 'So don't behave like one.
Now, I don't want any more nonsense tonight.'

Henry pursed his lips, but then evidently decided it
wasn't worth his while to make threats. Instead, he looked
at Helen slyly. 'Is that what you're wearing for supper?'
he asked. 'That man and woman are already here. Did you
know?'

Helen's stomach hollowed. She hadn't known. But then,
that wasn't so surprising. Her room faced away from the
terrace, where the Sheridans were no doubt entertaining
their guests.

'Oh—I expect I'll have supper in my room,' she declared
offhandedly, assuming an indifference she was far from
feeling. 'Now—you two settle down. If you're quiet, and
still awake when I come back, I may just read you a story.'

'Honestly?'

Henry sounded pleased, but she could see he was having
difficulty in keeping his eyes open. As for Sophie, she was
already on the edge of sleep, and Helen felt a reassuring
sense of pride in her achievement. After all, four months
ago she hadn't known the difference between pre-schoolers
and toddlers. Now, she could prepare nursery meals, mop
up every kind of mishap and handle childish tantrums without hesitation. To all intents and purposes, she was their

guardian, and while she might still have reservations she liked her work.

She was closing the children's bedroom door when she turned to find Andrew behind her. For an awful moment, she thought it was Chase Aitken, and her face turned quite pale in the lamplight.

'Are you all right?'

Whatever Andrew had been going to say, he'd noticed her sudden pallor, and she scrubbed her hands across her cheeks to produce some spurious colour. 'You—you startled me, that's all,' she said quickly. 'I was just getting Sophie a drink.'

'And then you're going to join us, right?' he essayed smoothly. His eyes twinkled. 'Though not in shorts and a T-shirt. I don't think Trish would approve.'

Helen caught her lower lip between her teeth. 'I don't think your guests are interested in meeting me,' she said carefully. Her hand went instinctively to her hair. 'I'm sure they'll be gone before I can put on a dress.'

'Don't you believe it.' Andrew was in annoyingly high spirits. 'I've invited them for supper. Now, hurry up and get ready.'

Helen felt indignant. Apart from anything else, now that Henry and Sophie were settled for the night, the Sheridans really had no right to order her movements. Besides, the idea of going out there and facing her mother was not something she wanted to anticipate.

'I'm tired,' she said, aware that although she'd washed her hair that morning her braid was less than tidy now. Strands of honey-blonde silk were nudging her ear-lobes, and there was a definite fringe of moistness at her nape.

'We're all tired, Helen,' said Andrew, his tone a little less conciliatory now. 'Don't be difficult. Aitken has already asked where you are this evening. I don't want everyone thinking that we treat you like some latter-day Cinderella.'

Helen sighed. 'They won't do that.'

'No, they won't. Because you're going to wash your face and hands and come and meet our guests. For heaven's sake, Helen, I thought you'd be amused. It's not as if you lead an active social life. Make the most of it while you can.'

Helen's jaw trembled. 'And if I don't?'

Andrew's expression hardened. 'Well, no one can force you,' he drawled. 'I'll tell Trish you're tired, shall I? I'm sure she'll be sympathetic.'

Helen was equally sure that she wouldn't. And Andrew knew that, damn him. That was why he'd said it. The next step was to ask her if she thought she really had the stamina to do the job she was employed to do. And, although she was sure it wouldn't be easy for them to find her replacement here, she couldn't take that chance.

'I'll be ready in fifteen minutes,' she mumbled, brushing past him to reach the door of her room, but he was determined to have his pound of flesh.

'What did you say?' he asked, though she was sure he'd heard her. And when she repeated it, her face flushed and mutinous, he smiled. 'Oh, good. I knew you'd change your mind. But make it ten minutes, will you? You don't want to miss all the fun.'

Helen closed her door in his triumphant face, wishing she wasn't such a coward. But, whatever happened, she still had a living to earn. However afraid—*apprehensive*—of facing her mother she might be, she couldn't afford to lose her job over it.

All the same, she viewed the contents of her wardrobe with some misgivings. What did you wear to meet the mother you hadn't seen for eighteen years? She had no desire for Fleur to think she was competing with her. But, the fact remained, her pride wouldn't let her dress without restraint.

She finally settled on a long-waisted, button-through voile with a flared hem. The dress almost reached her ankles, but the buttons ended at her knees, leaving a provocative opening that made walking that much easier. The pattern of tiny blue and green flowers on a cream ground was attractive, and with a V-neck and elbow-length sleeves, it was neither too casual nor too formal.

She brushed her hair and plaited it again for coolness, scraping it back from her face with a determined hand. The style made her look plain, she thought, unaware that her delicate features could never be deemed severe. Instead, the fine veins at her temple were exposed, and the sensitive curve of her neck.

A flick of mascara and an application of a plum-coloured lip-gloss completed her preparations, and she stepped back from her mirror with a quickening heart. She was as ready as she'd ever be, she thought, wetting her lips deliberately. She didn't think she resembled her mother, but time would tell.

She wasn't wearing any tights, and, stepping into high-heeled sandals, she gave her room a wistful look. What she wouldn't give to be spending the evening incommunicado. Tricia should have warned her that she wanted a slave, not an employee.

She heard voices as she approached the terrace—well, Andrew's and Tricia's voices, anyway, she conceded, wondering what Chase Aitken really thought of his hosts for the evening. She'd been absolutely amazed when Tricia had told her he'd accepted their invitation. She'd had the feeling at the airport that he resented people like them.

It was a beautiful evening. Barbados was lucky in that it had few annoying insects, and it was perfectly acceptable to serve a meal outside, even after dark. With that in mind, Tricia had had Maria set a table on the terrace, and flickering Spanish lanterns added intimacy to the scene.

To avoid looking at the group of people gathered around the drinks trolley, Helen paid particular attention to the table. A centrepiece of ivory orchids and scarlet hibiscus looked wonderful against white linen, the dark green leaves contrasting richly with the carefully chosen blooms.

Tall crystal glasses gave back a multitude of colours in the candlelight, and neatly folded napkins were set at every place. *Six* places, Helen was noticing curiously, when Andrew looked round and saw her.

'At last,' he said, and for all his suave smile Helen knew he wasn't suited. 'Our dear nanny has chosen to join us. Perhaps now we can have some food.'

'Drew,' reproved Tricia, with an apologetic smile for their guests. 'Ask Helen what she'd like to drink.' But she looked the younger woman over rather critically, and Helen had the feeling she wasn't pleased either.

'Hello, again.'

Chase Aitken's low, attractive drawl forced Helen to acknowledge the other people present. But she didn't look at him, or at the third female in the group. Instead, she allowed her gaze to alight on someone she didn't know. A stocky, fair man with glasses, who was none the less familiar.

'What would you like, Helen?' Andrew was asking, and glad of a moment's grace she pretended to give the matter some thought.

'Oh—um, a glass of white wine, please,' she said, aware that both Chase and Fleur were watching her. Her mouth dried in nervous anticipation as Tricia came with evident reluctance to perform the introductions.

'Oh, yes,' she said, and Helen was obliged to meet Chase's dark appraising eyes. 'Of course, you've met, haven't you? But, Fleur—this is our saviour. Helen—this is Mrs Aitken.'

He'd lied!

That was the first thing that came into Helen's mind as she turned to the colourfully-dressed female at his side. Chase was all in black—an appropriate choice for him, she thought—but, in a floral chiffon gown and incredibly high heels, Fleur looked like a bird of paradise beside a hawk. Her hair, which had once been a similar colour to Helen's, was tinted a pale silvery shade, and tied back with a scarf that matched her outfit. The ends were loose and flowing, and trailed seductively across her bare shoulder.

Helen swallowed. When she'd seen her mother at the airport it had been from a distance. She hadn't been able to see the ravages time had wrought. But it was obvious that Fleur had had at least one face-lift, and her skin had lost the dewy freshness of youth.

Even so, her mother looked totally at ease in these surroundings. As well she might, thought Helen bitterly, if the house she had glimpsed from the beach was anything to go on. The Sheridans' villa was modest in comparison. Andrew might be well off, but he couldn't compete in Chase Aitken's league.

But such considerations were just a way of avoiding the inevitable. She couldn't believe she was standing just an arm's length from the woman who had borne her. The fact that Tricia hadn't used her surname wasn't important. Couldn't Fleur see she was her daughter? Surely she must?

Evidently not.

'How do you do?'

Fleur was holding out a languid hand, and Helen had, perforce, to take it. But she drew her hand away again with some aversion—an aversion she hoped wasn't evident to anyone else but her.

'I must say, I think you're awfully lucky to be working in such lovely surroundings,' Fleur continued, apparently noticing nothing amiss. 'Believe me, not all employers are so generous. And working with children must be rather nice.'

How would you know?

Helen wanted to say the words out loud, but commonsense—*cowardice*—kept her silent. Besides, did she really want to have anything to do with the woman? Revealing her identity to her could only hurt herself.

'And I'm Lucas,' said the man Helen had thought she recognised, evidently getting impatient with the delay. He drew her attention away from the others and shook her hand warmly. 'I'm Matt's personal dogsbody, for want of a better word.'

Helen frowned. *Matt*? But Lucas was speaking again, and she had no time to give it any attention. 'I saw you at the airport, too.' His eyes twinkled behind his glasses. 'Just from a distance, I'm afraid.'

Of course. Helen managed a smile. That was where she'd seen him. He must have gone to meet Fleur from the plane while her husband waited with the Range Rover.

'There you are. One white wine, as requested.'

Andrew had returned with her drink, and his intervention enabled Chase to ease himself between her and his assistant. 'Something wrong?' he asked in an undertone, arms folded across the black silk at his midriff. 'I take it you don't like my house-guest either. Or are you simply averse to her because she's related to me?'

Helen pressed her lips together, aware that he had successfully isolated her on the edge of the group. 'You admit it, then,' she responded huskily. 'She is related to you!'

'Sure.' He frowned. 'But she's not my wife, as you assumed the other day. She's my sister-in-law, actually. She was married to my brother. But he was killed in a riding accident two months ago.'

Helen's jaw dropped. 'He's dead!' she breathed in a staggered voice. 'I didn't know.'

'Why should you?' He was regarding her dispassionately. 'It's not as if it would make the newscasts in England. Chase was a polo-player. Not a football star.'

'Chase...' Helen said the name again, almost wonderingly, and Matthew Aitken looked at her with curious eyes.

'You didn't know him, did you?' he asked. 'That's not why you were so agitated yesterday? I know we look—*looked*—a little alike, but he was eight years older than me.'

'No.' Helen couldn't let him think that. Who knew what he might say to her mother if he suspected there was some connection? 'I—I was just sorry to hear he was dead, that's all. I expect you miss him badly. I'm sorry if I was rude.'

'When?' Matthew's lips twitched. 'At the airport? On the beach? Just now?'

'At all,' said Helen firmly, realising he was getting far too friendly. 'Um—do you live on the island, Mr Aitken? Or is this just a holiday for you, too?'

'Matthew,' he said softly. 'My name's Matthew, but most people call me Matt. And, yes, I do live here, as it happens. I find the climate and the people suit my mood.'

'Could you go and tell Maria we're ready to eat, Helen?'

Tricia had just noticed the younger woman was monopolising their most interesting guest, and her eyes flashed warningly in Helen's direction. It occurred to Helen suddenly that she had only been invited to the party because Matthew Aitken had brought his assistant. Tricia hated uneven numbers, even if it did mean she'd been forced to ask the nanny to join them.

'Of course,' she said now, glad to put some distance between herself and her mother. For all she hadn't said anything, Helen had been conscious of Fleur's proximity, and of the fact that she looked at Matthew with hot, possessive eyes. Dear God, was she already looking for Chase's replacement? And, if she was, did Matthew share his brother's fascination for diminutive blondes?

The idea was distasteful, and as she hurried into the villa Helen had to admit that it wasn't just because Fleur was her mother. The thought of Matthew Aitken making love to his dead brother's wife was repulsive. In fact, the thought of her mother even considering it caused a violent sense of injustice to invade her heart. If only her father had known he was well rid of her. Instead of spending the rest of his life trying to prove himself a man.

CHAPTER SIX

'YOU'RE so lucky living here,' Tricia Sheridan remarked enviously as they sat at the dinner table later. 'Tell me— Matt.' She gave a coy little smile to cover her audacity, and then continued, 'What do you do with yourself all day?'

Matthew couldn't make up his mind about that. But, after all, his pen-name was *Mallory* Aitken. It was possible she'd never seen his picture on the back of one of his books. He'd just got so accustomed to people using his writing as a lever that he'd become rather cynical.

'Oh—this and that,' he volunteered now, his eyes drifting irresistibly across the candlelit table. They'd seated Lucas beside Helen, and he seemed to be enjoying himself. And Helen didn't look as anxious as she'd done when she first appeared.

He wondered what Lucas was saying to her, and then chided himself for even caring. It wasn't as if he intended to see any of them again. His initial reluctance to get involved with these people had probably been right. For all Helen had offered some kind of an apology, he still had the feeling he should quit while he was ahead.

'What kind of this and that?' Tricia persisted, and Matthew wondered if it was possible to escape these proceedings without telling the truth. The last thing he needed was spurious congratulation, but before he could make a comment Fleur intervened.

'Haven't you heard of Mallory Aitken?' she exclaimed, and Matthew knew it was a measure of her annoyance at being ignored that had caused her to speak so caustically. Besides which, she had always denigrated his success before, declaring that his novels were little more than fantasy. But, 'Good heavens,' she added now, 'I thought everyone had read at least one of Matt's thrillers. They sell in their millions. Isn't that right, darling?'

Matthew managed to disguise his frustration, and gave a careless shrug of his shoulders. 'They sell,' he agreed mildly, realising it had been a bigger mistake than he'd thought bringing Fleur here. And, dammit, if he hadn't been so bloody curious about the nursemaid, he'd have had the sense to see it.

'Don't be modest, darling,' Fleur protested, her shrill laugh drawing the attention of everyone at the table. 'I'm sure Lucas has been telling Ellen how lucky he was to land this assignment. He was just Matt's sound technician, you know, when Matt worked for the ITC.'

Ellen? Matthew's mouth drew down, and glancing at the young woman in question he glimpsed a look of anguish on her face. But why? What had Fleur said to upset her? Surely getting her name wrong wasn't a reason for such distress?

'I say, how exciting!' Andrew Sheridan joined the discussion before his wife could voice her reaction. 'Mallory Aitken, eh?' His eyebrows arched. 'What did you say you'd written, old man?'

'I didn't,' said Matthew, hearing the tightness in his voice and controlling his temper with difficulty. 'I'm afraid my sister-in-law exaggerates. D'you mind if we change the subject?'

'Oh, but you must tell me what you're working on at the moment,' Tricia enthused eagerly, apparently deciding that he didn't mean her, and Matthew sighed.

'I never discuss my work,' he told her flatly, lifting his wine-glass and surveying her over the rim. 'Tell me, Mrs Sheridan, when did you say you were leaving?'

'Leaving?'

For a moment she looked totally nonplussed, and Matthew felt an uncharacteristic surge of satisfaction at the

thought. It wasn't his nature to be deliberately malicious—
except with Fleur, he qualified bleakly—but he didn't like
these people, and he didn't care if it showed.

'I thought Lucas said Tricia and Andrew had just got
here.' Once again Fleur took the initiative, and in avoiding
her gaze Matthew looked straight across the table into
Helen's pale face. Her expression was guarded, he thought,
though vaguely apprehensive, and he wondered what she
was thinking as he forced her to meet his eyes.

'Did he?'

Matthew said the words carelessly, responding to his sister-in-law without deviating from his course. It irked him
when Helen looked away, and he was in no mood to be
polite.

'I expect I forgot,' he remarked now, putting his wine-
glass down on the table. 'Time goes so quickly when you're
enjoying yourself.'

It wasn't a compliment, and no one could have mistaken
it for one, but Maria's reappearance to collect the empty
plates provided a welcome diversion. What had he eaten?
Matthew wondered as the plates were taken away. Aspar-
agus, he thought, and then chicken. What was the matter
with him tonight? He didn't normally feel so aggressive—
even with Fleur.

'Anyway, we're here for a month,' Tricia declared at last,
evidently deciding not to take offence. 'I suppose you know
Laurie Parrish, don't you? The man who owns this villa.
He's a colleague of my husband's at the Foreign Office.'

'I've met him,' said Matthew evenly, wondering if he
was supposed to be impressed. 'But we don't do a lot of
socialising in the usual way. Lucas and I—we live a fairly
hermit-like existence.'

'Really?'

Tricia exchanged a glance with her husband, and
Matthew could almost feel what she was thinking about
that. Well, let her, he thought wearily. He had nothing to
lose. And it might keep the Sheridans off his back.

'Oh, I'm sure now that I'm here we can change all that,' Fleur put in insistently, determinedly undermining his intent. 'You must excuse my brother-in-law, Tricia. I can tell you from experience, his bark's much worse than his bite.'

Matthew's jaw compressed, but he didn't attempt an answer. Instead, meeting his assistant's eyes, he allowed a silent acknowledgement of Lucas's caution. But it was no stretch of his abilities to shift his eyes to Helen, and although he scorned his motives he couldn't help himself.

With the meal over, the Sheridans invited their guests to take coffee seated in the lounge chairs that had been circled on the opposite side of the patio. It gave Matthew an opportunity to escape Fleur's cloying presence, and, not risking another altercation, he removed himself from danger by sitting on the steps of the veranda. He knew Fleur wouldn't join him there, being far too afraid of ants and other crawling insects, and, eschewing anything but a brandy, he stared broodingly towards the starlit horizon.

'Is anything wrong?'

Lucas's enquiry disturbed his reverie, and looking up he found his assistant and the young woman who was causing him so much self-analysis standing looking down at him. He had the distinct impression that she wasn't there through choice, but Lucas was evidently immune to her feelings. Besides, why should he suspect that there was anything more than a casual encounter between them? Hell, there *was* nothing more than a casual encounter between them, Matthew told himself savagely. It infuriated him that he should even have thought it was anything else.

'What could be wrong?' he queried now, gripping the post and hoisting himself to his feet. His smile was thin. 'I'm having an absolutely—*spiffing*—time.'

'Matt!'

Aware of Helen beside him, Lucas was justifiably embarrassed, and Matthew allowed his narrowed gaze to encompass her taut features. 'Are you enjoying yourself,

Miss—? Oh, I'm sorry, but you never did tell me your name.'

'It's—Gr—Graham,' she stammered hurriedly, and then glanced behind her, as if she half expected someone to come and contradict her. 'And—yes. Your—er—that is, Lucas—he's been telling me about some of the dangerous places where he's worked.'

'Really?' Matthew's mocking eyes turned back to his assistant. 'None more dangerous than here, eh, Luke?'

'What is it with you, Matt?' Lucas was looking angry now, and, realising he was in danger of alienating the one person in this group who cared anything about him, Matthew lifted his shoulders in a placating gesture.

'I guess my liver is just objecting to the abnormally— rich diet,' he commented ambiguously, and had the doubt-ful privilege of noting their individual reactions. Helen just looked confused, but Lucas had caught the innuendo.

'You were the one who said we couldn't neglect Fleur while she was here,' he reminded him drily, and Matthew gave a rueful grin.

'Yeah, I did, didn't I?' he conceded, noticing almost in passing that Helen's face had grown taut. What had he said? he wondered. Was it his imagination, or had it been the mention of Fleur that had caused her to freeze up sud-denly? She couldn't be jealous, could she? There was only one way to find out. 'I'm afraid my sister-in-law can be a little irritating at times, Miss—er—Graham,' he added. 'Let me apologise on her behalf.'

Helen swallowed. He could see the sudden contraction of her throat, and, although it had not been his intention to remind himself of his own unwilling reaction to her, he couldn't help watching that slender column, or prevent his gaze from moving to the slight trace of cleavage revealed by the neckline of her dress.

She had small breasts, he observed obliquely. Small, but perfectly formed. Their *retroussé* peaks pushed rather too obviously against the cloth, and he felt himself hardening totally against his will.

God, he thought incredulously, was he so desperate for a woman that even the sight of an engorged nipple could push him over the brink? She was cold, perhaps, or apprehensive—though only the lord knew why. Certainly she'd given him no reason for behaving like a callow youth. For all her controlled indifference, he still sensed that she didn't like him at all.

In consequence, when she asked coldly, 'What are you talking about?' he knew an overwhelming urge to run a protective hand over his zip. He had no desire for her to know that she had disturbed him, whatever her real feelings might be.

It took an effort, but his response sounded reasonably cool, to his ears at least. 'Fleur called you Ellen,' he reminded her pleasantly. 'I'm afraid my sister-in-law only listens to what she wants to hear. It's a little foible of hers. You must forgive her. Since my brother died, I've noticed it more and more.'

There was an irony there, but obviously Helen didn't detect it. 'I'll never—' she began vehemently, and then, as if some inner restraint had kicked into gear, she faltered. 'That is—I mean—' She looked at both men with sudden apprehension. 'I—never noticed,' she amended herself hurriedly. 'If—if you'll excuse me, I've got to go and check on the children.'

She walked swiftly away, the skirt of her long dress flapping about her ankles. Matthew also observed the involuntary sway of her hips, and the unknowingly sensuous curve of buttock and thigh. Something he was not alone in approving, he sensed impatiently, finding Lucas's attention almost as objectionable as Fleur's at that moment.

'She doesn't like you, does she?' his assistant remarked drily, after Helen had disappeared through the French windows. 'I wish I hadn't felt sorry for you now. She and I were getting along rather well.'

'Were you?'

It was a distinct effort for Matthew to be civil, and Lucas, misunderstanding the reason for his employer's attitude, pulled a rueful face. 'Yes, we were,' he said earnestly. 'And, you must admit, you didn't look very happy. I guess Fleur has been getting to you, huh?'

Matthew scowled. 'I can handle Fleur,' he declared, finishing the brandy in his glass and regarding its base dourly. 'And I don't need you to feel sorry for me either. I can get along without your girlfriend's approval, believe it or not.'

Lucas made a careless movement of his shoulders. 'She's not my girlfriend, Matt, and you know it.' He pressed his lips together. 'Not yet, anyway.' He shrugged. 'I don't suppose there's much point in getting involved with her; they're only here for a month. But I do find her damn attractive. Did you know, she's only been the Sheridans' nanny for the last three months?'

'Really?'

Matthew managed to sound totally uninterested, but Lucas evidently didn't notice. 'Yes. Apparently, her father died six or seven months ago, leaving her virtually penniless. Whatever you think of Mrs Sheridan, at least she offered Helen a job.'

'How kind.'

Matthew's tone was sardonic, but inwardly he couldn't help wondering how a girl of her background should have wound up playing nursemaid for the Sheridans. Hadn't her father had any insurance? If he'd had a daughter like Helen, he'd have made damn sure she wouldn't be penniless when he died. He frowned. What the hell, it wasn't anything to do with him. When this unholy gathering was over, he'd make sure he never saw any of them again...

'Matt...'

Fleur's petulant voice sounded in his ear, and he turned to find her coming towards them. He hoped she was bored, that she was going to ask if they could leave, but her first words were the opposite of what he wanted to hear.

'Matt, darling, Drew—Andrew, that is—has suggested we have a rubber of bridge. It's years since I've played, but you never forget the rules. Come and be my partner. I'm sure Lucas and Ellen won't mind.'

'Her name's Helen,' said Matthew grimly, before he could prevent himself, but Fleur wasn't interested in anyone's identity but her own.

'Ellen, Helen—what does it matter?' she exclaimed impatiently. 'She seems hopelessly out of her depth, from the little I could see.'

'That's not true,' said Lucas fiercely, but Matthew found he didn't want the younger man getting involved in this discussion.

'Whatever,' he said, 'it's impolite not to remember someone's name. If you start making those kinds of mistakes, Fleur, people will think you're getting old.'

Fleur's lips tightened. 'You can be a real pain sometimes, Matt, do you know that?'

'I'm also not interested in playing cards,' he averred. 'Find yourself another partner, Fleur. I'm thinking of making my escape.'

Fleur gasped. 'But you can't.'

'Why can't I?'

'Because—well, because, to use your word, it would be impolite.' Fleur turned to Lucas. 'You know I'm right, don't you?'

Lucas hesitated. 'Well—'

'Then why don't you take my place?' suggested Matthew mockingly. 'I'm sure you'd be much better at it than me. I'll just help myself to another brandy.'

'Matt!'

'Oh, Matt!'

It was difficult to decide which of them sounded the most put out, Matthew thought wryly, sauntering away. But, hell, he'd done his good deed for the day by bringing Fleur here. He wasn't in the mood to jump through hoops, whoever was pulling the strings.

In the event, it was a fairly bloodless victory. Lucas was too polite to turn Fleur down, and the Sheridans were the kind of people who didn't question the motives of their guests. Besides, listening to Fleur explain that Matthew wasn't feeling up to it was interesting. It made him wonder what other lies she'd told without turning a hair.

He supposed he did feel a little guilty about Lucas, but he wouldn't admit that Luke had annoyed him, too. Dammit, what did he care if the other man made it with the nursemaid? Fleur was probably right; Helen acted as if she was only here on sufferance.

The card players went into the dining-room for their game. Candlelight was all very well, but it wasn't strong enough to play by, and besides, the breeze was apt to lift the cards from the table. It suited Matthew. It meant Fleur's flirtatious giggle was muted. It also meant he could avoid Lucas's patient face.

Depositing his glass on the tray, he abandoned any thought of pouring himself another drink and crossed the patio. Beyond the low stone wall that formed the boundary of the garden he could hear the gentle murmur of the ocean. Although there was no moonlight to speak of, the lights from the patio illuminated a portion of the beach, and as his eyes became adjusted he could see the curling tide.

It was odd to think that he had never seen the ocean from this angle. Usually he saw the villa from the shoreline, and he remembered the sensation he'd had of being watched. That was how he'd known the villa was occupied. Though he hadn't known by whom until Fleur arrived.

Stepping down on to the softer sand that had drifted against the boundary wall, Matthew kicked off his leather loafers. It was one of the advantages of living in a hot climate that he didn't have to wear socks, and the coral grains were pleasantly cool between his toes.

Tying the laces of his shoes together, he looped them around his neck and walked lazily towards the water. Soon he had left the softer going behind, and the damp sand, compacted by the ocean, was firm beneath his feet. When he'd first come here, he had often used to bathe by moonlight. The idea of being able to swim as nature intended had been a novelty. But these days he generally confined himself to the simpler delights of the pool.

All the same, there was still something rather appealing about stripping off his clothes and wading naked into the waves. It would certainly ease his frustration, he thought wryly. A good cold shower was just what he needed.

Which was ridiculous, he had to admit. It wasn't as if the Graham woman was particularly attractive, after all. Oh, she was tall and slim, and she had nice eyes—but so what? That description could apply to a dozen other women of his acquaintance, and none of them disturbed his concentration.

The water seeped around his toes as he stood there, and he knew he should roll the cuffs of his trousers up. But what the hell? he mused with some impatience. It wasn't as if he cared what anyone else thought.

And then he saw her.

She was coming out of the sea, perhaps fifty yards further along the beach, and for a moment he half believed that his thoughts had conjured her up. In that first, gut-wrenching awareness he thought that she was naked. And then, as he gazed like some dumbstruck youth, he realised that her dress was plastered to her body.

But she had been in the sea, that much was obvious, and, like him, she apparently hadn't cared what happened to her clothes. The skirt of the thin garment was sodden, and she bent to squeeze the hem as she stepped on to the damp sand.

Matthew swallowed, his breath escaping in short, uneven bursts. God, there was something almost—pagan—about her. Had she any idea he was watching her? Or was she totally immune to his eyes?

In a minute she'd be gone, and because this whole scene had all the unreality of a dream, Matthew found himself moving towards her. Perhaps he was imagining it; perhaps she wasn't really there. She was certainly the stuff of fantasy as she rubbed those long, sexy legs.

'Hi.'

His greeting caught her unawares; he knew that immediately. But at least she was all too disturbingly human as she turned her head towards him. Despite the poor light, he was instantly aware that she was no fantasy. Her warmth, her breath, her nearness assaulted his senses. He wanted to reach out and touch her to prove she knew it, too.

Of course, he didn't do any such thing. But he couldn't prevent his eyes from making a swift inventory of her body. Her breasts were far too provocative in profile, and the folds of her dress, clinging to her hips and thighs, were almost more erotic than if she'd been completely naked.

The shadows they created at knee and groin tormented him. He wanted to peel away the fabric and expose the flesh beneath. He wanted to put his hand between her legs, and feel her sweetness. He wanted to feel her close about him and lose all control...

'What do you want?' she asked, arresting his descent into madness, and Matthew forced his brain to function over the dictates of his sex. 'I thought you were playing cards,' she added, crossing her arms about her waist almost protectively.

'Well, as you can see, I'm not,' said Matthew evenly, relieved to find that his voice was only marginally affected by his mood. 'Tell me—' he endeavoured to strike a casual tone '—do you usually go swimming fully clothed?'

He thought she might have flushed, but the darkness revealed nothing but a faint glimmer in her eyes. 'Not usually,' she replied tightly. 'I was—hot, that's all. And I didn't want to disturb the children by getting changed.'

Matthew's mouth turned down. 'I thought you said you were going to check on them,' he reminded her smoothly, and she straightened her spine.

'I was. I did. But—they were restless.' She lifted her

shoulders. 'I expect they could hear the strange voices. The villa's walls are quite thin.'

'Mmm.' Matthew doubted that had been her motive, but it wasn't worth arguing over. 'It's funny,' he said, 'I was just thinking of doing the same thing. Oh—not plunging in with all my clothes on. But taking a swim.'

Helen's eyes widened. 'Here?'

She sounded quite appalled, and Matthew took his cue. 'Why not?' he asked. 'You've obviously enjoyed it.' He hesitated only a second before flicking the curve of one alluring breast with his finger. 'Was it cold? Is that why…?'

His meaning was obvious, and he could tell by the way her eyes sparked that she resented his familiarity. 'Why don't you find out?' she demanded, swinging round on him unexpectedly, and before he could guess her intentions she'd thrust both hands at his chest.

She was quite strong, he thought, but it wasn't her strength that defeated him. The element of surprise was what caused his downfall. That and a sudden depression of sand beneath his heel.

He tried to regain his balance, but the tide was working in her favour. The undertow sucked away his footing, and with an almighty splash he floundered on to his back.

God, it was cold—or perhaps he had just been incredibly hot. Whatever, the shock of it drove the breath from his lungs, and left him gasping for air. Like some wallowing sea creature, he struggled to regain stability, splashing about and soaking himself with every move he made.

It was her laughter that provoked him into action. Peal after peal of it broke over him as she stood there, apparently forgetting how vulnerable she was. It was as if she thought his position was irretrievable, and only when he scrambled to his feet did she take off.

But she was too late—too late and too slow, and hampered by the soaking folds of her skirt. Matthew's trousers were much less cumbersome, his legs much swifter. He lunged for her ankle without compunction, and wrestled her to the sand.

She was breathless, as much from the laughter his plight had evoked as from her belated sprint across the beach. She fell, a helpless victim to his superior strength, still choking on convulsive giggles as he rolled her on to her back.

'Beast,' she exclaimed, but it came out as a stutter as she tried frantically to crawl away from his hands. Thankfully, the sand was damp, or they'd have both been covered in it, and it squelched beneath his knees as he brought her down.

She was twisting and turning so much that he had to use his weight to subdue her. Even so, she wriggled increasingly under him, trying to draw up her knee between his legs. In the end, he forced her legs apart and lay between them, suffering the jab of her heels against his thighs.

'You didn't honestly expect to get away with it, did you?' he demanded, imprisoning her wrists above her head with one hand, and forcing her to look at him with the other. 'Dammit, what am I going to tell the others when I get back there? They're going to think I'm crazy or something worse.'

They were nearer the terrace now, and the faint illumination spilling from the lanterns caught the fleeting look of withdrawal in her eyes. But it was only a momentary aberration before she answered him. 'You should have thought of that before you made a pass at me,' she retorted. 'Now, will you get off me, you neolithic brute? It's not my fault if you've got some awkward explanations to make.'

'Isn't it?' Matthew made the obvious rejoinder, but he found he was enjoying himself too much to let her go. Beneath his chest her heart was pounding frantically, and a hot surge of awareness was pooling in his groin. His voice thickened. 'Who else's?'

'It's your own fault,' she panted, his weight causing a constriction in her lungs. 'But don't worry. I'm sure your—

your sister-in-law will believe you. She's sure to think it was me if you play nice.'

Matthew's eyes narrowed. 'What's that supposed to mean?'

'Nothing.'

Her reply was swift, but he had the impression she'd said more than she intended. Dammit, she couldn't be jealous of Fleur, could she? The implications of that possibility made his head swim.

He looked down at her suddenly, and the eyes that had been wide and imploring a moment ago were quickly veiled. Long lashes, several shades darker than her hair, made a dusky fringe against her cheeks, and for the first time he noticed the tinge of darkness that created a revealing shadow beneath their rims.

Either the children were keeping her awake, or she wasn't sleeping well for some reason, he decided. There was exhaustion in her pallor, and he wanted to know why. But, for the moment, he was selfish enough to put a hold on his compassion. Holding her like this, feeling her move against him, inspired thoughts of a totally different nature. He still wanted to comfort her, but in a very different way.

'You don't have to be jealous of Fleur,' he said, releasing her wrists to cup her face. 'She won't be staying long.'

Her outrage was evident in the violent thrust she made against him, but this time she didn't have a hope in hell of succeeding, he reflected smugly. Her anger only made him even more determined; her frustration made him settle even more surely against her. If she did but know it, she was exciting him by her actions. He could already feel the ache of longing between his legs.

'I don't give a damn how long that woman is staying,' she seethed, but her denial turned to a muffled moan beneath his lips. Giving in to the desire to taste her, his mouth cut off her angry protest, and although she fought his possession she couldn't win.

Groaning his satisfaction, Matthew moved over her, sub-

duing her flailing hands without too much effort. She tried
to clench her lips together, but he wouldn't let her, and his
tongue entwined with hers in an intimate dance.

He knew the moment when she stopped resisting him.
Until then, despite his efforts, it had been a fairly one-sided
affair. Her eyes were open and she stared at him in accusation. The sounds she uttered were protests that he ignored.

But suddenly, as if in spite of herself he'd touched some
vulnerable chord inside her, she gave in. Almost innocently,
it seemed, she surrendered to the sensual brush of his
tongue. Her lips parted to allow his hot invasion; when his
tongue seared across hers she met its fire with her own.

Her hands, which had been balled against her sides, slid
into his hair now. Her nails raked his scalp as he deepened
the kiss. She was heat and light and fire, and his blood
responded, thickening to a throbbing mass as she arched
beneath his thighs.

Did she know what she was doing? he wondered unsteadily, finding it difficult to think coherently with her passion beneath his hands. She was more, so much more than
he had ever expected, and his own senses were reeling in
eager response.

Her small breasts thrust against his chest, unbearably
provocative in his present state of arousal. The wetness of
their clothes was creating an urgent friction, and when he
released her mouth to take a breath, his eyes dropped to
the sensuous suction of their bodies.

He wanted to tear her clothes from her, he thought crazily. He wanted to strip off his own shirt and trousers, and
warm her with his heat. But, for all his whirling senses, he
knew they were far too close to the villa to allow such
madness. He contented himself with lowering his head, and
suckling her through the cloth.

Fire shot through him as he took that pert nipple between
his lips. For all that its dusky peak was hidden beneath her
dress, it tasted like the sweetest kind of heaven. Thrusting,

throbbing, it surged into his mouth, and, forgetting what he'd thought a moment before, he gave in to his instincts and unbuttoned her bodice.

Her breasts looked every bit as delicious as they had tasted. Tight and swollen, their pointed fullness tipped towards his mouth, and he took a moment to enjoy their provocation. His own body throbbed in anticipation, and he wondered if she could feel his urgent response. Between his legs his sex was aching, straining for a satisfaction she could give him.

He didn't delay any longer. Although her eyes had barely fluttered when he drew back from her, he was afraid she might suddenly change her mind. But when he took the knotted curve of her breast into his mouth, she barely shuddered. The sigh of contentment that escaped her was an involuntary admission.

Matthew groaned then, low in his throat, the sounds she was making intensifying his need. He wanted her, he thought shakenly. God, he wanted her so much it hurt. He was harder than he'd ever thought possible, and he couldn't hold out much longer.

Her hands slid inside his collar, cool against his spine. Small palms massaged his shoulders, peeling the shirt away from him, as she nuzzled his throat with her tongue. She was tasting him, he thought weakly, feeling that sensuous wetness against his skin. She must know how he was feeling. God, he was perilously near the brink.

A feeling of reckless hunger swept over him. Images of how slick and tight her womanly sheath would be filled his head. He could imagine the fulfilling sweetness of his possession. He could imagine burying himself deep inside her, stretching her to the limits, taking her with him to the mindless heights of oblivion...

Reason reasserted itself. It was lust, he told himself savagely, suppressing the urge to slide his hand up her thigh and discover her arousal for himself. The musky scent of her body and his was all around them, and he wouldn't have been human if he hadn't wanted what she could give. It was a long time since he had been with a woman—any woman—and he was horny. He needed the act, but not the complications. Seducing the Sheridans' nanny wouldn't just be foolish, it would be mad.

Yet, when she gripped his neck and brought his mouth back to hers, temptation hovered. His blood felt like liquid fire in his veins. The feel of her toes, caressing now, was almost driving him crazy, but with a muffled oath he let her go, and got unsteadily to his feet.

CHAPTER SEVEN

'WHEN are you waking up, Helen?'

The plaintive cry, accompanied by a persistent tugging at the sheet which was all that covered her, forced Helen to open her eyes. Sophie was standing beside her bed, still in her baby-doll pyjamas, her thumb tucked unhappily into her mouth.

Helen stifled a groan and blinked rapidly, trying to clear the sleep from her eyes. There was a heavy sense of apprehension hanging over her, which she couldn't quite interpret at this moment, and her head was throbbing dully, as if she'd slept too long.

'Oh, Sophie,' she said, struggling to focus on her watch. 'What time is it?'

'It's late,' replied Sophie defensively, making snuffling noises with her thumb. 'Mummy said I could come and wake you up. She says she's got a headache.'

Haven't we all? thought Helen with some resignation, rolling on to her back. For heaven's sake, what time was it? Tricia didn't usually surface before she did.

When she finally made sense of the pointers on her watch, she gave a horrified gasp. It was half-past eight. She could hardly believe it, but she'd slept long past her normal deadline. She'd acclimatised with a vengeance, and Tricia had a right to feel aggrieved.

And then, as she turned to Sophie to tell her she was sorry, the reasons why she had overslept surged over her. Oh, God, she thought, remembering why she had lain awake for several hours the night before, how could she have been so stupid? She'd actually let Matthew Aitken crawl all over her. She'd let the brother of the man who'd destroyed her father's life almost make love to her. And, what was worse, she hadn't stopped him. She'd encouraged him to do it.

'He—len!'

Sophie's protest was more of an angry whine now, as if she sensed Helen wasn't listening to her any more. Helen's eyes might be open, but she wasn't looking at her. She was staring right through her, and Sophie didn't like it.

'What?' With an effort, Helen forced her treacherous thoughts aside and struggled to pay attention. 'Oh—yes, I am late, aren't I?' she said ruefully. 'Go and tell your mummy I won't be long. I must just wash my face.'

'You slept in.' Henry's appearance in the doorway heralded another accusation, and Helen wondered if Tricia realised how like her her son was. 'You're not s'posed to sleep in,' he added reprovingly. 'You're s'posed to give us our breakfast.'

'And I will,' said Helen wearily, 'just as soon as I've cleaned my teeth and got some clothes on. Now—' she forced a smile '—why don't you two do the same? I'm sure you can manage to put your clothes on without me for once.'

'We're not s'posed—' began Henry, but Sophie cut him off.

'I'm staying here,' she declared, depositing herself on the end of Helen's bed. 'I want to watch you get dressed. I can, can't I? I'm a girl.'

'Well—'

'If you're staying, I'm staying,' announced Henry, and Helen pushed aside the sheet with a tired hand.

'You're neither of you staying,' she declared, making sure her nightshirt covered her thighs before swinging her legs out of bed. 'I won't be long, I promise. Now, be good children and go and brush your teeth.'

With the door closed firmly behind them, Helen drew the first unrestrained breath of the day. At least she had a few minutes to recover herself. She had the feeling she was going to need them this morning.

Examining her reflection in the mirror above the bathroom basin, she wasn't surprised to find the shadows around her eyes had deepened. Ever since she'd discovered that her mother was staying on the island she'd had a problem sleeping. But last night—and that encounter with Matthew Aitken—was something else.

Dear God, she thought, smoothing the fine veins below her eyes with the tips of her fingers, why hadn't she just kept out of the way, as she'd intended? Why had she gone for the walk along the beach? And why had she chosen to swim?

It had been such a crazy thing to do. Even now, with the benefit of hindsight, she couldn't honestly say what had driven her into the ocean. She'd been hot, of course, and restless, and her nerves had been taut and strung. But she hadn't intended to ruin her dress by soaking it with saltwater.

Nevertheless, that was what she had done, and until Matthew had come upon her she'd quite enjoyed the freedom to be herself. She'd told herself she wouldn't think about Fleur, wouldn't allow her to ruin this trip. But the trouble was, she'd already done that. Helen was never going to forget she was there.

Even so, Fleur hadn't recognised her. She wouldn't have made that stupid mistake over her name if she had. Giving Matthew a bogus surname had been reckless, of course, but with a bit of luck she might get away with it. She had the feeling they wouldn't be seeing either him or his sister-in-law again after last night. Even without what had happened, Matthew had been bored, and Tricia's attempt to get him to talk about his work had patently annoyed him.

Besides, if the name she'd given was ever questioned, she could always pretend that he had been mistaken. Gregory—Graham—they did sound sufficiently alike to support her theory, and she would like to think that Lucas would defend her.

She sighed. She'd liked Matthew's assistant very much. He'd talked to her a lot as she'd toyed with her supper, and, for all he worked for the enemy, he was one of the nicest men she'd met.

Yet she hadn't treated Matthew Aitken like an enemy, she reminded herself unhappily, unable to keep her humiliating thoughts at bay. For all her proud intentions, she'd given in without a contest, and if he hadn't pushed her away, she'd have let him prove it.

Oh, God!

Pressing her lips together, she stared painfully at her pale, drawn features, but she found no answers in her dry-eyed gaze. Although she wanted to cry, she wouldn't let herself. She wanted nothing to remind Tricia of the night before.

She had hoped she might sneak back to the villa without anyone seeing her, but, as everything else had worked against her that evening, she wasn't really surprised when she didn't make it. By the time she had dragged herself up from the sand, fastened her bodice and squeezed the water from her hem, the card-players had left the table. They were sitting on the veranda when she tried to slide past them and, despite her best efforts, Andrew had seen her.

It appeared, though she had learned this only incidentally, that Lucas was indirectly to blame for her exposure. Apparently he hadn't been able to grasp the rules of bidding, and the game had had to be abandoned.

But her appearance had provided a much more noteworthy topic for conversation, and Helen had had to stand there, feeling like one of her own charges, while Tricia took her to task for leaving the villa. Helen's explanation, that she had gone for a walk and fallen into the ocean, had not been received with any sympathy. It was madness, Tricia had declared, to go walking after dark on her own, and she had appealed to her husband to support her.

Helen had been uncomfortably aware that Andrew Sheridan was more interested in the way her wet skirts clung to her legs, and that her mother was watching her, too, with narrowed eyes. Dear God, she'd thought, she could do without this. And where was Matthew? Had he gone home to change?

In the event, it had been Lucas who'd taken pity on her. Although she suspected he had his own motives for helping her, he had suggested she ought to be allowed to go and dry herself. He'd made some comment about them not wanting their nanny laid up with pneumonia, and the veracity of this statement had rung a chord.

She hadn't returned to the party. For all she'd been curious to know how Matthew was going to explain his absence, she'd remained in her room for the rest of the evening. She'd told herself she didn't want to hear what lies he would tell to excuse himself, but the truth was she was too ashamed to see him again.

It also meant she hadn't had to speak to her mother again. And she supposed that was a blessing in disguise. The woman she remembered bore no resemblance to the brittle creature who'd sat at the Sheridans' table. Yet obviously this was the real Fleur, and not the childhood illusion she recalled.

The children were washed and dressed, and tucking into bowls of Rice Crispies when their mother came into the kitchen. For once Tricia was dressed, but whether that was to endorse the fact that Helen had slept in or because she had other plans, Helen couldn't say.

'Oh, so there you are,' she declared, as if Helen spent her time trying to avoid her. 'I was beginning to wonder if you'd decided to give notice. After last night's little fiasco, there was always a doubt.'

Helen refused to be intimidated, but she looked down at the barely touched croissant on her plate and made a pretence of spreading it with conserve. For all her determination, she didn't trust herself to meet Tricia's eyes without flinching, and the last thing she needed was for her employer to suspect she had something to hide.

'Did you want something, Tricia?' she asked, aware of the children looking on with interest. Henry, particularly, enjoyed any kind of altercation, and even Sophie's eyes were round as she looked at them over her spoon.

'Did I want something?' echoed their mother, and Helen's heart sank at the obvious aggression in her tone. 'I want an explanation, if that's not too much to ask. I assume you know that one of our guests left the party without saying goodbye? I want to know what you said that caused him to push you in the water.'

'Did someone push you in the water, Helen?' exclaimed Henry, his cereal forgotten in his excitement, but Helen had no time to feed his curiosity.

'No one pushed me in the water,' she exclaimed, resentful of the implication. 'I told you what happened: I fell. That's all there is to say.'

'Really?'

Patently Tricia didn't believe her, and Helen thought how ironic it was that the Sheridans had got totally the wrong end of the stick. 'Yes,' she said now. 'How could you think anything different? And—and as for one of your guests—leaving, perhaps you should ask yourself why, not me.'

Tricia gasped. 'What do you mean?'

Helen pressed her lips together. 'Nothing,' she said at last. 'I don't mean anything. But if we're talking about Matthew Aitken, I don't think he was exactly thrilled with the evening.'

'Mmm.' Tricia rested her chin on the knuckles of one hand. 'He wasn't the easiest of supper companions, I will admit. So—you didn't see him again, after we went to play cards.'

'I didn't say that.' Helen couldn't tell an outright lie. Fudging about how she'd got wet—that was prevarication. But if Tricia should ask Matthew, she couldn't be sure of what he might say.

'So you did see him?'

'Briefly.' Helen licked her lips. 'He was going for a walk, I think.' She crossed her fingers in her lap. 'He must have walked home.'

Tricia frowned. 'He didn't say where he was going?'

That was simple. 'No.'

'Was this before or after you—fell into the water?' asked Tricia slyly. Then, 'You know, I can't believe he'd abandon the party like that, in spite of what Fleur had to say.'

Helen stiffened. 'What did she say?'

'Oh, this and that.' Tricia gave her an irritated look. 'She asked where we'd found you, actually. I suppose you're not the usual sort of nanny.'

Helen took a breath. 'I—thought you meant she'd said something about—about Matthew Aitken,' she said, not sure whether she ought to be alarmed about Fleur's interest in her or not. Probably not, she assured herself ruefully. Her mother had only ever been interested in herself.

'Well, she did,' Tricia exclaimed now, rather petulantly. 'She made some excuse about him getting ideas at the most inconvenient times.' She sighed. 'I suppose I shouldn't have suggested playing bridge, but Fleur was so enthusiastic. She said she'd missed playing awfully since she went to live in the United States. Apparently, her late husband's father breeds horses, and naturally—'

'She said that?' Helen broke in, swallowing convulsively. 'That she'd missed playing bridge since she went to live in Florida?'

'Yes.' Tricia's eyes narrowed. 'But how do you know she lives in Florida? I don't recall her talking to you, and I certainly didn't tell you that.'

Helen felt her colour deepen. 'Oh—well, Lucas must have mentioned it,' she replied hurriedly. She forced herself to remain calm. 'Does it matter? I don't suppose we're likely to see them again.'

'You might not,' said Tricia tartly, 'but I'm sure Drew and I will get an invitation to Dragon Bay. It's only polite, in the circumstances. And Fleur knows how much I'd love to see the house.'

'But it's not her house, is it?' Helen pointed out, and then was relieved when Henry chose to speak. She'd said too much already. She should learn to keep her mouth shut.

'Can we come?' he asked, and for a moment both women looked blank. 'To Dragon Bay,' he added. 'Are there really dragons there? Sophie won't like it if there are.'

'I will, too,' declared his sister, digging him in the ribs, but their mother was in no mood to listen to their bickering.

'Just mind your own business, both of you,' she said. 'And only speak when you're spoken to. This is a private conversation. I'm talking to Helen, not you.'

'But are there dragons?' persisted Sophie, who was always slower than her brother, and her mother gave her a fulminating look.

'Of course there aren't,' she snapped. 'Don't you know when Henry's teasing you? Now, hurry up and finish your breakfast. And stop slurping into your food.'

Sophie's jaw wobbled, and she gave her brother a tearful glare. She usually got the worst of any argument, and Helen thought again how little Tricia understood her own children.

'Anyway,' she continued, just when Helen was beginning to think she'd got away with it, 'for someone who's supposedly not interested in seeing them again, you appear to have asked an awful lot of questions. Which reminds me, what did Matthew Aitken say when you—met him on the beach? I assume you didn't talk about the weather?'

Helen took a breath. Her thoughts were racing wildly, and she cast about for something trite to say. What had they talked about? she wondered. Aside from the sarcastic comment he'd made about her swimming fully clothed, she couldn't remember a thing. The trouble was, it was what he had *done* that was balking her memory. From the moment he'd touched her, it was all as painfully clear as a bell.

'He—we—talked about swimming,' she said at last, realising there was a danger in admitting it, but accepting it was the lesser of two evils. If she refused to answer, Tricia was bound to become suspicious, and making something up was almost as bad.

Liars had to have good memories, she acknowledged unhappily, and dealing with Matthew Aitken was far too fraught. The closer she stuck to the truth, the better. And it wasn't such an unusual topic, after all.

'Swimming?'

The other woman stared at her disbelievingly, but before she could say anything more there was an unholy crash. Helen guessed Sophie had been trying to pay Henry back for teasing her, and, in reaching across the table, she'd sent her dish tumbling to the floor.

The ensuing uproar successfully diverted the conversation away from Helen. Maria came rushing in, declaring that the milk would sink into the tiles and go sour. And Sophie, getting down from her chair, slipped on the mushy cereal. Somehow she cut her leg on a shard of china, and because it had started to bleed she began to scream.

It was too much for Tricia. 'Oh, for heaven's sake,' she exclaimed, looking disgustedly at her daughter, before leaving them to deal with the mess without her. And, although Helen wouldn't have wished Sophie hurt for the world, she couldn't help being grateful for small mercies.

'Will I still be able to go in the water?' asked Sophie later, sniffing into a tissue as Helen applied a strip of plaster to her thigh. 'You said we could play in the rockpools today, didn't you? I've got my bucket and spade all ready.'

'Your bucket and spade,' scoffed Henry, hands in pockets, watching the proceedings with a jaundiced eye, but Helen ignored him.

'I think we'll just do a little fishing with our nets this morning,' she declared, half wishing she'd never suggested going on to the beach now. They were too accessible there, too vulnerable. And although, after what had happened the night before, she didn't flatter herself that Matthew Aitken would want to see her, she'd no wish to reinforce his impression that she was easy.

Easy!

Oh, God! Straightening from her task, Helen got to her feet with a heavy heart. How had it happened? she wondered. How had she got herself into such a situation? It simply wasn't like her. She'd always considered herself so self-contained before. Naturally, she'd had men-friends. In fact, one man had actually got as far as asking her to marry him about two years ago. But she'd been quite content living with her father. And, although she'd expected to get married one day, she'd certainly been in no hurry.

Was in no hurry now, she appended, remembering that even in the depths of her despair she'd never considered taking that way out. Marrying someone just to provide herself with financial support had never been an option. In fact lately, since she'd come to work for the Sheridans, she'd begun to wonder if marriage was so desirable after all. Living with someone had to be easier. And, best of all, it kept your options open.

Last night must have been an aberration, she decided. She simply wasn't the type to act that way. She was exaggerating what had happened and punishing herself needlessly. For heaven's sake, the man had only kissed her. It was no big deal.

And yet, remembering how mindlessly abandoned she'd felt when he moved over her, it wasn't quite so easy to dismiss the whole affair. He hadn't only kissed her, he'd touched her intimately. And she'd wanted him to do it. She'd wanted him to do more...

'Why are you looking so cross, Helen?'

Sophie was gazing up at her with her thumb in her mouth, a sure sign that she wasn't totally convinced she hadn't done something wrong, and Helen forced herself to smile at her.

'I'm not looking cross,' she denied, not altogether truthfully. 'I'm just thinking, that's all. I believe I saw some shrimp nets in the cupboard, that the Parrish children must have left behind. Why don't we take them with us? You never know what we might find.'

'Which cupboard?' exclaimed Henry, proving he wasn't wholly immune to the delights of the beach, and Sophie pushed herself in front of him indignantly.

'I'll get them,' she said. 'Where are they, Helen? And I'll need my bucket, won't I? To put the fishes in.'

'Fish,' said Helen firmly, stopping Henry from pinching his sister's bottom, and giving him a reproving stare. 'We'll need the buckets to collect the fish. Well—the crabs and tiny molluscs we're likely to find in the rockpools.'

'What are moll—molluscs?' asked Henry with difficulty, but Helen just ushered him out of the door.

'I'll tell you when we find some,' she said. 'And I'll get the nets myself. I suggest you get your bucket, unless you want to be left out.'

With both children wearing hats, and their still pink limbs liberally coated with sun-blocking cream, Helen shepherded her charges on to the beach. Happily, from her point of view, it was completely deserted, and after dropping their towels in a prominent place she escorted them down to the nearest cluster of rocks.

The pools were warm, and for all her earlier apprehension Helen soon found she was enjoying herself. It reminded her of holidays she had spent with her father when she was a child. He had had endless patience with her, and it couldn't have been easy being a single parent in those days. Of course, she had had a nanny, too, but, unlike Henry and Sophie, she hadn't been abandoned to her own resources. Whenever possible James Gregory had looked after his daughter himself, and it was this that had created the bond between them that she'd found so hard to let go.

'Oooh, what's that?' asked Sophie, grimacing, and skipping out of the water as a weird-looking creature emerged from the shade of the rocks. Even Henry got out of the way as its spiny shell turned in his direction, and, recognising it as a sea-urchin, Helen scooped it out of the water.

'Not to be touched,' she said decisively, shaking it out of the net into another pool some distance away. 'Those spines can dig into your toes, and it hurts when you try to get them out.'

'Ugh.' Sophie gave a theatrical shiver, and Helen thought it had been a salutary lesson for them all. They weren't on the beach at Bournemouth, and for all its beauty this paradise did have one or two unpleasant inhabitants.

'I wasn't afraid,' declared Henry, brave after the event, and Helen gave him an old-fashioned look.

'Then I'll get you to deal with the next one we see,' she said pleasantly, and smiled as he looked anxiously about him.

Notwithstanding the heat, and the ever-present danger of the children falling over and hurting themselves, Helen found herself relaxing. Away from the house, and with no disturbing neighbour on the horizon, she could almost convince herself that nothing bad had happened. Even the thought of her mother, sunning herself on Matthew's veranda, only aroused a muted resentment. Despite the shock she'd had, she'd lived for almost twenty years without seeing her mother, and she had to be pragmatic if she wanted to keep her job.

Because they never stayed out too long, in a short while Helen peeled off her shorts and T-shirt and took them down to the water's edge. She reasoned that salt-water was unlikely to cause Sophie any problems, and it was so good to feel the comparative coolness on her skin after the undiluted heat of the sun.

Both children wanted to swim, but Helen didn't let them go out of their depth. For all it looked so idyllic, the current was quite strong. Henry grumbled, as usual, but he was still wary of finding another sea urchin, and Sophie splashed about quite happily in the shallows.

She was so busy keeping tabs on both children, however,

that she wasn't aware of anyone's approach until a woman spoke. And, because Henry and Sophie only stared at the visitor, Helen guessed who it was before she turned her head.

'Hello, Miss—Graham?'

Her mother was alone. Helen hadn't expected her to be, and she'd already steeled herself to meet Matthew's mocking gaze when she turned around. But only Fleur was standing there, looking like an exotic butterfly in billowing silk trousers and a poncho-like top of flowing chiffon. She was wearing dark glasses, too, which made her expression hard to read. But the fact that she was here at all caused a sudden sinking in Helen's stomach.

Oh, lord, she thought, grasping Henry's and Sophie's hands and drawing them closer, as if in protection. Did Fleur know who she was? Was that why she had come?

CHAPTER EIGHT

MATTHEW woke up with a hangover.

It wasn't the first time it had happened, and he didn't imagine it would be the last, but it was frustrating. He didn't enjoy working with a pounding head, and he wasn't in a particularly good temper when he stepped into the shower.

It was late, too, he noticed. It must have been after nine before he stirred. Too late for a walk, too late to go jogging; his whole schedule had been messed up. He preferred to be at his desk by nine o'clock and no later. He'd be lucky if he made it by ten the way things were going.

Not that it really mattered, he acknowledged edgily as he stood beneath the pummelling spray. It wasn't as if he had a deadline, or an editor breathing down his neck for copy. But he'd always believed it was essential to have self-discipline, particularly if, like he did, you worked for yourself.

It was a habit he had acquired during his days as a roving correspondent. Not that he'd had a desk to sit at in those days, but the discipline had been just as important. That was why he had been successful; why he had been on the spot when some of his fellow journalists had still been recovering from the previous night's excesses. Wherever he'd been, whatever he'd done—and he had to admit he had been as wild as any of them when he was younger—he'd always been around when he was needed.

Which was hardly a description of what had happened last night, he brooded angrily. He'd been on the spot all right, but it wasn't a memory he wanted to keep. Looking back, the whole affair had all the elements of fantasy. He didn't know what had possessed him; he could hardly believe how reckless he had been.

And the fact that that was the real reason why he had a hangover this morning was what was really bugging him. As soon as he'd opened his aching eyes, he'd remembered. God Almighty, he was too old to go cavorting about on the beach like some sex-starved adolescent; too old to arrive back at the villa soaked to the skin and howling with frustration.

Of course, he'd resorted to the only refuge he knew. By the time Fleur and Lucas came home, he was past feeling anything at all. Which was just as well, he reflected, turning off the shower. He hated to think he'd been so desperate that he might have turned to Fleur for comfort. Perhaps he was flattering himself, but he feared that was exactly why she was here.

He half expected Lucas to appear as he was dressing. They often discussed work, or the day's mail, before he returned to his study. But, like everything else this morning, his expectations didn't run to order. Lucas was sitting at the breakfast table, staring broodingly into space, when he entered the room.

A plate of scrambled eggs was congealing in front of him, and, judging by the almost-empty state of the coffee-pot, Matthew guessed the other man wasn't feeling like eating either. Still, at least he was alone, he thought with some relief. As only one place had been disturbed, it appeared that Fleur was still in bed.

'Hi,' he said, when Lucas only offered him a silent acknowledgement. For all he wasn't feeling in the mood to be conciliatory, he guessed Lucas was peeved because he'd abandoned them the night before. And, what the hell, it wasn't his assistant's fault that he'd behaved like an idiot. He deserved an explanation, but Matthew was loath to tell the truth.

Lucas's brows arched. 'Hi,' he conceded, after a moment. Then, with some enjoyment, 'You look like hell.'

'Thanks.' Matthew hooked out a chair and levered himself into it. 'I'll return the compliment some time.'

Lucas's expression wilted. 'Well,' he muttered, as if in vindication, 'that was a rotten trick you pulled last night. Do you have any idea what it was like, trying to mollify the Sheridans? Making excuses when there weren't any to make.'

Matthew pulled a wry face. 'I'm sorry.'

'So you should be.' Lucas warmed to his theme. 'It was bloody embarrassing, I can tell you. I don't often give Fleur any credit, but I have to admit, she saved your neck.'

Matthew's mouth turned down. 'Really?'

'Yes, really.' Lucas pushed the eggs aside, and poured himself the last dregs of the coffee. 'She made up some tale about you getting these sudden ideas, that had to be immediately recorded in case you forgot them. She assured those poor sods that you'd be working at your word processor until all hours.' He grimaced. 'Whether they believed her is another story, if you'll forgive the pun.'

Matthew scowled. 'Does it matter?'

'It does to me.' Lucas glared back. 'Until you had that clever idea of me playing cards instead of you, Helen and I were getting along nicely. She's a really interesting woman, Matt, and I'd hoped to see her again.'

Matthew suppressed the sudden surge of emotion he felt at hearing the other man talk about Helen so familiarly. He told himself it was irritation; he refused to consider that it might be anything else. For God's sake, she was just a little tramp, he thought repressively. He didn't care about her. It was Lucas he was thinking about. He didn't want his friend to get hurt.

All the same, he couldn't quite hide the rancour in his voice as he answered him. 'In what way was she interesting?' he asked. 'Whenever I looked in your direction, you seemed to be doing all the talking.'

Lucas flushed then, and Matthew felt even worse. He had enough guilt rolling round inside him already. Did he have to make fun of the other man just to satisfy his own perverted sense of justice?

'I admit—I did do most of the talking,' Lucas conceded now. 'But that was just because we didn't have enough time together. If you hadn't cut and run, I might have learned something more about her. I know I said she was only here for a month, but, hell—a month can seem like a lifetime.'

'Can't it just,' murmured Matthew drily. And then, as another thought occurred to him, 'She—er—she did go back to the party, didn't she?'

'Go back?' Lucas pounced on the words, and Matthew hurried to rectify his mistake.

'Well—yes,' he said. 'I—er—I met her on the beach. When I was walking back,' he added. 'I—think she'd been in the water.'

Lucas frowned. 'I wonder why she didn't say she'd seen you?' he mused. 'Still, as you say, she was wet.' His eyes narrowed. 'You had nothing to do with that, I suppose?'

'No.' Matthew made the denial without hesitation. 'As I said before, she was wet before she saw me. Perhaps she'd been swimming. People have done crazier things.'

Lucas shook his head. 'She said she'd fallen. In the water, I mean. But, as you say, who knows? In any event, she went off to change and didn't come back. Fleur and I had a couple of drinks, and then we came home.'

Matthew inclined his head, annoyed that he couldn't find anything in Lucas's story to lift his mood. Last night had proved to him that getting involved with Helen Graham would be madness. He didn't need that kind of complication in his life.

Ruth appeared just then, to ask him if he wanted his usual breakfast, but this morning he refused everything but toast and coffee. He needed the caffeine to alleviate his headache, and a slice of toast might help to calm the churning in his gut.

'So,' he said, after the housekeeper had gone, forcing himself to be civil. 'Where's my dear sister-in-law this

morning? Not that I'm worried,' he added swiftly. 'I just
like to keep ahead of the game.'

Lucas grimaced. 'She's gone out.'

'Out?' Matthew stared at him disbelievingly. 'Fleur's
gone out alone? I don't believe it.'

'Oh, it's true,' Lucas assured him. 'I saw her leaving the
garden myself. She seemed to be heading towards Dragon
Point. Perhaps she enjoyed the Sheridans' company better
than we thought?'

Matthew's stomach tightened. 'You're not serious!'

'Why not?'

Why not, indeed? Matthew didn't really understand the
sense of apprehension he was feeling himself. He just
doubted Fleur had gone to Dragon Point to see the
Sheridans. It wasn't in Fleur's nature to cultivate anyone
she couldn't use.

And yet, why else would she go there? Not to see Helen,
he was sure. Unless he'd said or done something to make
her think he was interested in the younger woman. Despite
the unwelcome implications of that thought, he wouldn't
like to see the girl terrorised by Fleur.

Unable to sit still with such thoughts churning his already
queasy stomach, Matthew thrust back his chair and got unsteadily to his feet. Dammit, what was he going to do? He
could hardly go charging after her like some latter-day cav-
alier.

'What's the matter?'

Lucas was looking at him curiously, and, realising he
was acting out of character, Matthew pulled a rueful face.
'Too much to drink, I guess,' he said, squeezing the back
of his neck and finding it clammy. 'And I'm not sure I trust
Fleur. What the hell is she playing at?'

Lucas frowned. 'Well, I must admit I wondered where
she was going,' he conceded. 'D'you want me to go after
her? She hasn't been gone long.'

Matthew hesitated, as though giving the matter some

thought. 'No,' he said at last, as if coming to a decision. 'I need some air myself. I'll go see what she's doing.'

'Is the water cold?'

Fleur stood safely out of reach of the incoming tide, her high-heeled sandals totally unsuitable for a walk along the beach. She had to keep moving to prevent her heels from sinking into the sand, and Helen doubted the salt would improve the expensive bronze leather.

But, with the children waiting to see what she would say, she was obliged to answer her mother. 'It's—quite warm, actually,' she replied politely. But she was under no illusions that Fleur's enquiry meant that she wanted to join them.

'I never liked swimming in the sea,' she declared now, making sure the creamy rivulets didn't reach her feet. 'Saltwater dries your skin, and the sand gets into everything. I hated that gritty feeling between my toes.'

'I like it,' said Sophie, letting go of Helen's hand and paddling out of the water. She splashed a bit, and Fleur stifled an impatient exclamation. But she didn't go away as Helen had hoped.

Henry hunched his shoulders and scowled at Helen. 'Who is she?' he asked in a stage whisper. 'What does she want?'

'Oh—' Helen bit her lip. 'Um—this is Mrs Aitken, Henry. You remember: she came to supper with Mummy and Daddy last evening. She's staying at the house beyond the headland.'

'Where the dragons are?' asked Sophie at once, and Helen wished they'd stayed in the garden after all.

'It's called Dragon Bay,' said Fleur, keeping well away from danger. 'But there aren't any dragons. Who on earth told you there were?'

'Maybe you're a dragon,' said Henry rudely, responding to the edge of contempt in the woman's tone. 'And how do you know there aren't any dragons? You don't live there.'

'He has a point,' drawled another voice, a male one this time, and Helen wondered what she'd done to deserve this fate. She'd been so busy worrying about something that wasn't going to happen, she'd overlooked the very thing that had.

'Oh, Matt!'

For all she was sure that her mother had expected this, Helen glimpsed a trace of impatience in Fleur's eyes as she turned to her brother-in-law. Just for a moment, she had the feeling that Fleur was as shocked to see him as she was, but it might have been because of what he'd said.

'Good morning,' he said now, encompassing all of them in the greeting, and Helen decided that this was her chance to escape. Without looking at him at all, she offered a muffled greeting, and then shepherded the children before her up the beach.

'My bucket—I've forgotten my bucket,' protested Sophie loudly, and, adjuring the children to stay where they were, Helen ran back to get it. She was not unaware that, in her green-and white-striped bikini, she was at something of a disadvantage, but she snatched up the bucket quickly, and turned to make her escape.

'I hope we haven't spoiled your plans for the morning,' Matthew remarked drily, and she was forced to acknowledge him then, or arouse her mother's suspicions.

'Not at all,' she said stiffly, clutching the bucket to her midriff. 'We never stay out long. It's much too hot for the children.'

'For you, too, by the look of it,' he commented, and she wondered if he was being deliberately unkind because Fleur was looking on.

She didn't need him to tell her that her face was like a lobster. She was burning with humiliation inside as well as out.

'Don't be cruel, Matt.' Her mother came to her rescue,

but once again Helen sensed she had her own reasons for doing so. 'Come along, darling. We've taken up enough of Miss—Graham's time.'

'If you'll excuse me…'

Helen just wanted to get as far away as possible—from both of them. It seemed obvious to her that whatever Matthew Aitken had said there was something going on between them. It sickened her, not just because of who Fleur was, but because of her own vulnerability. In God's name, why had she let him touch her?

The image of his dark, sardonic face accompanied her back to the house. That, and the unwelcome memory of Fleur clinging on to his arm. He had strong arms, dark-skinned and muscular, covered with a light coating of dusky hair, just like his legs.

Andrew was just coming out on to the patio as they reached the house, and he viewed her half-naked state with obviously appreciative eyes. 'Well, well,' he said. 'Nurse's uniforms get better all the time.' He grinned at Helen's discomfort. 'You appear to have caught the sun.'

'We saw Mr and Mrs Aitken,' declared Sophie, evidently assuming Fleur's familiarity with Matthew meant they were married. Relationships were always simple in the little girl's mind, and Helen stifled a sigh when Andrew frowned.

'Mr and Mrs Aitken?' he echoed. 'Would that be Fleur and Matthew Aitken?'

'Who else?' replied Helen, heading for the children's bedroom. 'Come along, you two. Let's go and take a shower.'

'Can I come?' asked their father, in an undertone only she could hear, and Helen hoped Andrew was not going to prove a nuisance on this holiday. The little she'd seen of him in London had not led her to believe he might become a problem, but since his arrival three days ago she'd been on her guard.

There'd been that business at the airport, for example. And while Helen knew it had just been a game on his part,

she'd been left with the feeling that Andrew liked to tease.
With her mother to contend with, she didn't need any more
problems. She half wished they could just pack up and go
home.

The rest of the day passed reasonably uneventfully. To
Helen's relief, Tricia took her husband off to have lunch
with some friends in Bridgetown, and after their afternoon
nap both Henry and Sophie were disposed to be friendly.
She suspected it was the heat as much as anything that was
sapping their energy, and they were quite content to splash
about in the swimming-pool, which was partially shaded by
a stand of palms.

The Sheridans didn't come back until after six, and by
then Helen had the children bathed and ready for bed. She'd
eaten her evening meal with them, to avoid having to join
her employers, and she spent the evening reading, and trying to come to terms with what she should do.

Now that she was certain that Fleur was her mother, it
had put her into something of a quandary. For all she told
herself that her mother had deserted her, that she owed her
nothing, the ties of blood couldn't be wholly ignored.
Whatever she felt about Fleur, however much she resented
the fact that she'd been thrust into her orbit, the fact remained that it had happened. Could she just forget about
her? Or did she owe it to her father's memory to tell her
mother who she was?

It would be hard explaining why she'd lied about her
surname to Matthew, of course. Would Fleur believe that
it had just been a knee-jerk reaction, brought about by her
initial desire to hide her identity from her? She couldn't
deny the panic that had gripped her when she'd first been
faced with the woman. Was that why she'd succumbed to
Matthew's lovemaking? Because she'd already used up all
her resistance with Fleur?

It was too simplistic a solution, of course. The truth was,
she didn't know why it had happened. She'd been dis-

tressed, perhaps, but hardly incoherent. Yet, when Matthew had laid his hands upon her, she'd melted like jelly in his arms.

And, unhappily, that had complicated an already complicated situation. Yet her involvement with him had started even before she'd recognised her mother. From the moment he'd accosted her at the airport, she'd been aware of him as a man. It was crazy, because he'd made it perfectly obvious he found her foolish. Beyond stripping her of her dignity—among other things—he'd just treated her with contempt. He was probably like his brother, she thought unhappily. He didn't care about anyone else's feelings but his own.

The thing she didn't want to think about was what his relationship with her mother might be. For all she and her father had lived a fairly free and easy existence, because she had been with him so much she was pitiably ignorant when it came to men like Matthew. Her own experience told her he probably didn't have a conscience, and if Fleur needed another protector, she could probably do a lot worse.

She half regretted not having supper with the Sheridans later, when she lay awake for hours, wishing the dawn would come. A couple of glasses of wine might have solved her sleeping problem, and it didn't help that she could hear Tricia and Andrew arguing through the thin walls of their bedroom.

Eventually she did sleep, however, though this time she awakened in good time to get the children's breakfasts. Despite her disturbed night, she felt reasonably rested, and she reflected that it sometimes happened that way. The previous day she'd overslept, and she'd felt heavy-eyed all morning.

It was after seven, however, when she opened the shutters and stepped out on to the veranda. Long after she might have expected to see Matthew, she acknowledged with some relief. She hadn't asked him if he'd seen her, but as she'd seen him it was always possible. She wouldn't like him to think she was haunting him. After what had happened, she'd be wiser to keep her distance.

Nevertheless, she couldn't deny a sudden mental image of her mother and Matthew in bed together. Brown skin on pale flesh; straight dark hair mingling with silvery blonde curls. A hairy leg wedged between two pearl-pale thighs... Dear God, she thought in horror, what in heaven's name was happening to her? She'd never had thoughts like these before she'd met that man.

Henry and Sophie were less amiable this morning. Some time during the night Henry had hidden Matilda, so Helen had to spend most of the time before breakfast looking for the rag doll. Of course, Henry said he hadn't touched it, but Sophie didn't believe him, and after finding the doll hidden beneath the little girl's mattress Helen didn't believe him either.

Consequently, they were late getting their showers, and late turning up for breakfast. Much to Helen's dismay, the children's father was already at the table, and she had to spend the meal parrying his teasing, which became increasingly personal.

'Your father was a yachtsman, wasn't he?' Andrew said idly, as Helen was about to usher the children out of the door. 'I'm thinking of renting a sailboat. Can I count on you to crew for me?'

'Oh—' Helen licked her lips, as much disturbed by his thoughtless question as by the implications it evoked. 'I—don't think I'm much good, actually. My father often sailed alone. I was never very keen.'

Which was another lie, she thought unhappily, wondering if being a forecourt attendant at a petrol station wouldn't have been less troublesome after all. It was all very well congratulating herself on the success of her relationship with the children, but nobody had warned her that her relationship with the parents might require a degree in social studies.

'Mmm.'

She had the feeling Andrew didn't believe her, but she hoped, if he mentioned the matter to Tricia, that her erst-while friend might understand her reluctance to get in-volved. It had been tactless to mention her father, particu-larly in connection with sailing, and if her motives were more personal, Tricia was not to know.

Although she was loath to take the children on to the beach again, the idea of staying by the pool, and perhaps being dragged into another of the Sheridans' arguments, didn't give her much of a choice. Besides, she doubted they would encounter the Aitkens a second time. A coincidence was a coincidence, but once was surely enough.

The children had brought their buckets and spades, and Helen spent the first half-hour helping Henry construct a castle. He had very definite ideas of how high he wanted it to be, and where they should put the moat, and keeping Sophie from jeopardising the project took all her concen-tration.

Nevertheless, some sixth sense seemed to alert her the moment Fleur appeared from the belt of palms that fringed the end of the beach. Once again, her mother was alone, and the connotations of that circumstance couldn't be ig-nored. She had to have a reason for coming here, whether Matthew had aborted the purpose of yesterday's visit or not. Helen's nerves tightened unpleasantly, but there was no way she could avoid the woman's presence.

'It's Mrs Aitken,' cried Sophie, being less interested in the castle and therefore more easily diverted. She looked at Helen. 'D'you think she's come to see us?'

'I doubt it.' Helen tried to be casual, merely casting the woman a polite smile before continuing with her task. 'Henry, pass me that shell, will you? I need to shore up the sides of the gateway.'

'Good morning.'

Fleur was evidently determined to create as much dis-ruption as possible, and Henry looked up at her with a critical frown. 'We're making a castle,' he said. 'Do you want to help us? We need someone to fetch the water, and Sophie always spills it.'

'No, I don't.'

'Yes, you do.'

The children started one of their usual pointless arguments, and Helen, who could see the half-built castle coming to a sorry end, got automatically to her feet. Henry was pushing Sophie now, and she was trying to retaliate, stepping all over his carefully laid foundations, and wringing a cry of anguish from her brother.

Helen moved to separate them, glad she hadn't shed her T-shirt and shorts as she'd done the previous day. Her mother, cool and elegant in flowing lemon trousers and a long silk sweater, was watching the proceedings with a resigned expression, her pale eyes hidden as before beneath a pair of dark glasses.

'Leave them to it,' Fleur said carelessly, and Helen thought how incongruous it had been of Henry to ask her to join them. The idea of Fleur fetching water or helping Henry build his castle was ludicrous. Helen doubted she'd ever been that kind of mother. Even when she was young. She was more at home beside a swimming-pool than braving the ravages of the beach.

So why was she here?

'Can we talk?' Fleur added quietly, glancing rather apprehensively about her. 'I'm sure these two can amuse themselves for five minutes, if we just saunter down to the ocean.'

Helen held up her head. 'Why should I want to saunter down to the ocean with you?' she asked tersely. 'We hardly know one another.'

'That's true.' Fleur didn't attempt to deny it. 'But there's something we have to talk about, and I think you know what it is.'

Helen's mouth dried. *No*, she thought unsteadily. *No*, she had nothing to say to this brittle woman, who she suspected was only here now because she was afraid of what Helen might tell the Sheridans. Through all the years she'd thought about her mother, and wondered what she was like, she'd never imagined confronting her like this. Dear God, she didn't even like her. It would have been so much simpler if they'd never ever met.

'I—don't think so,' she said at last, bending down to rescue one of Sophie's plastic sandals, which was in danger of being buried in the sand. Just go away, she begged silently. I really don't want to talk to you. I'll keep your dirty little secret, never fear.

'Please, Helen.' Fleur took off her dark glasses and gave her an appealing look. 'Don't you think I deserve a few minutes of your time? Is that really too much to ask?'

Helen took a breath. 'We've got nothing to say to one another,' she declared in a low voice, and Fleur sighed.

'Yes, we do,' she retorted. 'There may be some way I can help you. D'you think I like to see my—my daughter skivvying for someone else?'

Helen glanced anxiously towards Henry and Sophie, but to her relief they were still intent on destroying the castle. Henry appeared to have joined his sister now, in trampling down the battlements, and Helen wondered why she'd bothered to take so much trouble.

Without giving in to her mother's suggestion that they put some distance between themselves and the children, Helen compromised by turning her back on her charges. 'I don't need your help, thank you,' she said, without admitting their relationship. 'The Sheridans have been kind to me. Since—since Daddy died, I've learned who my real friends are.'

Fleur caught her lower lip between her teeth. 'I read— about what happened. I still have friends—acquaintances— in England, who thought it their responsibility to let me know that Jimmy had drowned. I would have got in touch with you then, but I was having—problems. Chase—Chase died a couple of months ago. I expect you knew that, too.'

'No. No, I didn't,' said Helen, not bothering to mention the fact that Matthew had told her. After all, what did it matter? She'd had no love for Chase Aitken.

'Well, he did.' Fleur visibly wilted. 'It was a terrible shock for—for all of us. He was such a young man.'

'My father was a young man, too.' Helen didn't attempt to sympathise with her. 'So—I suppose we've both lost a loved one. That's the only thing we've got in common.'

'No, it's not.' Fleur stretched out her hand, then, as Helen flinched away, she withdrew it again. 'Don't you want to know how I recognised you? It wasn't your name, Miss— *Graham*.'

Helen coloured. 'I didn't want you to recognise me,' she said, casting an unnecessary glance towards the children. 'I don't want you to recognise me now. It's been too many years; too many things have happened. I don't want to talk about it. I just wish you'd go away.'

Her mother sucked in her breath. 'You're very bitter.'

Helen stared at her. 'Wouldn't you be?'

'Perhaps.' Fleur had the grace to be honest. 'But, now that we've met again, can't we at least speak civilly to one another?'

'We are speaking civilly to one another.' Helen sighed. 'Look—just say what you have to say and go. Oh, and you needn't worry that I'll tell anyone about this meeting. Strange as it may seem, I've got some pride, too.'

Fleur bit her lip. 'You're just like me, you know.'

'No—'

'Yes.' Fleur hesitated. 'When I was your age, I looked a lot like you. Oh, you're taller, and you wear your hair longer, but that's not important. When I saw you at the party I was staggered no one else had seen the resemblance.'

Helen's lip curled. 'Is that supposed to be a compliment?'

Fleur laughed. 'Perhaps.' She lifted her shoulders. 'I see

you've inherited Jimmy's arrogance. That's exactly how he'd have reacted if I'd said it to him.'

Helen bent her head. 'Is that all you wanted to say?'

'No.' Fleur regarded her with an expression that was hard to define. 'Believe it or not, I wanted to tell you my side of the story. I should never have married your father. Did he tell you that?'

'Frequently,' said Helen, though in truth James Gregory had never discussed his relationship with his wife. Like everything else about her mother, it had been banished. If he'd had any remorse, he'd never relayed it to her.

'Mmm.' Her mother absorbed what she'd said with a jaded smile, and Helen guessed she didn't believe a word. She had to remember that Fleur had known James Gregory rather well. And he simply hadn't been the type to expose his real feelings.

'Well,' Fleur said at last, 'you'll know, then, that our relationship was doomed from the start. Your father married me because he wanted children. I married him because I was a woman of passion. I needed a man's—attentions— to make me whole.'

Helen caught her breath. 'I don't want to hear this.'

'Why not?' Fleur seemed almost amused by her daughter's revulsion. 'It should reassure you. It should make you see that when I left I wasn't punishing you. I was punishing your father, I suppose, if that's relevant. You can't imagine what it was like. Our life was so dull!'

'Don't say any more.'

Helen tried to turn away, but Fleur continued relentlessly. 'Can't you even try to imagine how frustrated I was? All your father wanted was a brood mare. As soon as I'd had you, he began talking about how soon we could have another child, maybe a son this time. I stuck it for as long as I could, but when he found out I'd been using a contraceptive, he became impossible.'

'Please.'

Helen wanted to put her hands over her ears and run

away, but with Henry and Sophie only yards from them
there was little she could do.

'Listen to me,' Fleur persisted. 'Your father was a good
man, but he was boring. I needed someone more—vital.
Someone who wanted me, not just my genes.'

Helen gave her a tortured look. 'You found what you
wanted with Chase Aitken, I suppose?' she said harshly,
horrified to find she was on the verge of tears. 'Well, don't
expect me to betray my father. He cared for me. He cared
for me deeply. You—you only cared for yourself.'

Fleur pulled a face. 'I knew you'd say that.'

'It's the truth.'

'Is it?' Fleur's lips twisted. 'I wonder. What if I told you
I regretted marrying Chase, too? You see—' her small teeth
tugged at her lower lip '—I think I married the wrong
brother. But I'm hoping to get it right next time. Will you
wish me luck?'

CHAPTER NINE

'WHAT?'

Lucas stared at him as if he couldn't believe his ears, and Matthew had to admit his statement had caused himself some astonishment, too. The only time he gave dinner parties was when his publisher or his agent came down from New York. He certainly didn't socialise with his neighbours, or invite them into his house.

'Well,' he said now, his tone revealing a defensiveness he would rather not have exposed, 'I've got to do something to get Fleur off my back. She's driving me crazy. God knows when I'll get this book finished.'

Lucas regarded him dourly. 'And how will giving a dinner party for the Sheridans get Fleur off your back?' he demanded. 'Dammit, you said you didn't even like them. Why invite them here?'

'Because it will give Fleur something to do—organising the menu, that sort of thing,' declared Matthew quickly. 'And as I've persuaded my father to leave the ranch for a couple of days, the least I can do is provide some entertainment.'

'Since when did Ben care about being entertained?' asked Lucas impatiently. 'And if you're doing this for me, then I'd sooner make my own arrangements, thank you.'

'For you—?' began Matthew blankly, and Lucas gave him an old-fashioned look.

'Yeah. So I can see Helen again,' he exclaimed, his expression becoming somewhat whimsical. 'If it's all the same to you, I'd as soon take her to the Greenhouse. The food there is excellent, and we won't have to worry about any of the Sheridans butting in.'

Matthew looked down at the pile of uncorrected manuscript on the desk in front of him, and mentally drew a
breath. Anything to avoid looking into Lucas's open face.
For God's sake, the idea that Lucas might misinterpret his
motives that way hadn't even occurred to him. He was so
wrapped up with his own selfish problems he hadn't given
the other man a thought.

'Besides,' went on Lucas doggedly, 'I thought the last
thing you'd want to do is appease the woman. Arranging
parties for her is just playing into her hands. She'll get off
both our backs much sooner if we ignore her. If there's one
thing Fleur doesn't like it's to be bored.'

Matthew sighed. 'Maybe.'

'What do you mean, maybe? You know it's the truth.
How long is she expecting to stay anyway? She's already
been here over a week.'

Tell me about it, Matthew brooded to himself irritably,
remembering the days before his sister-in-law's arrival with
some nostalgia. Days before he'd met Helen, too, he acknowledged, before he could push the thought away. Which
might prove even more significant, unless he could get her
out of his head.

'I'm hoping that—given a little sweetener—she may decide to travel back to the ranch with my father,' he replied
at last, though he doubted she'd go willingly. And was it
fair to unload his problems on to the old man? he wondered
grimly. Even with the financial settlement he had in mind,
he sensed it wouldn't be that easy.

Lucas hunched his shoulders. 'Well, I think you're mad.
And Ben will think so, too, when he gets here. You don't
owe her a thing, Matt. She was your brother's wife, not
yours. If he didn't make any sensible provision for her, why
the hell should you?'

Because...

Because he'd once let Fleur think he was interested in
her? Why else would she have come to his room that night,
if not because he had been giving out the wrong signals?

She'd believed he'd wanted her. Had she told Chase about that? Was that why in recent years he'd seen so little of his brother? And, God forbid, was that the reason Chase had been drinking before he played that final—fatal—match?

'You're not—interested—in her, are you?'

Lucas had misinterpreted his silence, and his doubtful enquiry brought Matthew swiftly to his senses. 'Goddammit, no!'

Lucas breathed more easily. 'I'm glad to hear it. For a moment there, I wondered.'

Matthew's jaw tightened. It was impossible to discuss his original reasons for giving the party with Lucas now. For a while there, he'd forgotten how smitten with Helen his assistant was, and he felt ashamed when he considered what he'd been planning to do. In his experience, there was only one way to get a woman out of your system, and, while he'd known of the obvious dangers, he'd decided to take the risk.

But now...

'So you won't have any objections if I include Helen in the invitations?' Lucas went on, happily unaware of his employer's feelings, and Matthew gave a grudging shrug of his broad shoulders.

'Why should I?' he asked tautly, as if that wasn't exactly what he had been planning to do anyway. 'Though you may find the Sheridans won't appreciate the gesture.'

'Why not?' Lucas frowned. 'Oh—do you think they'll need her to babysit? I hadn't thought of that. You may be right.'

'I am right,' said Matthew equably, though until that moment he'd never even thought of it. He felt a growing swell of relief. 'Never mind, Luke. I'm asking the Longfords. They can bring Hazel along instead.'

Lucas gave him a dry look. 'Hazel Longford is a kid,' he said flatly. 'And I don't care to babysit myself.' He paused. 'Unless it's with Helen.' He looked suddenly thoughtful. 'I wonder how the Sheridans would feel about that?'

'Whatever the Sheridans would feel, I'd be bloody angry,' declared Matthew heavily. 'Forget it, Luke. I need you here.' Then, ignoring the mocking tug of his conscience, he added, 'If you want to see the woman, do it on your own time.'

The conversation ended soon after, and although Matthew had expected the other man to object to his heavy-handedness he hadn't. Lucas had probably put his attitude down to the continuing problem he was having with Fleur, he reflected. It was bloody hard not to feel guilty with so many paragons around.

An hour later, with the pile of manuscript hardly touched, Matthew had to concede that he was getting nowhere. His mind simply refused to concentrate on fiction, when his own life seemed to be running out of control.

With a feeling of raw impatience, he pushed his chair away from the desk. What was the matter with him? he thought irritably. Why couldn't he put the Graham woman's face out of his mind? And not just her face, he recalled unwillingly. He could still feel her small breasts against his chest…

He scowled at his watch. It was barely eleven o'clock. Far too early to think about meeting his father at the airport. Ben wasn't due to arrive until three-thirty. Even allowing for the time it would take to get there, he'd still got more than a couple of hours to fill.

Getting up from his chair, he walked broodingly over to the long windows. Beyond a flowering hedge, the still surface of the pool gleamed in silent invitation. But beside the pool, stretched out beneath a striped umbrella, Fleur was enjoying the brilliance of the day. Like the serpent in his particular Eden, she basked in the sun while he sweated in his study.

Matthew's scowl deepened. If Fleur hadn't been there, he would probably have taken a swim. A refreshing dip in cool water was exactly what he needed to clear his head. And cool his blood, he acknowledged tersely. It wasn't just the temperature that was making him hot.

But Fleur was there, and there was no way Matthew was going to join her. In his present state of mind, he might just say something he'd regret. Besides, he wasn't totally convinced that his body wouldn't betray him. And the last thing he wanted was for her to think she turned him on.

He swung away from the window and propped his hips against the broad sill. He ought to work, but doing so was no more inviting now than it had been minutes before. He needed to get out of the villa. He needed to put some space between his actions and his thoughts.

He'd go into Bridgetown, he decided abruptly. There was a book shop in Broad Street, and it was some weeks since he'd checked out the latest titles. Whenever he finished writing, he always enjoyed the relaxation he found in reading. It was such a relief to let some other author carry the story, and work out the final dénouement.

Lucas was working in the outer office, and he looked up in some surprise when his employer appeared. 'D'you want some coffee?' he asked. 'I can ask Ruth—'

'I don't want anything,' said Matthew firmly, realising that Lucas would think he was acting out of character. 'I—er—I thought I'd take a ride into town. I feel like having a break. I won't be long.'

'I'll come with you,' said Lucas at once, but Matthew pressed him back into his seat with a purposeful hand.

'No need,' he said, tempering his refusal with a grimace. 'I guess Fleur is getting me down. I need to cut me a little space, OK?'

'OK.'

But Lucas regarded him with doubtful eyes. What was he thinking? Matthew wondered ruefully as he strode along the cool marble tiles of the corridor. That he was seeking to assuage his conscience? That, however he denied it, he *was* attracted to his dead brother's widow?

A louvred door gave access to the rear of the villa. Here a pleasantly-shaded courtyard gave on to a range of out-buildings. This was the oldest part of the estate, with some of the buildings dating back to the eighteenth century. Un-like the house, which had been rebuilt from the foundations, what had once been the servants' quarters had been con-verted into a string of garages.

There were stables here, too, though Matthew didn't keep any horses. If he wanted to ride, there were hacks available, but, having been brought up with the cream of horseflesh, he was loath to accept anything less. Besides, when he visited the ranch—which wasn't often, he admitted ruefully—he spent most of his days on horseback. His fa-ther was a tireless rider, and he'd taught both his sons to appreciate the sport.

Too well? wondered Matthew wryly, adjusting his jean-clad thighs beneath the wheel of an open-topped buggy. He hoped his father wasn't blaming himself for Chase's death. His brother had always been mad on horses, right from being a schoolboy, and becoming a professional polo-player had seemed a natural progression.

The traffic into Bridgetown was fairly hectic, and, like every other tourist resort, the town was thronged with eager sightseers. Skins of every colour mingled in the busy shops along Broad Street, and Matthew thought he was incredibly lucky when he found a parking space just off the square.

Unlike some Caribbean resorts, however, Bridgetown had a distinctly British appeal. Many of the Gothic struc-tures dated from the reign of Queen Victoria, and a mon-ument to Lord Nelson stood impressively in Trafalgar Square.

Leaving the buggy, Matthew negotiated a narrow lane that led down into the main thoroughfare. To his left the inner basin of the Careenage provided a tranquil harbour for luxury yachts. It was a far cry from the busy port it had once been, its erstwhile warehouses converted now into pretty cafés and shops. To his right, St Michael's Row led along to the cathedral. One of the oldest surviving churches in Barbados, the cathedral had been rebuilt after its destruction in the hurricane of 1780.

Leaving the square, Matthew started along Broad Street. As well as shops, there were several office buildings here, their wrought-iron balconies giving the place a colonial feel.

Graftons, the book store he sought, was situated on the corner of Maize Street. Small and personal, it nevertheless stocked an enormous collection of reference books and novels, with guide books for the tourists and paperbacks for everyone.

The owner, Becky Grafton, was a grey-haired Barbadian, and she greeted Matthew with her usual cheerful smile. 'Morning, Mr Aitken,' she said. 'What can we do for you this morning?'

Matthew grinned. 'Nothing, thanks. I've come to browse.' He grimaced. 'Unfortunately, you don't stock inspiration, do you?'

'Depends what kind of inspiration you're looking for, man,' chuckled her assistant, Larry Kamada. 'I'm told folks get all kinds of ideas from some of the books we sell.'

Matthew was nodding good-humouredly when he glimpsed a familiar figure beyond the shelves. With his stomach tightening unwillingly, he felt sure it was Helen Graham. He'd have recognised that braid anywhere, and the slender elegance of her figure.

Fortunately someone came to pay for their books at that moment, and it enabled Matthew to excuse himself from Becky and her assistant. And, although common sense dictated that he leave his browsing until later, he ignored the warning voice and followed his senses.

He found her in the furthest corner of the shop, half hidden behind the final fixture. He was fairly certain she had seen him now, and was hoping to avoid him. But her pale limbs were too noticeable, particularly as she was only wearing a short denim skirt and a pink sleeveless vest.

'Good morning,' he said, forcing her to look up from the volume of poetry she was studying. 'Are you a fellow reader, Miss Graham?'

'It's—' she began, and then broke off, flushing. 'Um— yes. I enjoy reading. When I have the time.' She paused, and, having regained her composure, gave him a cool look. 'I haven't read any of your books, however.'

'It's not obligatory,' said Matthew, apparently unfazed, though the faint contempt in her voice wasn't welcome. 'What do you read, Miss Graham? Apart from—' he dipped his head '—my namesake, Matthew Arnold?'

Helen thrust the anthology back on to the shelf, and moved as if she would have gone past him. 'Lots of things,' she said. 'So long as they're interesting.' She took a short breath. 'Excuse me.'

'Novels?' Matthew knew it was crazy, but he wouldn't let her pass him. Not until he'd got her to relax with him at least. For God's sake, if Lucas had his way, she'd be invited to Dragon Bay. They couldn't meet with animosity between them.

'Occasionally,' she acknowledged now, and he knew she was only answering him to avoid an argument. But, hell, when he was with her, he couldn't help being aware of her. For some reason, she disturbed him in a wholly unfamiliar way.

'You're alone?' he persisted, wondering where her charges were this morning, and he could fairly feel the antagonism surging through her.

'For the moment,' she said tightly. Then, 'Will you please move out of my way? I've some other errands I want to run and you're making me late.'

Matthew took a deep breath, and folded his arms across his chest. He looked relaxed, he thought, but his fingers were digging into the dark blue silk of his sleeve. He'd rolled the sleeves back to his elbows, and the muscles in his forearms tightened reflexively. But he'd never get another chance like this, and he wasn't about to lose it.

'What do you mean?' he said at last. 'You said, "for the moment". Do I take it the little horrors are with you? Or have you left them back at the house?'

Her tongue appeared and circled her lips. It was a pink tongue, Matthew noticed, and there was something unknowingly sensual in the way she moistened her lips. Not that she was aware of it. He'd gamble on that assumption. She was simply weighing the odds of lying to him or simply telling the truth.

The truth apparently won out. 'If you mean my charges,' she replied stiffly, 'they're spending the day with their parents. Tricia and Drew—Mr and Mrs Sheridan, that is—are visiting some friends in Speightstown. And, as their friends have got children, they've taken Henry and Sophie with them.'

'Really?' Matthew felt an unwarranted surge of exhilaration. He felt as if someone had just handed him a present, but one which he wasn't supposed to accept.

'Yes, really,' Helen repeated shortly, clearly eager to be on her way. 'Now, will you let me pass? Or must I call the assistant? As you're apparently known here, I don't suppose you'd like it if I screamed.'

Matthew's lips compressed. 'So you did see me come in,' he remarked, ignoring the implied threat. 'Was that why you panicked and hid in this corner?'

'I did not panic.' But her nervous lips betrayed her. 'I simply didn't want to speak to you, that's all.'

'Why not?'

'Why not?' She regarded him with frustrated eyes. 'I should have thought that was obvious, in the circumstances.' Then, as if gathering some courage from his silence, 'For a writer, you're extremely unimaginative. If you give it some thought, I'm sure you'll understand.'

Once again, she attempted to go past him, but this time she came up against the unyielding wall of his body. If she'd thought that by insulting him she'd cause him to lose interest, he reflected, then she didn't know him very well at all.

'It's a little late to play hard to get, isn't it?' he asked, as she recoiled from the heat of his chest. 'Just because I didn't finish what I started, don't pretend you spent the whole time fighting me off.'

Her colour deepened then, and in spite of himself Matthew was intrigued. She was such a curious mixture of sensuality and innocence, and although he didn't believe the latter, he wanted to prolong this encounter.

It took her a minute to compose herself again, and then she said in a low voice, 'If you've finished, I'd like to go. Please.'

Matthew frowned. 'And if I'm not?'

'Not what?'

She was confused now. He could tell by the blank look in her eyes that his earlier accusation had found its mark. But, contrarily, it didn't please him. Her submission was no more appealing than her retaliation had been.

'Not finished,' he said almost gently, and, acting purely on instinct, he stepped aside. 'Look, can we just forget what happened last week? Let's put it down to experience. Why don't you let me buy you lunch, to prove there's no hard feelings?'

'I can't.'

Her immediate denial annoyed him, but at least she hadn't rushed away. 'Why can't you?' he asked evenly. 'There's a café just round the corner.'

'I've got to get back,' she said automatically, but he sensed that she was weakening. 'Mr Aitken, there's no need for you to do this. We'll say no more about it.'

Matthew sighed, controlling his impatience with an effort. 'You said yourself that the Sheridans are away all day,' he reminded her.

'I know.'

'So there's really no reason for you to hurry back?'

'Perhaps not.'

He took a gamble. 'But you find my company objectionable? You'd rather eat alone.' He shrugged. 'Well, OK, if that's the way you feel, there's nothing more to say.'

'No.'

She did move then, tucking the strap of her bag over her shoulder and starting towards the door. Matthew was just consoling himself with the thought that she'd probably done him a favour, however unlikely that felt at the moment, when she glanced back over her shoulder and stopped.

'Just around the corner?' she said, coming back on what were obviously reluctant feet. 'The café? That is what you said, isn't it?'

Matthew's stomach contracted. 'Yeah.' He paused. 'Down on the quay, if you know where that is.'

'I do.' She hesitated. Then, 'Why not?' She shrugged. 'If you really meant it, that is. If you weren't just being— polite.'

All the air seemed to go out of Matthew's lungs, and all he could do was nod. And, with a gesture of compliance, Helen turned again and sauntered towards the exit. He knew she couldn't be feeling as nonchalant as she appeared from behind, that if he looked into her eyes he'd see the uncertainty that still lingered, but he had to admire her confidence all the same.

He watched her as she traversed the aisle ahead of him, and he was aware of the possession in his gaze. But hell, the tail of that neat braid, bobbing about at her waist, was absurdly sexy, her slim legs long and curvaceous below the short hem of her skirt. He wouldn't have been human, he told himself, if he hadn't remembered how she'd looked that evening nearly a week ago. He'd wanted to make love with her then, and he wanted to now.

There was a half-moon of sunburned skin above the scooped neckline of her vest, and as he came up behind her at the entrance he knew the craziest urge to bend and soothe it with his tongue. But then his eyes encountered

Larry Kamada's and he quickly stifled the impulse. He was letting his senses rule his reason, and it had to stop.

The café he took her to overlooked the Careenage, and for a while, as the waiter took their order and Helen's attention was diverted by the gleaming yachts lying at anchor, Matthew was able to convince himself that he'd imagined the way he'd felt. She was attractive and sexy, and—hell!—she probably knew it better than he did. That diffidence was just an act; he was sure of it.

They sat outside, at a table shaded by a huge umbrella. With the sun dazzling on the water, and the sound of muted conversation all around them, it was all very normal and civilised. Matthew decided that anyone watching them would assume they were holidaying together.

Or perhaps not, he considered. His arms and legs were tanned while Helen's skin was still fashionably pale. Like the back of her neck, where the sun had caught her, her skin turned pink. An indication of its delicacy that he was loath to admit he'd noticed.

They ate shellfish and salad—juicy island shrimp served with mixed greens and papaya. There were spicy sauces to accompany the food, and Matthew noticed Helen avoided them. But she did drink several glasses of the dry Californian wine he'd ordered, and he guessed that she was thirsty.

'Nice?' he ventured, after their plates had been taken away, and because the wine had relaxed her Helen nodded.

'Very nice,' she conceded, elbows lodged on the table, her wine-glass cradled between her palms. 'Thank you,' she added belatedly. 'It was kind of you to bring me here. My—my father and I used to come to Barbados many moons ago.'

Matthew hesitated. 'But your father's dead now,' he averred softly, and she gave him a guarded look.

'How do you know that?'

Matthew sighed. 'Oh—Luke told me, I think.' He hoped he hadn't spoiled the mood. 'It's not a secret, is it?'

'A secret?' Her lips twisted suddenly, but, although he'd been half-afraid he'd said the wrong thing, she shook her head. 'No, that's not a secret. He—died seven months ago.'

'I'm sorry.'

'Yes.' She grimaced. 'So am I.' Then, with a sudden change of direction, 'How long were Fleur and your brother married?'

Matthew didn't want to talk about Fleur at this point, but he humoured her. 'Oh—about seventeen years, I guess,' he said carelessly. 'I was sixteen when Chase brought her to live with us. They weren't married then, of course. Fleur's husband hadn't divorced her.'

Helen put down her glass. 'She was already married, then, when your brother found her?'

'What is this?' Matthew was impatient, and it showed. But, dammit, why was she interested in Fleur? It wasn't as if the two women even liked one another.

'What do you mean?' A faint trace of colour had entered her cheeks again, and Matthew wondered how it was that he could disconcert her so easily. And then he thought he had the solution. She was talking about Fleur to prevent him from saying anything provocative.

Shaking his head, he said, 'OK. She was married, right? But if you're implying that Chase broke up a happy marriage, you couldn't be more wrong. There'd been men before him, I'm convinced of it. If you knew Fleur as well as I do, you'd know she's one hungry lady!'

Helen's colour dissolved as quickly as it had appeared. In seconds her face was completely white, and Matthew knew an unfamiliar sense of concern. He guessed the combination of the heat, the dazzling sun and an unaccustomed amount of wine was responsible for her pallor. She needed somewhere cool and shady, where she could relax for a while.

'Are you all right?' he asked, and she looked at him with unexpectedly wounded eyes.

'I'm fine,' she said quickly, though she clearly wasn't. 'Um—thank you for lunch. I've got to go—'

'Not yet,' said Matthew firmly, grasping her wrist when she would have risen from the table. 'Let me get the bill, and then I'll see you back to the villa.'

'No—I—I've brought Maria's car,' she protested, but Matthew knew she was in no condition to drive.

'I guess they have laws about drinking and driving here, too,' he informed her softly. 'Now, just sit still a minute. You're in no fit state to go anywhere alone.'

'Wine doesn't make me drunk,' she exclaimed faintly, after Matthew had summoned the waiter and arranged to pay. 'Please, let me go. Everyone's looking.'

'Only because you're making a scene,' Matthew informed her drily. 'Take it easy, can't you? We'll be out of here directly, I promise.'

He noticed, with some relief, that her colour was returning as they left the table. But he retained his hold on her arm, just in case she felt a little weak. Besides, although he didn't want to admit it, he enjoyed looking after her. He liked the feeling of her fine bones beneath his hand, though he sensed her resistance was only dormant and not totally suppressed.

At the corner of Broad Street she halted. 'I think this is where we part company,' she said, obliging him to release her. 'Thank you again for lunch. It was most—unexpected.'

Matthew drew a breath. 'You're going to drive back?'

Her brows arched. 'Of course.'

'Then, where are you parked? I'll follow you. Just to make sure you're all right.'

Helen's mouth tightened. 'There's no need.'

'I think there is.'

'Why?' She gazed at him angrily. 'Aren't there any *hungry* ladies for you to annoy around here?'

Matthew's lips parted. 'Did that upset you?' he exclaimed. 'Was that why you looked so sick back at the restaurant?' He shook his head. 'Hey, I've never satisfied

Fleur's particular appetite. If you think I was speaking from experience, you were wrong.'

'It's of supreme indifference to me,' she declared, turning away. 'Goodbye, Mr Aitken. I don't suppose I'll see you again.'

The hell you won't, Matthew muttered to himself irritably. For God's sake, what was wrong with what he'd said? Fleur was nothing to her; they hardly knew one another. Yet there was no denying she'd reacted to his words.

He gnawed broodingly at his lower lip as he walked back to where he had left the buggy. It wasn't until he was on his way home that he remembered he hadn't bought the books he'd intended to buy. Meeting Helen had put everything else out of his head, he thought frustratedly. And for all she'd had lunch with him, he was fairly sure she still resented him like hell.

And why? Because he'd come on to her one time? Well, maybe more than come on to her, he admitted honestly, but it wasn't as if she'd been wholly opposed to what he'd done. If he hadn't come to his senses as he had, he had the feeling she wouldn't have stopped him. Was that what was eating her? Was she blaming him for being a tease?

If she only knew, he reflected bitterly, feeling the tight constriction of his trousers. What he really wanted was for them to spend the afternoon in bed. Then maybe both of them could get it out of their systems. There was no denying his frustration as he drove back to Dragon Bay.

CHAPTER TEN

'WHERE did you go today?' Tricia asked at supper, and Helen wished she'd had more warning of the question. She'd foolishly assumed that the Sheridans would think she'd spent the day at the villa. But evidently Maria had been talking, and there was no escape.

'I went into Bridgetown this morning,' she replied, aware of Andrew's eyes upon her. But then they'd been on her since she had joined them at the table, and she wished she'd worn something less revealing.

But it was so hot tonight, and the ankle-length skirt and chiffon blouse had looked perfectly adequate in her bedroom. It was only now that she was aware of the blouse's transparency, and the fact that the skirt was slit to the knee.

'Yes. Maria said you'd taken her car,' Tricia remarked, with some impatience. 'I'd have thought you'd have welcomed some time alone instead of rubbing shoulders with a crowd of tourists.'

'We're tourists,' put in Andrew mildly, but Tricia was obviously in no mood to accommodate her husband.

'Not that kind of tourists,' she said. 'We're sort of staying with friends. In any case, I thought Helen might be tired.'

'She's not an old woman,' Andrew inserted, and earned a malevolent look from his wife.

'Like me, you mean?' she countered. 'I know that's what you were really saying. You embarrassed me at the Rutherfords as well.'

Andrew gave a resigned sigh. 'I did not embarrass you,' he retorted. 'But if you must go around telling everyone

128

what a saint you are, you must expect a little fire and brimstone in response.'

Tricia's eyes flashed. 'I did not tell everyone I was a saint—'

'As good as,' countered Andrew laconically. 'And I doubt Helen would approve of her affairs being gossiped about indiscriminately. You had no right to tell them about her father. Or her mother either, as it happens. It's nothing to do with—'

'What have you been saying about my mother?' Helen, who had been congratulating herself on avoiding any mention of Matthew Aitken, now felt a sudden twinge of alarm. 'What do you know about my mother?' she protested anxiously. 'I—I've never even mentioned her to you.'

'I haven't said anything,' denied Tricia irritably, though the glance she cast in her husband's direction promised retribution later. 'I simply told them you were my nanny, and someone—I don't remember who—asked if you were James Gregory's daughter. Of course I had to say you were, and that was that.'

'But what did they say about—about him?' she finished lamely, realising she couldn't mention Fleur's name without creating more confusion, and Tricia sighed.

'Nothing that you haven't told me yourself,' she replied impatiently. 'Drew's exaggerating, as usual. For goodness' sake, it's not a secret, is it? It was in the papers when it happened.'

'What Trish means is that people are naturally curious,' Andrew declared now, evidently deciding the joke had gone far enough. 'If she hadn't made such a big thing out of employing someone without any previous experience, I doubt your name would have come into it. But as she compared her actions to those of Mother Teresa—'

'That is not true!'

Tricia was incensed, but Helen didn't find their bickering amusing any more.

'Well, you were waxing lyrical about how generous

you'd been to Helen,' Andrew persisted unrepentantly. 'For heaven's sake, after spending a day in the offspring's company, I'd say she deserved a medal, not you.'

'They're your children,' retorted Tricia, but her eyes flickered somewhat remorsefully in the younger woman's direction. 'Oh—what does it matter anyway?' she exclaimed with feeling. 'Nobody knows you here.'

Except Fleur, thought Helen uneasily. And how would she react if these friends—whoever they were—knew Matthew, and mentioned it to him? So far, he only knew her as Helen Graham. But even he might make the connection if he was pushed.

At least her own activities weren't questioned any further. So far as the Sheridans were concerned she had spent the morning in Bridgetown, and that was that. Besides, Matthew Aitken had been the last person she'd expected to meet in a bookshop. Although, now she came to think of it, it wasn't as unlikely as all that.

In any event, they'd never suspect that he might have bought her lunch. Encountering him was one thing; having him spend time—and money—on her was another. She didn't even know why he'd done it. He certainly didn't know that Fleur was her mother.

Which was, of course, why she had accepted his invitation. Without the fact that she'd wanted to question him about his brother's relationship with Fleur, she'd never have spent any longer with him than she had to. As it was, she'd found out rather more than she'd expected, and, although she'd told herself that she didn't believe everything he'd said, she couldn't forget what her mother had said about marrying the wrong brother.

The next few days passed reasonably uneventfully. Now that Andrew was here the Sheridans went out occasionally in the evening, either to friends' houses or to dine at one of the better restaurants in the area. Thankfully Helen wasn't expected to accompany them, and she spent most of her evenings reading, or listening to the World Service, which she could tune in to on Maria's radio.

Henry and Sophie had settled down to a regular routine, and to Helen's relief her mother didn't try to contact her again. Whether she would, when Helen was back in London, was another matter. For all she told herself she didn't want to see Fleur again, the memories still hurt.

Then, towards the end of their second week, an invitation arrived. It was from Dragon Bay, from Matthew Aitken, and Tricia couldn't wait to tell Helen that she'd been right.

'I knew he'd invite us to his house,' she declared. 'It would have been terribly rude if he hadn't. Apparently his father is staying with them, and he'd like us to join them for lunch tomorrow.'

'Lunch?' echoed Helen in surprise, and Tricia bridled.

'Yes. He says we should bring the children along as well.' She grimaced. 'I bet that was his assistant's idea. What was his name? Lucas? I noticed his interest in you, and I suppose it's the only way he could get you to come, too.'

'Me?' echoed Helen, aghast, and Tricia nodded.

'Yes, you,' she exclaimed shortly. 'I forgot to mention it. Your name's on the invitation as well.'

Helen spent the next twenty-four hours wondering how she could get out of going. She didn't want to see Matthew's house, and she was fairly sure her mother wouldn't want her there either. Whatever Matthew had said, Fleur evidently thought she had some hope of achieving her ambitions. Helen didn't want to watch her trying. She just wanted to get on with her life.

Besides, she thought unhappily, she didn't want to have to explain to Tricia and Andrew why she hadn't mentioned meeting Matthew in Bridgetown. And as for admitting they had had lunch…

It was all getting horribly complicated, and it was all Matthew Aitken's fault. Why did he have to play his games with her? Wasn't one member of her family good enough for him?

Of course, he didn't know who Fleur was, and she had no intention of telling him. The opinions he'd voiced about her mother were hardly flattering. The last thing she wanted was for him to think that she was like that, too.

And yet, who could blame him if he had misinterpreted her actions? But, until that incident on the beach, she'd never imagined she could lose control. Perhaps due to her father's unhappy experience, she had kept her relationships with men strictly casual. She'd reached the ripe old age of twenty-two without ever giving her heart—or herself—to anyone.

Unwillingly, the memory of how she'd felt when Matthew cornered her in the bookshop came back to haunt her. She hadn't believed it when she'd heard his voice, and she'd taken cover almost instinctively. But he'd seen her. His sharp gaze had located her, hidden behind the book-shelves. She'd snatched up that anthology of Matthew Arnold just seconds before he'd appeared.

She wondered if it was fate that had caused her to choose *Matthew* Arnold. Goodness knew, there had been any number of other writers she could have picked. But her hand had reached unerringly for the nineteenth-century poet, although she couldn't remember a word she'd read.

She sighed. It had amused Matthew. Accusing her of panicking, forcing her practically to beg him to get out of her way. And watching her with those cool green eyes, enjoying her disconcertment. She'd been afraid he was going to touch her, but he'd been far too clever for that.

Her mouth felt dry just remembering how he'd made her feel. Her breasts had suddenly felt absurdly tender, and there'd been a disturbing pain low in her stomach. She'd felt hot, too, hot and sticky, especially between her legs. She'd been so afraid he'd notice; so afraid he'd do some-thing to embarrass her all over again.

And, despite her protestations, panic had won out. She

had tried to get past him, tried to force her way to the door through the immovable wall of his chest. She hadn't succeeded; not until he'd let her. All she'd gained was a trembling awareness of the sensual heat of his body.

She hardly remembered what they'd said. She knew he'd made some comment about her choice of reading material, and she'd retaliated by putting him down. But she hadn't read any of his books, she defended herself fiercely. And his head was quite big enough without her adding to his ego.

Of course, he had derided her resistance to his teasing. And if she'd had any sense, she'd have made her escape as soon as he let her go. But, instead of that, she'd agreed to have lunch with him. And however honourable her motives had been, she'd been aware of him every second they were together.

Yet, she sighed inwardly, it hadn't been all bad. When Matthew wasn't baiting her or asking awkward questions, he could be really nice. And the food had been delicious, the surroundings equally as good. With the yachts rocking at anchor, and the sun dancing on the water, it had been absolutely heaven—until she'd asked about Fleur...

Did she believe him? That was the point. Did she want to believe him, and was she in danger of condemning her own mother on the strength of what Matthew had said? And, finally, was she any better? Had she just not had the opportunity to expose her own unstable nature?

By the following morning she had resigned herself to the fact that she had to go. For her own peace of mind, if nothing else. She had to prove to herself, once and for all, that Matthew Aitken meant nothing to her. That the animosity she'd felt towards her mother was not simply—jealousy.

'Are you going like that?' Tricia exclaimed disparagingly, when she appeared on the terrace in her usual attire of T-shirt and shorts. 'You are going for lunch, Helen.

Don't you think a dress—or even a skirt—would be more suitable?'

'Well, I think Helen looks very nice as she is,' remarked Andrew, with predictable arrogance. 'You should wear shorts, Trish. Then your legs wouldn't look so deathly white. Helen's acquiring quite a tan, even though her skin's as fair as yours.'

'Helen isn't a redhead,' retorted Tricia, stung, as usual, by her husband's ability to put her down. 'And I think wearing shorts is *passé*, especially on a formal occasion. Though I suppose Helen will be eating with the children...' She paused. 'Perhaps she has a point.'

Helen didn't choose to comment. Between them they'd succeeded in making her feel like the poor relation, but perhaps that was to her advantage. And she was poor, if not an actual relation. And it would suit her very well if she had only Henry and Sophie to deal with.

'Will we see the dragons?' asked Sophie, after she and her brother and Helen had been installed in the back of the estate car, and her mother gave an exasperated sigh.

'How many more times?' she exclaimed. 'Sophie, there are no dragons. It's just the name of a house, that's all. Now, please, sit down and shut up.'

It took about fifteen minutes to reach Matthew's house by road. Helen had half expected they'd go via the beach, as Matthew and the others had done the evening they'd dined with the Sheridans. But Tricia had insisted that she couldn't walk so far in the blazing sun. It was different after dark, she'd added. It was cooler, and one didn't perspire quite so much.

Which was true, Helen reflected, if one had a car with air-conditioning. The Parrishs' estate car had no such refinements, and the heat in the back was almost unbearable. Tricia had insisted that Andrew couldn't possibly have all the windows open or her hair would lose its style. And, as she'd spent most of the morning getting ready, Helen wasn't really surprised.

Nevertheless, by the time they reached the private road leading to Dragon Bay Sophie was feeling sick, and Helen's nerves were stretched as tight as violin-strings. She assured herself it was the child's health that was troubling her, and not the thought of their destination, but she wasn't convinced. Still, if Sophie was ill, perhaps she and the children could go home. She doubted Tricia would object. She hadn't wanted them here in the first place.

Stone gateposts marked the entrance to Matthew's property, and they crunched down a coral shale drive, between hedges of flowering hibiscus. The perfume of the flowers invaded the car, filling the air with a heady fragrance.

Further on, acres of manicured lawns came into view, their lushness enhanced by the continual use of sprinklers. They could see the house now, too, a sprawling two-storey dwelling, and Tricia exclaimed excitedly, delighted she'd got her way.

But it was an attractive house, even Helen had to concede that. Peach-coloured brick, weathered to a creamy radiance, was topped by a pink-tiled roof, whose eaves drooped protectively over wrought-iron balconies. A profusion of pink and white bougainvillaea trailed delightfully over the walls, and many long windows were trimmed with shutters.

'What a place!' breathed Tricia, nudging her husband's arm, as they reached a tree-shaded courtyard. A stone nymph holding a pitcher tipped water tirelessly into a basin, creating an illusion of coolness in its lily-strewn depths. 'All this, and the ocean, too,' she added enviously, nodding towards the turquoise water just visible beyond the adobe wall that enclosed the stables. 'Imagine living here in such luxury! No wonder Fleur wants to hang on to her connection with the family.'

Her words disturbed Helen, but Sophie chose that moment to wail, 'I'm going to be sick!' and Helen tumbled her out of the car before it happened. In consequence, she was attending to the little girl when Matthew appeared around the side of the house, and she wondered if she was ever destined to meet this man on equal terms.

But, before Matthew could speak to her, Tricia thrust open her door and intercepted him. 'I'm so sorry,' she said, by way of a greeting. 'I'm afraid my daughter is a proper pain. She doesn't seem able to travel a hundred yards without having this problem. It was kind of you to invite the children, but perhaps you shouldn't have bothered.'

'Nonsense.' Matthew, in a black silk shirt, open down his chest to display the smooth brown skin of his torso, gave Tricia's apologies short shrift. He ran a careless hand over the light covering of dark hair that thickened around his navel, and despite herself Helen's eyes were drawn to the way it arrowed beneath his belt. Tight black jeans, worn to a comfortable softness, moulded his powerful thighs, and she had to tear her gaze from the muscles that bulged against his zip. 'I can remember not being a particularly good traveller myself at Sophie's age. Especially in hot weather,' he appended drily, and Helen was sure he'd noticed that all the car windows were shut.

'Beautiful place you've got here, old man,' Andrew remarked, evidently deciding not to make an issue of the children. 'What is it? An acre or so?'

'Two acres of gardens, and a further half-dozen that are uncultivated,' replied Matthew shortly. He glanced at Helen again, who was drying Sophie's face with a tissue now. 'Come along. I'll introduce you to my father. Then I'll show Helen where she can wash Sophie's face.'

'Oh, I'm sure that's not—' began Tricia protestingly, but Henry disconcerted her by running up to Matthew and grabbing his hand.

'Are there really no dragons?' he asked, proving he was not as sophisticated as he'd pretended, and Sophie pursed her lips because he'd stolen her thunder.

'Only little ones,' Matthew replied good-humouredly, pointing out one of the tiny lizards that clung to the trunk of a tree. 'Of the animal variety, anyway,' he added, with another glance at Helen. 'But we do have some monkeys as neighbours, and you might see one of them if you're lucky.'

'I hope you're not referring to us, old man,' exclaimed Andrew, laughing, but Tricia didn't find that amusing at all.

'It's so hot,' she said affectedly. 'I'm looking forward to a cool martini. Oh—look, what a delightful pool! It's not like that poky one back at the villa, where you can't even get a decent swim.'

As Tricia hadn't even wet her toes in the pool at the villa, Helen couldn't quite see her argument, but it was true that the huge swimming-pool, nestling among flowering cannas and ginger lilies, was spectacular. A row of cabanas provided a colourful side-screen, with striped chairs and loungers set beneath tall umbrellas. Above the cabanas an arched bell-tower added a touch of character, and gave an indication of the Mediterranean style of the villa.

The back of the building, which faced the sea, was built on three sides of a paved courtyard. A cloister-like veranda, threaded with flowering vines, jutted out at the first-floor level. Above this there were balconies, shadowed, as before, by the hanging eaves. Helen guessed all the rooms inside the house would be cool and shaded. Whoever had designed the building had had its occupants' comfort in mind.

In the centre of the courtyard, matching the one at the other side of the house, a fountain played incessantly. And it was around the fountain that a selection of chairs and tables had been arranged, carefully protected by a shady canopy.

Fleur, dressed more modestly today in a simple apricot sheath, was seated beside an older man with greying dark hair. Matthew's father, obviously, Helen decided, hanging on to Sophie's sticky hand. He got to his feet as they stepped into the courtyard, and his warm smile was disturbingly like his son's.

Matthew made the introductions while Fleur looked on, and Helen saw—to her relief, she told herself—that her mother had no intention of betraying their relationship. The smile she cast in her daughter's direction was no more and no less condescending than the smile she offered their other guests. She didn't even get to her feet to greet them. She simply proffered a languid hand.

'Sophie's been sick,' Matthew announced, after acquainting his father with the names of their guests. 'I'm just going to show Helen to a bathroom where she can clean the little girl up. Dad, can I leave you to give these people a drink? I know Tricia would like a martini.'

'No problem,' said Ben Aitken easily, giving Helen a knowing look. 'Don't worry about us. We can look after ourselves. Show her the house, why don't you?'

The look Matthew exchanged with his father was no less exasperated than the look Fleur cast at her daughter. 'Surely—Helen—can manage on her own,' she said. 'There's a bathroom off the gallery. You don't need to escort her, Matt. She's not a child as well.'

'But I want to,' replied Matthew smoothly, causing Helen no small twinge of anxiety, and she felt like assuring all of them that she was here against her will. Only Sophie seemed delighted at the unexpected attention, and, trying to remember the child's feelings, she followed Matthew into the house.

Her impressions, such as they were, were of cool marble tiles and tall, pale walls. A shallow staircase wound against one wall, flanked by a banister made of some dark wood that had been polished to a mirror-bright sheen. Then darkly-polished floors, strewn with thick Chinese carpets, and cool air from a system that controlled the atmosphere.

There were pictures on the walls lining the staircase, set at intervals between long windows. There were carved occasional tables that supported bowls of flowers, and urns of some stemmed foliage that gave off a fragrant scent.

They passed several pairs of double doors before

Matthew halted before those at the end of the long corridor. Taking a handle in each hand, he threw the doors open, and indicated that Helen and Sophie should precede him inside.

Despite her determination not to be impressed by him or his house, Helen couldn't quite stifle the gasp that escaped her as she viewed what she could only assume was a guest suite. A sitting-room, elegantly furnished in olive leather and pale oak, gave access to the bedroom beyond. Through a wide archway, Helen glimpsed an enormous square divan, spread with turquoise silk. Long curtains, whose colour matched the bedspread, moved gently in the controlled air, allowing a view of the balcony, with the sun-kissed ocean as a backdrop.

Helen would have liked to stand and stare some more, but Matthew was already heading across the sitting-room to another door. 'It's in here,' he said. And, at her momentarily dazed look, 'The bathroom. I'll come back in a few minutes to take you downstairs.'

'Oh—oh, yes.'

Helen blinked her eyes and, tightening her grip on Sophie's hand, hurried across the thick Chinese rug that lay like a magic carpet in the middle of the polished floor. He probably thought she was stupid, she thought, acting like a schoolgirl in a sweet shop. But even the places she'd stayed with her father hadn't prepared her for this, and, like Sophie, she was silenced by her surroundings.

'Just use what you like,' he said as she stepped into a pale green cave, whose walls were finely veined marble tiles, inset with mirrors. Their reflections were diffused into a thousand different images, and Helen felt her colour deepen as she saw the way her clothes were clinging to her.

But it had been so hot in the car, and the scoop-necked T-shirt she'd worn over her swimsuit was already pasted to her back. Her shorts clung, too, delineating the cleft of her bottom, and crumpling up between her legs to expose her upper thighs.

But it was the way her breasts were outlined against the front of the T-shirt that caused her the most embarrassment. The reaction she had to Matthew Aitken was evident in every thrusting line. Despite her swimsuit, and the cotton shirt, her nipples pressed against the cloth, and she had no doubt that he'd noticed it as well.

Taking a trembling breath, she turned to close the door and found him gone. While she had been steeling herself to meet his mocking gaze, Matthew had left the suite. There was no one in the sitting-room, no one in the bedroom, as far as she could see. Just herself and Sophie, and these very beautiful rooms.

CHAPTER ELEVEN

'WHAT'S this?'

Unaware, Helen had released Sophie's hand, and now the little girl was poking her finger into a bowl of dried flowers standing at one end of the vanitory unit.

'Oh—um—pot-pourri,' Helen said absently, still glancing over her shoulder. And then, trying to regain her confidence, 'It's scented, sweetheart. Leave it alone.'

The bathroom was huge, with an enormous whirlpool bath and a shower cubicle besides. A bank of soft cream towels resided on a rack beside the twin basins, and a glass shelf displayed an assortment of bath-oils, gel and other preparations.

Helen noticed all the preparations were of a masculine variety. And, as she ventured to peep inside the glass cupboards, she found shaving-soap and razors, and deodorants for men. It couldn't be, she thought; he wouldn't allow them to use *his* bathroom. Yet, unless the room was Lucas's, who else's could it be?

Deciding she had spent quite enough time speculating about unessentials, Helen plucked Sophie's questing finger out of a jar of shower gel and handed her a tablet of soap instead. Then, turning on the gold taps, she filled one of the basins and, using a facecloth from the pile, she quickly washed the little girl's face.

'Mmm, this soap smells lovely,' said Sophie, enjoying herself immensely, and Helen's hopes of leaving the party early died a death. The child was always like this—down one minute and up the next. Once she was out of the car, she soon recovered her spirits.

'Well, hurry up and wash your hands,' said Helen a little

tersely, realising she was blaming Sophie for something
that was all her fault really. But, heavens, the idea that this
was Matthew's bathroom, that he had stood naked before
these mirrors, excited her in ways she didn't comprehend.
She only knew that it wasn't wise for her to be here. She
was far too vulnerable at the moment.

The sound of the outer door opening gave her a start,
but the woman who appeared presented no problem. She
was small and round and maternal, and Helen guessed she
must be in her fifties. With salt-and-pepper hair and button-
black eyes, she had a smile that split her swarthy features.

'You all finished?' she asked, and Helen wondered if
she'd come to clear up after them. She'd tidied the basin
as best she could, but it was no longer in its previously
pristine condition. And Sophie's fingermarks were probably
everywhere. The little girl had an inquisitive nature.

But, 'Yes,' she said now, managing a rueful smile.
'Thanks very much.'

'It's no trouble.' The woman's accent was faintly mid-
dle-European. 'Come.' She held out her hand to Sophie.
'We will see if we can find some lemonade. And perhaps
some ice-cream, hmm?'

Sophie looked up at Helen. 'Can I?'

'I don't see why not,' agreed Helen, patting her shoulder.
'You go along with Mrs—'

'It's Ruth,' said the woman. 'Just Ruth.' She took Sophie's hand in hers and smiled confidingly. 'Your brother
will be envious, eh? Only little girls who've been unwell
are offered my ice-cream.'

'And it's delicious,' declared Matthew, appearing behind
her, and Ruth looked up at her employer with teasing eyes.

'How would you know?' she asked. 'You're not a little
girl, are you?' She glanced down at Sophie again. 'He's
just trying to butter me up.'

'What does that mean?' asked Sophie, as Ruth urged her
past her employer and into the corridor beyond. 'Do you
use butter to…?'

The child's voice grew indistinct, and, realising she hadn't moved since Matthew appeared, Helen quickly gathered herself together. 'She—she's very good—your housekeeper?' she finished questioningly. And, at his nod, 'Thanks again. I was feeling rather—sticky.'

Matthew inclined his head, but he didn't move out of the doorway, and, realising she couldn't hear Sophie any more, Helen took an uneasy breath. 'I'd better go,' she said. 'And—and join the others. Tricia will be wondering where I am. Henry can be such a handful.'

'But he is *her* handful,' Matthew pointed out, without budging, and Helen shook her head.

'I'm—I'm supposed to look after both children,' she said. 'That's why the Sheridans employ me. And if I know Tricia, she'll already be annoyed that I've seen your house and she hasn't.'

'But you haven't seen my house,' pointed out Matthew evenly. 'Only the hall and stairs, and these apartments. There are five other suites, sitting-rooms, dining-rooms and a couple of offices. Not to mention a library, my study and the kitchen.'

Helen expelled a nervous breath. 'Very impressive.'

'It wasn't said to impress. I was only stating what there was to see.' He glanced around. 'These are my apartments. Would you like to see the view from the balcony? It encompasses the whole of Dragon Bay.'

'Oh—well, I—' Helen licked her dry lips. Once again she had been put in the position of indebtedness to him, and to refuse what, on the face of it, was a simple request seemed rather churlish. 'Why not?'

'Good.'

He smiled, an unguarded smile this time, but she noticed he closed the doors behind him before advancing across the floor. They were shut into these rooms now, alone in his apartments. She wouldn't have been human if she hadn't been faintly alarmed.

Yet, following him into what was obviously his bedroom, she found herself able to give her surroundings the attention she'd craved. Once again the furnishings were spare but elegant, with carved antique cabinets at each side of the huge bed and a carved antique chest of drawers between the windows. Another door led into what appeared to be a dressing-room, with yet another bathroom beyond. The ceiling was high and richly carved, and a selection of misty water-colours adorned the walls. The whole ambience of the room was cool and understated, yet no one could pretend its simplicity was there by chance.

While Helen had been admiring the room's appointments Matthew had unlatched the long windows, and a draught of warm air swept into the room. It reminded Helen of how hot she'd been when she arrived here, and a hasty glance at her shorts and T-shirt showed her how right she was to feel apprehensive.

Matthew was obviously waiting for her, however, and, trying not to feel self-conscious about the way her clothes clung to her, she stepped past him on to the balcony.

The view was, as he had implied, magnificent. The curving arms of the headland were joined by the reef, and the ocean exposed its teeth with every surging tide. Right now the water was receding, laying bare the rocky promontory, and seabirds swooped unceasingly for the flotsam left by the tide.

'It's beautiful,' she said at last, aware that although the balcony didn't overlook the courtyard it was just a few yards away. The last thing she wanted was for Tricia—or Fleur—to look up and see her. It was going to be hard enough to explain her absence as it was.

The sound of Henry yelling his head off caused her to look beyond the courtyard, to where the pool was now in use. The party had evidently moved to the chairs on the poolside sun-deck, and Andrew must have found some shorts, because he was in the pool as well.

'I'll have to go,' Helen said with some consternation, realising she had already been longer than she'd thought.

'Can you imagine what—what Tricia will be thinking? I'm supposed to entertain the children; that's why I'm here.'

'No, it's not,' said Matthew quietly, easing her back into his bedroom and closing the windows. 'You're here because I invited you. Unfortunately, I had to invite the Sheridans also.'

Helen swallowed. 'Well, that's very—kind—'

'It's not kind at all, and you know it.' He was standing very close to her, just inside the windows, and she could feel the disturbing heat of his body. 'I wanted to see you again. Don't ask me why. I find you very attractive. Is that enough?'

Helen's legs seemed to have lost the ability to move. Which was silly, because he wasn't touching her, and she certainly wasn't frozen to the spot. On the contrary, she was sweating; an actual droplet of perspiration was trickling down her spine. Perhaps her legs were stuck together too, she thought. There had to be some reason why she didn't step away.

'I don't think—' she began, but his knuckles, tracing the line of her cheek before dipping beneath her jawline, silenced her.

'What don't you think?' he asked softly. 'That this is a good idea? Oh, it is, believe me.' His lips twisted. 'For me at least, it's imperative. Unless you want to drive me mad.'

Helen's breath escaped on a gasp. 'Mr Aitken—'

'Matthew.'

'Matthew, then.' She moistened her lips with a nervous tongue. 'Whatever you think—whatever impression I've given you by my behaviour—I'm not—I'm not used to— Well, you know what I mean. I—I'm flattered, but I'm not interested. Now, please, I'd like to go back to the others.'

'Would you?'

His hand dropped to his side, but although he was no longer touching her she was as conscious of him as if he was. It was the way he was looking at her, she thought uncomfortably. As if he could see through her clothes, as if he could see through her *skin*. And, God help her, her body was responding to him, without any volition on her part.

'Yes,' she managed finally, but, when at last she got her legs to move for her, his hand at her nape caused her to falter.

'You're hot,' he said, and she knew he must be feeling the line of wetness beneath her braid. 'Why don't you take a shower instead?'

'A shower!' The words were more of a squeak than anything else, but he didn't demur.

'Why not?' he asked gently. 'I find the idea—tantalising. There's something very sexy about a woman when she's wet.'

Helen stared at him. 'You're not serious!'

'Yes, I am.' His thumb invaded the neckline of her T-shirt and stroked softly over the fine bones that formed her shoulder. 'Your shirt and shorts are sticking to you. Despite the fact that you're obviously wearing a swimsuit. You can keep that on, if you like. I'll enjoy taking it off myself.'

Helen gulped. Then she shook her head. 'You're mad,' she said in a strangled voice. 'Absolutely mad!'

'Just aroused,' he corrected her huskily, pulling the loose neckline of the T-shirt off her shoulder. He bent his head and touched her bare shoulder with his tongue. 'So are you.'

'I am not.'

Helen's denial was as spurious as the hand she raised to stop him. In all honesty, she didn't understand what was happening to her, for, although she'd shared amorous interludes with men before, she had never felt the way Matthew made her feel. The lovemaking she'd experienced before had been strong on affection and weak on sex, but with Matthew she knew it would be different; when he touched her she started to burn.

'OK,' he conceded now, letting her have the way of it, but she sensed he didn't believe her any more than she believed herself. Why else would his hand reach for her, caressing her at her midriff, sliding beneath the hem of her shirt to spread his palm against her back?

'Mr Aitken—Matthew—' Her mouth was so dry she could scarcely get her tongue round it, and it didn't help when he moved nearer and rubbed his chest against her breasts. The hand she'd raised between them was crushed against hair-roughened muscles, and the fibres were surprisingly soft where they curled against her palm. 'We can't—*you* can't—do this.'

'Do what?' he taunted, looking down at her with sensual indulgence. 'What am I doing, for God's sake? Just inviting you to get cool. I can't help it if your puritan soul reads something more into my intentions. You are hot. I can feel it. And I think you can feel it, too.'

It was all double meanings and innuendo. For all her ignorance in some things, she wasn't unaware of what he really meant. Almost involuntarily, her eyes dipped to where his chest-hair arrowed beyond his navel. His brown flesh was smooth and masculine, his stomach taut and flat. But below his belt the fabric was taut, and her eyes tore away in panic.

'Please—' she begged, half aware that the solution was in her own hands. She had only to pull herself away from him, put the width of the room between them, and he wouldn't touch her again. Something told her she could stop him. Matthew Aitken didn't have to force himself on anyone.

'Please, what?' he asked, the tips of his fingers invading the waistband of her shorts now. The back of her swimsuit dipped low over her hips and he didn't have to push it aside to find the curve of her taut rear. Her muscles clenched instinctively as his finger found the damp cleft of her bottom, and a wet heat flooded between her legs as he urged her closer against him.

'Mmm, sweet,' he murmured huskily, his teeth fastening on to the skin of her shoulder and nipping the yielding flesh. 'You know what I want to do, don't you? It's not easy for a man to disguise his needs.'

His meaning was all too obvious. The way he was holding her was bringing her into intimate association with his body. And, although until that night on the beach she had had little experience of a man's arousal, there was no mistaking the solid feel of his sex pressed against her thigh.

Her breathing trembled. What she should do and what she shouldn't do were just abstracts, suspended in her brain. Thinking was becoming a problem; coherence was almost impossible. And, when he lifted his head and found her mouth, her sigh signalled her inevitable surrender.

His mouth was so sensual, slanting across hers first one way then the other, nibbling kisses at her lips until they were forced to part. Her hands, balled into fists, provided her only resistance. But when his tongue plunged into her mouth, every muscle felt suspended.

His hands cupped her buttocks now, lifting her against him. She could feel the whole length of him hard against her mound. His tongue performed a sensuous dance, miming what his body demanded. And, almost without volition, her hands crept to his neck, grasping handfuls of his hair, pulling him closer.

'God,' he groaned as she strained against him, her small breasts almost bursting out of her swimsuit. 'We are wearing far too many clothes. We've got to do something about it.'

'I don't want a shower,' protested Helen weakly, briefly sobered by his hands pushing her shorts down to her thighs.

'Well, not right now,' Matthew agreed, as her shorts puddled about her ankles. He lifted her legs about him and carried her to the bed. 'Maybe later, hmm?' he added, as she felt the coolness of the bedspread against her midriff. He tugged the T-shirt over her head and then frowned. 'What happened to the bikini?'

Helen caught her breath. 'I—it's too revealing,' she got out tremulously, and he uttered a lazy laugh.

'And this isn't?' he teased her softly, peeling the one-piece *maillot* down to her waist. 'Oh, God, Helen, let me touch you. I've been wanting to do this for days.'

Helen had the feeling that this was all some incredible dream. She couldn't be here, in Matthew Aitken's bedroom, letting him undress her without doing anything to stop him. She wasn't beautiful. She wasn't the kind of woman to drive a man mad with desire. As a matter of fact she was fairly ordinary—an awareness she'd felt even more strongly since she'd seen her mother again.

Matthew had shrugged off his shirt now, and, tugging her braid towards him, he went to work on her hair. In no time at all he had loosened the plait and drawn the sun-streaked strands over her breasts. Then, as she lay there, too dazed to feel embarrassed, he bent his head and took one erect nipple into his mouth.

The feeling that swept through her as he suckled on her breast was amazing. It was like an exquisite kind of pain that she didn't want to stop. It caused her to close her eyes, so that the sensual feelings filled her head. But when her lids flickered open, and she saw his bent head, the weakness she was feeling only intensified.

Dear God, she wondered, was this what it was like to want a man? Was the dampness between her thighs and the trembling in her legs a forerunner to what he meant to do to her? Knowing what happened was one thing; experiencing it was something else. Did she want this man to be the one to teach her, to show her how it could be?

She was in no state to decide, she thought, realising she was ducking the issue, but incapable of doing anything else. It had all happened too fast; she was still coming to terms with her own sexuality. And there was still that element of fantasy, of not believing that this was happening to her.

But it was. The heat of Matthew's body splayed beside her, his warmth, his passion, his smell—they were unmistakable proof of what he was doing. For some incredible reason he wanted her, and her bemused senses couldn't handle anything else.

His mouth moved to her other breast, his teeth tugging an even greater response from her. She was weak, helpless, in the grip of emotions too strong to deny. Her pulse was racing, the blood rushing through her veins like liquid fire. She was on fire, she thought wildly. She was drenched in sensual flames.

When he drew her hand down to the bulge that swelled his jeans, she no longer tried to stop him. 'Help me,' he said. 'Touch me. Open the zip—that's right. Oh, God!' He caught his breath as she took hold of him. 'Oh, yes! Yes. That's so good.'

Helen's head swam. Was she really doing this? Was the living, throbbing thing in her hand a part of him? She knew it was. She could feel the blood beating beneath the sensitive skin, could feel his pulse racing against her palm. Hard and velvety smooth, it filled her with alarm as well as excitement. He was so big, so overpowering. And, although she was no foolish teenager, age did not necessarily bring reassurance in its wake.

Her fingers moved involuntarily, sliding up and down the length of him, so that he swore, quite explicitly, and removed her hand. 'If you do that, I can't be responsible for the consequences,' he told her thickly. Then, with unsteady fingers, he tugged her swimsuit down her legs.

She should have been embarrassed, and momentarily she did think of trying to cover herself. But somehow he'd managed to push his jeans away, and his hairy thigh came between her legs. Then he nudged the melting source of her femininity, and it was far too late to hide herself from him.

Her hips rose off the bed, almost in protest, but his fingers were already taking the place of his knee. They threaded between the moist curls, and she caught her breath instinctively. Then he rubbed the tiny nubbin hidden in the folds.

'Is that good?' he asked against her lips, as his tongue made another greedy foray into her mouth. His fingers moved again, sliding inside her, and a swelling sense of anticipation spread through her stomach and down her trembling legs.

'Don't—that is—I haven't—' she began chokingly, but the sudden eruption of her senses left her weak. A wave of shattering sweetness washed over her. She jerked against his fingers in helpless fervour as the feeling spread.

'Relax,' he breathed when she subsided again, but the shuddering that had gripped her body wouldn't stop. 'It was that good, hmm?' he added softly. 'You sure know how to drive a man insane.'

Then he was kneeling between her legs, his palms tantalising her breasts for a moment before dipping to draw her legs wider apart. His thumbs probed the soft creases, and she knew he was watching her reaction as he did it. But that didn't stop her bucking helplessly when he touched the place where he'd caressed her before.

She had to tell him, she thought dizzily, wondering if he was in the habit of making love to virgins. Or did he know? Had he guessed? For all he'd succeeded in arousing her, far beyond anything she'd imagined, surely he must know she was painfully ignorant of what came next?

But when his finger slid inside her again and found her wetness, the groan he uttered made it impossible for her to offer any last-minute confession. Besides, if she was honest with herself, she would admit that she didn't want to tell him. She didn't want him to think she was so inexperienced, so lacking in sex-appeal, that no man had touched her.

'God, Helen,' he muttered, as she lay there gazing at him with an unknowingly sensual invitation in her eyes. 'I wanted to make this last, but I don't think I can. There's a limit to my endurance, and I guess we just reached it.'

There was still time. As he reached towards the drawer in the cabinet beside the bed and pulled out a foil wrapper,

Helen tried to find suitable words. But she saw what he was doing, and her mouth dried in helpless anticipation. He was protecting himself—and her. She had nothing to worry about. Nothing—nothing could go wrong.

How wrong she was.

His hands cupped her bottom, lifting her against him. The solid bluntness of his arousal was touching her now, there, in that place between her legs that suddenly seemed too small for what he expected it to do.

Yet he was still caressing her, his fintertips between her legs, holding her apart, drenching her in her own heat as she responded without volition.

And it was good. The feelings she had felt before flowered again as he caressed her, and when he pushed against her, her muscles expanded to meet him.

It was going to be all right, she thought, relaxing and letting her body receive him. She could feel him now, hard inside her, and her hips arched almost instinctively to meet his powerful thrust.

And then a sob escaped her. The pain was excruciating for a moment. Dear God, she hadn't dreamed it would hurt so much. All pleasure vanished as he pushed his way inside her.

'God!'

Matthew's exclamation was no less fervent than hers, but, although he looked down at her with hot, accusing eyes, there was no way he could prevent what was happening. Her cry, her sudden resistance, had caused her muscles to convulse around him, and the constriction was enough to send him shuddering into release.

He collapsed on to her, almost winding her with the weight of his heavy body. All the air exploded from her lungs in an unwary gasp and she lay there, gulping for breath, as his hips jerked helplessly against her.

CHAPTER TWELVE

BY THE time Matthew was capable of lifting his head, Helen was already beginning to move restlessly against him. Dismay, pure and simple, was mirrored on her expressive face; her eyes were bright with unshed tears, looking anywhere but at him.

And, curiously, it was her obvious distress that dispelled his own feelings of anger and accusation. Despite the undeniable relief he'd felt in slaking his own needs, his gratification had been tempered by the knowledge of what he'd done. Contrary to her belief, he was not in the habit of ravaging inexperienced women. And, if he'd known she was a virgin, he'd have probably let her go.

Or would he?

The point was moot, but no longer debatable. And, looking down into her drowned grey eyes, he wondered if he'd have found the strength to do anything differently. He'd wanted her—more, in fact, than he'd wanted any woman ever before. And, what was more, he still wanted her. He could feel himself growing hard at the prospect of doing it all again.

'Please…'

Her voice, soft and tremulous, nevertheless contained a note of recrimination. She was trying to get up, but his body wouldn't let her. She obviously wanted to get away from him, but he didn't want her to go.

Instead of complying with her wishes, Matthew lifted one hand and shaped the curve of her jawline. She jerked away from his touch, but she couldn't avoid it, and he allowed his thumb to invade the softness of her mouth.

'How old are you?' he asked suddenly, and she stopped struggling long enough to give him a wary look.

'Does it matter?'

He inclined his head. 'Humour me.'

She hesitated. 'Twenty-two.' Then, with some dignity, 'As—as you've got what you came for, can I get up?'

Her words irritated him more than a little, but he contained his anger and said quietly, 'So—how did you get to the age of twenty-two without—without—?'

He couldn't find the right words, but in the event he didn't need to. 'Just unlucky, I guess,' she responded, with obvious sarcasm, but he knew that she was hurting, and not just in a physical sense.

He sighed then. 'It's incredible.'

'Incredibly boring, don't you mean?' she retorted tightly. 'Perhaps I never had the opportunity. We're not all like—like that, you know.' He was fairly sure she'd been about to say 'Fleur', but she swallowed the distinction and gave him a guarded look. 'I'm sorry if I wasn't what you expected. If it's any consolation, you weren't what I expected either.'

Matthew traced the outline of her lower lip with his thumb. 'Is that your way of telling me you were disappointed?' he enquired gently, and her face suffused with scarlet colour.

'No!' she exclaimed hotly. And then, more steadily, 'You're only making fun of me again. Well, fine. The joke's on me. I should have had more sense than to stay.'

'I'm not making fun of you,' Matthew informed her evenly, his hand dipping into the hollow of her shoulder, before moving on down her arm. He could feel her trembling beneath his touch and he knew an inexplicable feeling of protection. Which was ridiculous in the circumstances, he thought. When he'd been the one to abuse her trust.

Needing to detain her now, as much for his own needs as hers, he added, 'Why did you? Stay, I mean? I would have let you go if you'd told me. I'd never have forced you, if that's what you believe.'

'I don't—that is—' His questing hand had found her breast, and a little shudder feathered her smooth flesh. 'I—don't know why I did,' she admitted honestly. 'Perhaps I was curious.' Her lips twisted ruefully. 'Someone—some *man*—had to do it.'

'And you chose me?'

'No. Yes.' She shook her head. 'I don't know.'

She was getting frustrated. He could sense it. Even though she refused to look directly at him, even though she refused to acknowledge how her own body was betraying her, a kind of raw panic was setting in. She was afraid of herself, he thought, with sudden intuition. She didn't understand her own needs. And, dammit, he'd done nothing to explain them to her. He'd just gone ahead and had his way.

Ignoring the protest of his own body, whose needs were all too understandable to him, Matthew levered himself up on his hands and withdrew from her. But when she would have rolled away, he grasped her shoulders. 'Wait,' he said, and something in his voice stilled her instinctive protest. 'I think it's time we took that shower. Come on, I'll show you where it is.'

She wanted to protest, he knew, but a glance at her inner thighs had her covering herself defensively, and, not giving her a chance to escape him, he swung her up into his arms.

The shower cubicle in the adjoining bathroom was plenty big enough for two, but she gazed at him in horror when he joined her. 'You can't,' she said, when he turned the taps on. 'I—my hair's going to get wet.'

'I'll dry it for you,' he replied softly. 'Now, stop making a fuss and enjoy it.'

He found himself in the unusual position of wanting to please her. When she reached for the soap he let her take it, even though his hands itched to do it himself. It was incredible, he could hardly keep his hands off her. And when he saw the water streaming off her breasts, and the upturned thrust of her nipples, he thought how frustrating it was to be good.

But at last she was finished, and, giving in to the urge he'd had all along to caress her wet skin, he pulled her back against him for a minute. 'Do you have any idea what you're doing to me?' he asked, nuzzling her shoulder. Then, with intimate enquiry, 'Do you feel better?'

Helen quivered, but he noticed she didn't pull away from him this time. 'I—I suppose so,' she said, squeezing her legs together when his fingers spread down her stomach. 'If—if you'll give me a towel, I'll get dried. I don't think my hair's very wet.'

'I'll do it,' said Matthew unevenly, letting her go with some reluctance. 'Step outside the cubicle. The towels are beside the bath.'

Forcing himself not to look at the way she curled in on herself in embarrassment, Matthew collected a huge bath-sheet and wrapped it about her shoulders. 'Is this what you do with Sophie?' he asked, trying to distract her, but as he rubbed her trembling shoulders the towel slipped down to her waist.

Matthew's eyes sought hers then, and what he saw there had him reaching for her. She was nervous, no doubt, but she was also aware of his arousal. And he told himself that excused his disgraceful lack of control.

Gathering her up in his arms again, he carried her back to the bed, and although she whimpered something about her hair being wet he didn't respond to her plea. God, he thought, he'd never felt this way about any other woman. She was everything he wanted, and so much more.

It was strange, because usually he was such a restless animal. Once he'd had his way with a woman, he'd been glad to leave. And, apart from a couple of abortive affairs in his teens, he'd remained emotionally inviolate. He guessed Fleur's behaviour had something to do with it. Certainly he'd never trusted a woman since.

But suddenly this woman was making him feel emotions he'd considered were for mutts and school-kids. Ownership, the need for possession—he was aware he was feeling them both. Not to mention jealousy, he acknowledged tautly. The thought of some other man touching her drove him mad.

Her lips were pressed together when he touched them, but, as if the caressing brush of his tongue was all that was needed to break the spell, her jaw sagged almost instantly. The sweetness of her breath was like nectar in his nostrils, and, although he'd determined restraint, his tongue surged helplessly into her mouth.

Desire, hot and fluid, poured through his veins. And he wanted to pour himself into her just as urgently. Dear God, she was so sweet, so responsive, so passionate. He wanted her so badly, he didn't know how he was going to stop.

Then her hands crept up his chest, and he felt incredible. When they linked behind his neck and drew him closer, he felt as if he was actually on fire. The feel of her small breasts pushing against his chest was unbelievably erotic, and he tucked one hand between them to stroke her swollen core.

To his amazement, she didn't stop him. And, what was more, he could feel her musky arousal on his fingers. For some amazing reason she still wanted him. And his body ached to show her how it should be.

'You don't know what you do to me,' he got out unsteadily, and winced when her nails dug painfully into his shoulders.

'I—know what you do to me,' she whispered, and he realised what he'd hoped might be going to come true. She wound her arms around his neck. 'Do you think I might enjoy it more this time?'

'Depend on it,' he said huskily, parting her legs and bending to press his face against the damp cluster of honey-gold curls. 'Don't stop me,' he added, as she jerked a little nervously. 'Just let yourself go with the flow.'

*   *   *

Matthew remembered those words later, when he lay panting beside her. Lord, he thought, she was every man's dream come to life. Despite her inexperience, she'd responded without inhibition, and the pleasure he'd found with her had been intense.

In fact, he realised tautly, he'd never felt this way before either. Always, when he'd made love to a woman, there'd been some part of himself he'd held back. He'd found satiation, but not satisfaction; release but not relief. Yet, with Helen, he'd felt no sense of restriction. With her, he was a whole person; together, they were complete.

It was at once awesome and frightening. He'd never let anyone have that kind of control over him before. In many ways, he was an emotional virgin, he thought wryly. But, God, she made him eager to shed the shackles that state had wrought.

Realising he needed reassurance that he wasn't the only one who felt that way, he turned his head and looked at Helen. She was lying within the circle of the arm and leg he'd thrown possessively across her, but she seemed to sense his sensual appraisal because she slanted him a sleepy gaze.

'I can't stay here much longer,' she murmured ruefully, but he could hear the reluctance in her voice.

'I know,' he said, drawing a finger line from her breastbone to her navel. 'We've got to talk, I guess. And it's not easy to be rational in this position.'

'No.' Her lips parted, and for a moment she looked as anxious as she had done before. 'But was it—? I mean— it was all right, wasn't it? The second time, I mean. I didn't do anything wrong.'

Matthew's lips tilted lazily. 'You tell me.'

Helen licked her lips. 'It was—amazing. I didn't know— I didn't think—that is—'

His finger over her lips silenced her, and then he bent and replaced his finger with his mouth. 'I get the picture,' he said, when they were both deliciously breathless. 'We'll talk about that later. When the others have gone.'

'The others!'

Helen gazed at him with horror-stricken eyes, but Matthew wouldn't let her get away.

'I'm sure they've guessed what's going on,' he said flatly. And, at her anxious gasp, 'Does it matter? They're going to find out anyway.'

Helen swallowed. 'They are?'

'Aren't they?'

A twinge of her anxiety touched him then, but before she had time to formulate a reply the doors to the outer room were flung open and Fleur marched into the suite.

Matthew had never felt so furious—or so helpless—in his life. That Fleur should be here in his house was bad enough. That she should have the effrontery to burst into his private apartments unannounced was intolerable.

And short of confronting her—nude—there was no way he could throw her out again. An option that wasn't an option, in his present protective position.

Helen's reaction had been equally as violent, though he guessed she was more shocked than angry. Beneath his palm—the palm which moments before had been teasing the swollen bud of her breast—her heart was racing madly. And, although she hadn't a hope of dislodging him, her elbows were scrabbling for purchase on the pillows.

He wanted to wring Fleur's neck, he thought savagely. She had ruined his life once before, and he was damned if she was going to ruin it again. It was time he told her what he really thought of her. It was time to get her out of his life. She couldn't be allowed to embarrass Helen. Whatever happened, that was one thing of which he was sure.

But before he could speak, almost before he had had time to drag the silk sheet over their naked bodies, Fleur charged into the bedroom, with Lucas at her heels. Matthew guessed his assistant had come upstairs with Fleur to try and restrain her, but what he saw in the bedroom set him rocking back on his heels.

However, before Matthew could say anything in his own defence, before he could try and explain that this was not what it looked, Fleur screamed. Her cry, raw and anguished, echoed and re-echoed around the vaulted ceiling of the apartment. It caused Helen to jerk violently beneath him, and he soothed her pained expression with a kiss.

'Trust me,' he said, for her ears only, but she didn't seem to be listening to him any more. Her eyes were on the woman who had haunted him since his youth, and the anger he'd felt initially rekindled anew.

Deciding there was only one way to handle this, and that wasn't lying down, Matthew jack-knifed off the bed, taking the quilt with him. Then, wrapping it about himself, he faced Fleur with eyes that were as cold as glaciers. 'What the hell d'you think you're doing?' he snarled. 'Get out of here, before I throw you out myself.'

Lucas's face was haggard. 'I tried to stop her,' he said stiffly, as Fleur snatched a tissue from her sleeve and dabbed her eyes. 'I didn't know—I didn't think—' His expression mirrored his contempt. 'For God's sake, Matt, there are people downstairs! What are they supposed to think?'

'I don't give a damn what they think,' said Matthew harshly. 'Just get this mad woman out of here. I want her packed and out of my house.'

Fleur drew a dramatic breath. 'And can I take my daughter with me?' she enquired haughtily, drawing an anguished breath from Helen. Fleur threw the crumpled tissue on the floor. 'Oh, yes—' this as Matthew stared at her disbelievingly '—didn't she tell you she's my daughter? Why else do you think she came here, if not because of this?'

'That's not true!'

At last Helen spoke, and Matthew gathered the quilt about him as he turned to look at her. 'What's not true?' he found himself asking. 'You're not her daughter? Or—

she—isn't why you came here? Why you let me take you to bed?'

Helen's face paled. 'I am her daughter—' she began, but he wouldn't let her finish. Like a house of cards, the world he'd been building for the two of them, ever since he'd realised how he felt about her, came tumbling about his ears. She was Fleur's daughter! The woman who for a few short minutes he'd thought he'd loved was the offspring of that vile creature. He couldn't believe it. He wouldn't believe it.

But he was very much afraid it was true...

CHAPTER THIRTEEN

'THERE'S a letter for you, Miss Gregory.' Helen's landlady came out of her door as her tenant came running down the stairs. 'Couldn't climb all those stairs,' Mrs Reams added, patting her ample chest as if she was already breathless. And, as she weighed considerably more than her five-feet-two-inch-frame could support, Helen could quite understand her dilemma.

'That's all right, Mrs Reams,' she said now, taking the letter with barely a glance and tucking it into her trouser pocket. 'It's a lovely morning, isn't it?'

'Mmm.' Mrs Reams looked disappointed. 'Aren't you going to open your letter, dear? It might be something important.'

'I doubt it.'

Helen felt a fleeting twinge of sympathy for the garrulous old lady. Mrs Reams had probably examined the letter very thoroughly before handing it over. In the three months since Helen had been living in her top-floor bed-sitter, she'd learned that Mrs Reams was extremely inquisitive. It frustrated her considerably that her tenant remained so obstinately close-mouthed.

'Well—' Mrs Reams gave it one last shot '—it's not one of those advertising circulars. I'd say it was from a woman. Your mother, perhaps?' she queried. 'Or your sister?'

'I don't have a sister,' replied Helen dampeningly. 'And I've really got to go. I've got a class in half an hour, and I can't afford to miss it.'

Mrs Reams adopted a resigned face. 'Oh, very well,' she muttered, turning back into her ground-floor apartment. It was obvious she was getting nowhere, and she was missing her game-show on the telly.

Meanwhile, Helen jogged determinedly towards the bus stop. She hadn't been lying when she'd said she had a class at half-past nine. She was taking an intensive course in word-processing and other secretarial skills, and she'd already learned that missing a class was to her disadvantage, not theirs.

But at least she was doing something positive with her life at last, she thought firmly. And a six-month secretarial course was all she could afford right now. She would have preferred to work with children, but that would have entailed a lengthy course at college. And the money she'd saved wouldn't last that long.

Still, the prospect of becoming a secretary was much preferable to working at a filling station. And she'd be supporting herself for the first time in her life. When she'd worked for Tricia, she'd always felt indebted to her. Now she was making her own decisions, and the outcome was up to her.

The bus arrived, on time for once, and after paying her fare Helen found a seat and dumped her haversack beside her. It was only then that she extracted the letter from her pocket. She couldn't delay reading it any longer, however fruitless the exercise might be.

It was from Tricia. She'd seen that at once, as soon as Mrs Reams had handed it to her. Her erstwhile employer had written to her twice since she'd terminated Helen's employment: once to convey her feelings, and once to send her a cheque.

In consequence, she couldn't possibly imagine what Tricia might want now. She'd made her feelings plain enough, and she'd sent her final salary. There didn't seem much else to say, unless Andrew had been causing trouble again.

Slitting the envelope, she extracted the thin sheet of writing-paper. It was a handwritten note, short and to the point.

Helen,

I've been contacted by Matthew Aitken's father. He'd like you to get in touch with him. His address is given below.

Tricia Sheridan.

Helen swallowed, and folded the slip of paper back into the envelope. Then, turning her attention to the window, she stared resolutely at the street outside. They were passing a park, and she could see children with their mothers. There were dogs, too, and an old man rummaging in a bin.

What was he looking for? she wondered, noticing that his clothes were fairly clean. Perhaps he was looking for something he'd lost, she reflected grimly. She'd lost something, too, but it wasn't something she was likely to find.

The letter was still in her hands and, forcing herself to act normally, she folded the envelope in half and stuffed it back into her jeans. When she found a bin she'd dispose of it, she told herself. If she left it on the bus, someone might return it to her.

The secretarial college was the next stop, and, hefting her bag, she got to her feet and made her way to the front of the bus. 'Lovely morning,' remarked the driver, responding to the slim young woman with her chunky braid of hair. 'Too nice for working, eh? How'd you fancy going for a spin on my bike?'

'No, thanks.'

Helen's smile was distracted, and, as if realising he was wasting his time, the driver stood on the brakes with a heavier foot than was necessary. 'Ooh, sorry, love,' he said, as Helen was thrown against the handrail, but she knew it had been deliberate.

'It doesn't matter,' she said disparagingly, and sauntered down the steps.

But once the bus had pulled away her defiance left her, and Joanne Chalmers, a young woman she had become friends with in the six weeks they had been sharing the course, came to meet her with anxious eyes. Joanne was the same age as herself, but she was already married with a family. In consequence, she mothered all the girls and Helen in particular.

'Hi,' she said, falling into step beside her. 'What's wrong?'

'Oh—' Helen looked at her a little defensively. 'Um—nothing. Not really.' Then, realising Joanne would expect an explanation, she added, 'The driver was a bit fresh, that's all. He nearly tipped me off the bus.'

'Men!' Joanne pulled a sympathetic face. 'Aren't they just the limit! Barry and me had a bit of a barney this morning. Lindsey's got a rash, and he thinks I should take her to the doctor's.'

'Oh, dear.'

It was a relief to think about something other than her own problems, and Helen listened while her friend extolled the virtues of being single. 'I should never have had a baby at seventeen,' she said. 'My mother was right, only I wouldn't listen.' She grimaced. 'Mothers usually are right, aren't they? Oh—sorry. I forgot yours had done a bunk.'

Helen shook her head and turned away, in no state to think about Fleur at present. The letter from Tricia—and its connotations with Matthew—had resurrected the whole sorry mess, and she was unutterably relieved when a group of their fellow students came to join them and she had time to regain her composure.

Joanne probably thought mentioning her mother had upset her, Helen reflected ruefully, feeling the other woman's eyes watching her with some compassion. She'd told Joanne her father was dead, and that her mother had left them when she was a baby. It was the truth, if somewhat encapsulated, and it had prevented a lot of unnecessary questions.

Now, however, she found herself wondering what Joanne would say if she was completely honest with her; if she told her friend that her mother had accused her of seducing the man she loved. And what if she added the rider that the man in question had believed her, that he'd actually thought she'd done it to avenge her father's death?

Oh, God, she thought later that morning, as she stared blankly at the keys of the word-processor, she'd believed she'd got over it—or over the worst, at least. But the pain was no less acute because she'd been ignoring it for so long. On the contrary, it felt as if it had festered and infected her whole body.

She couldn't eat any lunch and, reassuring Joanne that she was just feeling under the weather, she decided to skip the afternoon's classes and spend the time in the park. She could have gone back to her bed-sitter, but Mrs Reams was bound to be curious, and she didn't want her asking questions that she wasn't prepared to answer.

It was a warm June afternoon and, finding an empty bench, Helen folded up her sweater and stuffed it into her haversack. The heat was pleasant on her bare arms, now exposed by the cotton vest she was wearing, and she tilted her head wearily and turned her face to the sun.

But the warm day was too reminiscent of that other warm day she had spent at Dragon Bay, and although she'd planned to throw the letter away she pulled it out of her pocket. The folds she had made bisected the paper; it would be incredibly easy to destroy. She should tear it into little pieces, she thought, and drop it into the nearest rubbish bin.

Instead, she extracted the slip of paper from its envelope again, and smoothed the creases out on her knee. The words were the same; Tricia was evidently still at odds with her. But this time she read beyond her signature; this time she read the address.

'Ryan's Bend,' she mused aloud, after taking note of the fact that apparently it was a stud farm. 'Benjamin Aitken, Ryan's Bend, Kinsville, Tallahassee, Florida.'

There was a telephone number, too, and Helen thought that if she had intended to contact Matthew's father, that was how she'd have done it. But, as she didn't intend to

contact him, as she had no wish for another verbal bludg-
eoning, there wasn't much point in noting it down.

She sighed. She was surprised Tricia had agreed to convey the message to her. Since the events of that morning
at Dragon Bay, Tricia had scarcely spoken to her at all. It
had been Andrew who had informed her her services were
no longer required, Andrew who had contemptuously dismissed her anxious attempts to explain.

'I always thought you were a sly minx,' he'd said, after
they were back at the Parrishs' villa. 'Butter wouldn't melt,
and all that. But you were holding out for richer game.'

Of course, Tricia hadn't been around when he'd said that.
Or she might conceivably have wondered what he'd meant.
No, Tricia had retired to bed with a headache. And Helen
had borne the brunt of Andrew's temper.

She had wondered afterwards whether Tricia might not
have found it in her heart to overlook what had happened
if Andrew hadn't put his spoke in. After all, her work
hadn't suffered. And the children liked to be with her as
well. But Andrew had insisted that they couldn't continue
to employ her; that she might be a bad influence on Henry
and Sophie. And although in her stronger moments Helen
had known that he was jealous, she'd despised herself so
bitterly that she'd packed her bags.

One of the worst aspects of the whole affair was the
suspicion she had that she'd proved to be no better than
her mother. After all these years of despising Fleur for
abandoning her home and family, it had only taken a couple
of weeks for Matthew Aitken to get her into his bed. How
had it happened? When she'd gone to Dragon Bay that
morning, she'd had no inkling of how it would end. Even
now, with the knowledge of that self-betrayal behind her,
she found it difficult to accept what she had done.

And yet, if she was honest, she had to admit that at no
time had Matthew ever forced her to stay. True, he'd kissed
her, and caressed her, but he hadn't tied her down. She
could have left at any time. She had had only to open the

door. But somehow he had bewitched her, and she hadn't
wanted to leave.

But why?

Three toddlers were playing ball under the protective eye
of their parents, and Helen watched them, too, trying to put
all thoughts of Matthew Aitken out of her mind. But although the children were beguiling, and so trusting in their
innocence, she couldn't forget Matthew's face when Fleur
had accused her of using him.

Fleur...

Helen's hands clenched together in her lap. She hadn't
heard a word from Fleur since she had left the villa that
morning. Her mother hadn't even tried to contact her and
demand an explanation. It was as if she didn't exist, as if
their brief reunion on the island had never happened. She
knew now that Fleur had only been using her to ensure that
her identity was never revealed.

The fact that Fleur herself had revealed it was immaterial
now. Obviously, the shock of finding Helen and Matthew
together had temporarily unhinged her mind. The way she'd
looked, the bitter fury in her gaze when she'd seen her
daughter, was forever imprinted in Helen's subconscious.
That woman didn't love her. Helen thought she probably
hated her now, for making her betray the truth.

A pain knifed through her stomach.

As always, it was the memory of Matthew that hurt the
most. He had been so ready to believe Fleur; so ready to
accuse her. It was as if he'd been expecting it; as if he'd
wanted to believe the worst. And why? Had she just been
a morning's diversion? He obviously hadn't cared about
her feelings.

Not as she'd cared about him...

Helen frowned. Now where had that come from? She
didn't care about him. She *couldn't* care about him. He was
Chase Aitken's brother. The brother of the man who'd destroyed her father's life.

And yet...

Pulling out a tissue, she quickly blew her nose. She must be getting a cold, she thought tautly. Maybe that was why she was feeling so down. It wasn't the letter, or the weight of memory that came with it. It was just a dose of summer flu that was going around.

Her eyes watered suddenly and, scrubbing the heels of her hands across them, she felt an overwhelming sense of desolation. Who was she kidding? she chided herself painfully. Of course she'd cared about Matthew. That was why she'd been so desperate, why she'd tried to contact him again before she left.

She cringed now, thinking of that phone call. She'd been at the airport, waiting for the evening flight to London, and she'd been half afraid his number would be unavailable. But it hadn't been. The operator had given it to her directly. And she'd dialled Dragon Bay with trembling fingers, praying that Matthew would be there.

She'd wanted to explain, she'd told herself. Fleur had had her say, but Helen had been too stunned to defend herself. Besides, with Lucas there it had seemed such a fiasco. And Matthew had left her to it. He hadn't even said goodbye.

Lucas had answered the call, she remembered now. And, when she'd first heard his voice, she'd believed she was in luck. Lucas knew her; he knew she wasn't capable of the things her mother had accused her of. He'd understand why she wanted to speak to Matthew. He'd be on her side.

But he hadn't been. As soon as he had realised who it was, his voice, his manner, his whole attitude had changed. Matthew wouldn't speak to her, he'd informed her coldly. Matthew wasn't speaking to anyone. And he'd particularly mentioned her. He didn't want to speak to her again.

She'd hung up with a feeling of total annihilation. She'd boarded the plane to London and spent the whole trip in a daze. What she was going to do, where she was going to live—those problems hadn't touched her. It wasn't until she landed in England that she'd realised what she had to face.

Fortunately, the cold air of a March morning had helped to clear her head, and by the time the airport shuttle dropped her at Victoria she had a little idea of what she had to do. A bed and breakfast to begin with; and then somewhere more permanent to settle down; and a job—not necessarily in that order. She would never again rely on so-called friends.

In the event she hadn't found a job, but she had enrolled at the secretarial college. Six weeks of looking for work, and of spending her nights crying for something she could never have, had given her a new perspective on her future. She was alone, yes, but that didn't mean she had to take any employment that was offered to her. She had a little money saved and, if she was careful, she could take the secretarial course. Good secretaries were paid accordingly, and she intended to be very good.

But now this, she fretted, looking at the letter again. Why couldn't they leave her alone? Hadn't they done enough? Besides which, she hardly knew Matthew's father. She'd only met him briefly that one time. Which brought her thoughts round full-circle. Oh, God, why hadn't she destroyed the letter straight away?

She sniffed, feeling a burning behind her eyes that had nothing to do with influenza. She felt as if she'd been nursing an injury and now someone had exposed it, tearing aside the fragile skin that had been growing over the wound.

She read Ben Aitken's address again. A stud farm, she thought, trying to drum up the resentment she knew she should be feeling. No doubt that was where Chase Aitken had got his polo ponies. Did Matthew play polo as well?

No, she reminded herself, he was a writer. Since coming back to England, she'd learned he was a fairly successful one as well. She'd even borrowed one of his books from the library, but she hadn't been able to read it. The words were far too close to him, and she'd severed even that connection.

Stuffing the letter into her pocket again, she hoisted her haversack and got to her feet. Sooner or later they'd realise that she wanted nothing more to do with them.

The next few days weren't easy, but, like with everything else, time put a welcome buffer between her actions and her thoughts. She was busy with the course, and she even had supper with Joanne and her family one evening. She was making a life, she told herself. She didn't need anything—or anyone—else.

Then, one evening, when she got back from college, Mrs Reams came to meet her with a conspiratorial smile. 'You've had a visitor, Miss Gregory,' she exclaimed confidingly. 'A gentleman. I said he could stay with me until you got in, but he didn't want to. He said he'd come back later.' She frowned. 'Are you all right?'

Helen felt limp, her legs like jelly. 'A gentleman?' she echoed, not having got past that initial announcement, and Mrs Reams nodded, giving her an anxious look.

'That's right, dear. An American gentleman, he was. Not young, you understand, but ever so handsome. Treated me like a lady, he did. He said he didn't want to trouble me. Well, of course, I said it was no trouble at all, but he still insisted he wouldn't wait.'

Helen let out her breath on a trembling sigh. 'He's coming back?' she swallowed. 'When?'

'I don't know, dear. Tonight, I expect. I said you were usually at home. I told him you were studying to be a secretary.'

'Is there anything you didn't tell him?' asked Helen sharply, and then felt sorry when Mrs Reams looked taken aback. 'Oh—it doesn't matter. I'm just feeling tetchy.' She hesitated. 'Did he give you his name?'

'His name!' Easily reassured, Mrs Reams gave a girlish laugh. 'Oh, my, yes, aren't I silly? He told me his name was Aitken. He said you'd know who he was.'

Helen's head sagged. 'Thank you.'

'You do know who he is, then?' the landlady persisted, and Helen gave her a rueful look.

'Yes. He's—a friend of my previous employer. I expect he's visiting London on business, and decided to look me up.'

It was a poor excuse, but Mrs Reams didn't seem to notice it. 'Your previous employer?' she said chattily. 'And who would that be, dear? I didn't realise you'd been working. I thought you said you couldn't find a job.'

'I couldn't. That is— Oh, it's a long story.' Helen didn't want to get into that right now. 'Um—well, if he comes back, I suppose I'd better see him. Will you send him up, Mrs Reams? I shan't be going out.'

However, later that evening, Helen had cause to regret her rash words. Seven o'clock passed, then eight, with no sign of Matthew's father. If he had been going to come back, surely he'd have been here by now. Instead of which she was sitting here like a pigeon, just waiting to be knocked off its perch.

Apprehension set in, and a not-unexpected feeling of panic. Why was he coming to see her? she wondered. To confirm she'd got his message? And, if so, what had that message meant? Surely Fleur hadn't sent him, not after the way she'd behaved. And if she had, Helen didn't think she wanted to know.

And then, at about half-past nine, when she was thinking of getting ready for bed, there was a knock at her door. Her mouth dried, and her tongue felt as if it was glued to the roof of her mouth, but she had to answer it. She'd told Mrs Reams to send her visitor up. And the landlady knew she hadn't gone out.

For all her complaints that climbing the stairs was bad for her, Mrs Reams was standing beside the man waiting outside. It was Matthew's father, Helen saw instantly. And the tiny hope she'd nurtured, that Matthew might be with him, died a death.

'Here we are,' said Mrs Reams triumphantly, and Helen

guessed her curiosity had got the better of her. The landlady evidently wanted to see for herself how Helen would greet him, and when Ben Aitken held out his hand she was obviously disappointed.

'Sorry to be so late,' he said apologetically. 'I'm afraid I went back to my hotel and fell asleep. I flew over last night and I never can sleep on aircraft. Too much noise and turbulence. I hope you'll forgive me.'

So polite!

To Helen, who didn't quite know what she had expected, but certainly not such courtesy, his words were like a balm. Unexpectedly, she felt that awful pricking behind her eyes again. Turning away, so he shouldn't see it, she said, 'Please, come in.'

'I'll leave you, then,' said Mrs Reams regretfully. She turned to the man. 'It's good for Miss Gregory to have some company for a change. Quite a recluse, she is usually. Hardly goes out at all, and I should know.'

'Thank you, Mrs Reams.' Helen recovered sufficiently to give the landlady a reproving look, and the old lady pulled a face before starting down the stairs. 'I'm sorry,' said Helen, closing the door, 'I'm afraid Mrs Reams is rather nosy. But she means well, and she's been very kind to me.'

Ben Aitken stood just inside the door, looking politely round the room. Seeing it with his eyes, Helen was instantly aware of its shortcomings, but it was clean and neat and serviceable, and it was her home.

'Won't you sit down?' she asked, pointing to one of a pair of worn plush armchairs and moving towards the electric ring. 'Can I get you a drink? Some coffee, perhaps? I'm afraid I don't have anything cold.'

'Nothing for the moment,' replied Matthew's father easily, lowering his long length into the chair she'd indicated. He looked round again. 'So this is where you live. Mrs Reams told me you're studying at college.'

'Just secretarial college,' said Helen quickly, taking the

armchair opposite and folding her hands in her lap. 'I—don't have any formal qualifications, you see, so I—'

'I'm not here to question what you choose to do with your life,' he declared at once. 'Just to—ensure that you're all right. We— That is—my son—was afraid Fleur might make things difficult for you.'

Helen swallowed. 'Fleur?' she echoed faintly, and Ben Aitken nodded.

'You have seen your mother, haven't you?'

Helen shook her head.

'But she—we—' He was obviously finding this as awkward as she was, because he looped his hands over the arms of the chair and fixed her with a troubled stare. 'You haven't seen your mother? She hasn't been in touch with you at all?' He sighed. 'Oh, dear, Matt was right. She is only interested in herself.'

Helen took a breath. 'If—if it's any consolation to you, I don't mind. Not seeing her, I mean. I—we have nothing in common, whatever you believe. I thought we might have for a while, but I was wrong.'

'Even so—' Matthew's father looked uncomfortable. 'She was—supposed to come and see you. To make sure that you were all right. Matt knew you'd lost your job because of him, and he was anxious. He wanted to offer some—recompense.' He coloured. 'It was the only thing he could think of to do.'

'Matt!' Helen stared at him, aghast. 'You mean, Matt asked my mother to offer money to me? Ugh!' Her revulsion was obvious, and she sprang to her feet with distaste. 'I think you'd better go, Mr Aitken. I appreciate that this isn't your problem, but I've heard enough.'

Ben Aitken sighed. 'Miss Gregory—Helen—please—'

'No, I don't want to hear your excuses,' she told him stiffly. 'I know you thought what you were doing was right. But people do things differently on this side of the Atlantic. And if your son thinks he can buy—'

'He doesn't,' interrupted Ben Aitken heavily. 'Darn it, I

knew I'd go about this the wrong way. Matt isn't trying
to—buy—anything, Miss Gregory. He just wants to know
you're—secure.'

'Why?' Helen's lip curled, and Ben Aitken looked up at
her with rueful eyes.

'I would have thought that was obvious,' he said. 'He's
concerned about you. He thought Fleur wasn't to be trusted,
and it appears she wasn't.'

'So he thought he'd get you to offer me money instead.'
Helen trembled. 'I find that insulting.'

'Do you?' Ben Aitken pulled a wry face. 'Well, where I
come from they say pride doesn't put butter on your
greens.'

Helen flushed. 'Well, you can tell—your son—I manage.
Even if I didn't, I'd still want nothing from him.'

'Yes, I think he knows that,' affirmed Ben wearily.
'When you didn't answer his letters, he surely knew. But
that doesn't stop him worrying about you, let me tell you.
Goddammit, the man's hurting! Why else d'you think I
agreed to come?'

CHAPTER FOURTEEN

HELEN sagged against the back of the chair. 'What did you say?' she asked weakly, and Matthew's father gave her an impatient look.

'Ah, hell!' he exclaimed. 'Matt'd kill me if he knew what I'd just said. Look here, Miss Gregory, I want you to forget it. It's not even relevant to why I've come.'

'It is.' Helen stared at him intently and then hauled herself round the chair and into the seat. 'What was that you said about—about letters? I haven't had any letters. Well, not from—from Matt, anyway. Just from Tricia.'

'Tricia?'

Ben looked confused, and Helen quickly explained that she meant Mrs Sheridan. 'The only communication I've received from the United States was when she sent me your address.'

Matthew's father frowned. 'But—Matt wrote to you. Twice, that I know of. It must be—two or three months ago now. Before he and Luke had that bust-up. Oh—you won't know—Luke has left.'

Helen blinked. 'Lucas doesn't work for Matthew any more?'

'No.' Ben looked rueful for a moment. 'Oh—you probably know—the guy was infatuated with you. Finding you with Matt that time—well, I guess it blew his mind. At any rate, he and Matt had the most godawful row a couple weeks afterwards.' He grimaced. 'Wrecked the office, they did. Chucked his goddamn computer on the floor.'

Helen gasped. 'Matt?'

'What? No—Luke did it. I think it was aimed at Matt, but, thank God, he missed.' He gave a short laugh. 'That

176

would have given Matt more than a mild concussion. As it was, I had to fly down and help Ruth put things straight.'

Helen swallowed. 'You're saying Matt had a concussion?'

'Just a mild one,' said Ben drily. 'And you should have seen Luke's face. No—' he grimaced '—Luke didn't brain him; he hit his head on the metal cabinet. But it knocked him out, and Luke decided to get out while he still could.'

Helen shook her head. 'I don't understand.'

'Don't you?' Ben snorted. 'Well, I'm beginning to. Matt must have given those letters to Luke to post, and my guess is he didn't do it. I can't prove it, of course, but it makes sense. I think Luke would have done anything to keep you two apart.'

Helen tried to absorb what he was saying, but after all these weeks she'd given up on ever hearing from Matthew again. And even now she didn't really know what his father was doing here. What did he mean, Matthew was hurting? He couldn't mean because of her—could he?

And then another thought struck her. 'The day—the day I left, I tried to ring Matt,' she said carefully. 'Lucas— Lucas answered the phone, and he said Matt—Matt didn't want to speak to me.' She licked her lips. 'Do you—do you think he was lying? I never got a chance to explain, you see.'

Ben sighed again. 'This would be the day after—well, the day after you and Matt—' He broke off significantly. 'I don't know. I suspect he might have been telling the truth.' And when Helen's lips parted in consternation he added hurriedly, 'No one could speak to Matt for several days after that.'

Helen tried to be casual. 'Oh? Why?'

'Because—' Ben grimaced. 'Because he went on quite a bender. He took it hard, you see, you being Fleur's daughter. I guess he didn't tell you, but that woman blighted his young life.'

Helen's voice was barely audible. 'How?'

'Oh, you don't want to know.'

'I do want to know,' insisted Helen tautly. 'Please, I have a right to know. She is my mother, after all.'

'Which is why— Oh, what the hell?' Ben lay back in his chair and gazed wearily into her face. 'When Matt was twenty-two, she tried to seduce him. And he's blamed himself for it ever since.'

Helen's breath caught in her throat. 'But—she was married to his brother.'

'I know.'

'Well—where was he when—when this was going on?'

'Nothing went on,' Ben informed her flatly. 'And Chase was away at the time. He often was.'

Helen hesitated. 'But—how do you know it was—it was like Matt says? Perhaps he—'

'Because it happened to me, too,' snarled Ben with sudden anger. 'Goddammit, what do I have to say? The woman's psychologically sick!'

Helen felt sick, too. 'I didn't know.'

'How could you?' Ben sighed. 'She's not your problem. But why do you think Chase had been drinking before that fatal match? Because he'd found her with some other man the night before.'

Helen trembled. 'And—Matt knows this?'

'He does now.'

'What do you mean?'

'I mean, I told him. As soon as I could talk some sense into him. I guess it was a couple of days after you left. I told him he couldn't believe a word she said.'

Helen moved her head. 'And he—believed you?'

'You mean, is that why he wrote to you? Yeah, I guess that sounds about right. But by then I think he'd come to the conclusion that he wanted you, whatever.' He scowled. 'I've never seen him in such a state before.'

Helen pressed her damp palms to her knees. 'I—don't think I understand.'

'Sure you do.' Ben sounded almost sardonic now. 'He

sent me here because he believes you never want to see him again. He wouldn't listen to your explanation, so why should you listen to his?'

'I see you haven't eaten your lunch again,' Ruth chided her employer reprovingly. 'And that won't aid your digestion,' she added, nodding at the glass of whisky in his hand. 'I don't know what's the matter with you. You always used to like my cooking.'

'There's nothing wrong with your cooking, Ruth,' Matthew assured her evenly. 'The quiche was really delicious, and the apricot mousse just melted in the mouth.'

'But not your mouth, hmm?' Ruth observed wryly. 'Will you be working this afternoon, or shall I tell Vittorio he can have the afternoon off?'

Matthew scowled. 'What a trial you are, woman. No, I shan't be working. Tell Vittorio to come back tomorrow morning. I'll probably be working then.'

'Probably.'

Ruth went away, muttering to herself, and, leaving the table, Matthew carried his glass to the windows. The housekeeper could be a nuisance, but he knew she only had his best interests at heart. But the trouble was, he didn't have any enthusiasm for anything these days. He had more money than he needed, and his writing was too demanding in his present state.

He sighed, raising his glass to his lips and draining it in one gulp. Whisky, he thought. The total panacea. But unfortunately even that was losing its potency. In the last few days, he'd found nothing would dull the pain. Perhaps he should have taken his father's advice and gone to see her. But after what had happened—and the fact that she hadn't answered his letters—he'd chickened out.

All the same, he'd have thought the old man would have had a result by now. All he'd had to do was ring the Sheridans and get Helen's address from them. They couldn't know what Matthew had written in those letters.

But they must have had an address to forward them or they'd have sent them back.

But yesterday afternoon, when he'd phoned the hotel where his father was staying, Ben had been decidedly vague. He'd spoken to the Sheridans, he'd said, and yes, he had Helen's address. But she was staying somewhere out in the suburbs, and he hadn't had the energy to see her yet.

Naturally, Matthew had been concerned, but when—seizing the opportunity—he'd offered to fly over and join him, Ben had insisted that he stay where he was. He'd be all right, he said. He was only tired. But Matthew intended to ring again today, and if he was still feeling under the weather...

He looked down at his empty glass, and then turned back to where he had left the decanter. But although he removed the stopper he didn't pour any. Until Ben had spoken to Helen nothing was going to do any good.

The phone rang just then, and he practically lunged across the room to answer it before Vittorio could beat him to it. But then he remembered. He'd given Vittorio the afternoon off. His new assistant was a young Barbadian, and he lived in Bridgetown with his wife.

'Dad?' he exclaimed into the receiver, and then suppressed a savage curse when he heard his publisher's voice. 'Oh, hi, Marilyn. Yeah, I know, I did promise. But I did have a concussion, I told you that.'

Marilyn wasn't appeased. And Matthew guessed he couldn't blame her. The book was now three months overdue, and he was slacking. OK, he'd had his problems, but he was supposed to be a professional, for God's sake.

'Three weeks,' he said at last, having driven her up from the ten days she'd first suggested. 'Yeah, I'll deliver it myself. You have my word. I know, I've said that before, but this time I mean it. Just give me a few more days to get my head together.'

'It looks all right to me,' said a soft voice behind him,

and Matthew swung round so sharply that the base of the phone went crashing to the floor.

He could hardly believe it: Helen was standing just inside the door. Then, as Marilyn protested, 'God—what? Oh, I'm sorry. I dropped the phone.'

She looked so good, he thought incredulously, hardly aware of what Marilyn said after that. A sleeveless green tunic, slit to the waist, over clinging white ankle-length leggings, gave her a sinuous, sensuous beauty. And her hair was loose for once, drawn back loosely at her nape with a white ribbon.

'Dammit, Matt, are you listening to me?'

Dragging his eyes from Helen's increasingly nervous gaze, Matthew knew he had to get rid of Marilyn without delay. Why Helen was here, what the old man had told her, were questions he needed answering. There was nothing more important. Whatever his publisher might think.

'Look, I've got to go,' he said, as Helen smoothed her palms against the panels of the door behind her. 'Um— something's come up. I can't talk now. Leave it with me, and I'll get back to you. Just don't hold your breath, eh, Marilyn? There are more important things in life.'

He saw the way Helen's expression changed when he mentioned the other woman's name and, drawing courage from that revelation, he said huskily, 'My publisher,' as he put down the phone. He swallowed. 'She's on my back because I haven't been doing any writing.' He shrugged. 'I guess I've had other things on my mind in recent weeks.'

'Like a concussion?' Helen suggested, proving his father had been talking, and Matthew felt a momentary anger towards the old man.

'It wasn't serious,' he said, with a taut grimace. 'I guess my skull's too thick to do it any real harm.'

'All head injuries are serious,' she retorted swiftly, and then, with a nervous twitch of her spine, 'I'm sorry. That is, I had no idea Lucas felt that way about me. I didn't give him any encouragement. I'm not like—like Fleur, whatever you think.'

Matthew conceded the point, suddenly aware that he hadn't shaved that morning, and that there was an unbecoming shadow of stubble on his jaw. The dining-room wasn't the place he'd have chosen to have this discussion either. But it was too hot outside, and he was loath to remind her of the last time she was here.

'Well, it's over now,' he said at last, when it became apparent that she had nothing more to say. 'Luke's gone back to working in television. I got a request for a reference from a news station in New York.'

'Oh.'

Helen nodded, and, realising he couldn't restrain himself any longer, Matthew decided to confront his fears right off. 'Yes,' he said, massaging the tense muscles at the back of his neck with unsteady fingers. 'Was—was that the only reason you came?'

Helen straightened then. 'Not exactly,' she replied, and Matthew felt a tightening in his loins. 'I came to—to tell you I—didn't get your letters. Your father said you'd written to me, but I didn't know.'

Matthew blinked. 'Son of a—' He broke off abruptly, and stared at her with uncomprehending eyes. 'But the Sheridans knew where you were living, didn't they?' He shook his head. 'They must have. How else did the old man get your address?'

'Oh, yes.' Helen moistened her lips with the tip of her tongue, and Matthew wondered if she had any idea how much he longed to feel that tongue in his mouth. 'Tricia had my address, and she wrote and told me that your father wanted me to contact him. But—' she coloured '—I thought it could only be because—because of what had happened. And, well—I didn't want to go through all that again.'

Matthew stared at her. 'Let me get this straight. You

didn't get my letters, but you did get the message from my father?'

'Yes.'

'So what happened?' He scowled. 'If Sheridan held them back, I'll—'

'He didn't.' Helen hesitated. 'At least, your father and I don't think so. Mr Aitken said you probably gave them to Lucas to post, and—well, maybe—maybe he didn't.'

Matthew swore. 'So—when my father came to see you— I'm assuming he did come to see you—yesterday?'

'The day before.'

'Until then, you thought I still believed what Fleur had said?'

She nodded.

'Dear God!' He raked back his hair with an aggressive hand. 'And here was I, thinking you still hated my guts for what I'd done.'

Helen lifted her slim shoulders. 'I—never—hated your guts,' she told him softly, and Matthew felt some of the misery he'd been carrying around since she left lift from his shoulders. 'What happened—happened because I wanted it,' she went on carefully. She took a breath. 'Your father said you were worried about me. Does that mean you've forgiven me for who I am?'

'There was nothing to forgive,' said Matthew gruffly. He'd waited so long—without any hope of redemption— to hear her say those words, and even now he could scarcely believe she was here. 'I had no right to accuse you. My God, you're not your mother's keeper. And you were the best thing that had ever happened to me, besides.'

'Was I?' she asked faintly, and he uttered a sigh.

'Of course,' he said, 'but I guess that's why I found it so easy to believe the worst. What Fleur said— God! It made a horrible kind of sense. And after what Chase had done to your father...' He shook his head.

'Oh, Matt!'

'I know, I know.' He gripped the back of his neck with

painful fingers. 'But I'd never felt that way before, and I was hooked. Fleur and me—well, let's say she has reason to resent me.' He grimaced. 'I was one of her—disappointments, and she doesn't forget.'

Helen hesitated. 'I know.' Then, at his look of surprise, she added ruefully, 'Your father told me. He's worried about you, too, but I expect you know.' She shook her head. 'There's a lot of things I don't know about my mother. But I don't think I blame Chase any more for what happened to my father.'

Matthew's eyes narrowed. 'And me?' he said. 'What about me? Can you ever forgive me for treating you as I did? I should never have let you leave the island. I should have trusted you. You're nothing like Fleur, and I was a fool to let you go.'

Helen swallowed. 'It doesn't matter.'

'It does, too.' He took a step towards her and, stretching out one hand, he brushed the back of his knuckles against her cheek. 'Are you going to stay? Are you going to let me make it up to you? I never thought I'd be grateful to the Sheridans for anything, but I'm really glad they fired you right now.'

Helen stiffened. 'You don't have to feel responsible for me.'

'But I do.'

'No.' She dashed her hand across her cheek, as if to remove the imprint of his fingers. 'You don't understand. I didn't come here because I want you to—to help me. I've saved some money, and I'm taking a secretarial course so that I can get a decent job.'

Matthew closed his eyes for a moment. 'But I thought—'

'What did you think?' she demanded, suddenly distraught. 'That as soon as your father contacted me, I saw a meal-ticket for life?' She caught her breath. 'I'm not like that. I don't need your money. I've seen what money can do, and I'm not impressed.'

Matthew took another step towards her. 'And me?' he

said. 'What about me? What if I need you? Doesn't that count?'

Helen shook her head. 'You don't need me.' She spread her hands. 'You don't need anyone. Besides, there are any number of beautiful women more than eager to do anything you say. I was just—a novelty. A silly virgin. But that doesn't mean you have to look after me for the rest of my life.'

Matthew drew a steadying breath. 'And what if I want to?' he asked. 'What if I tell you that's why I thought you'd come here? Because I thought you shared the way I feel? My father told you so much about me. Didn't he tell you I was crazy about you, too?'

He saw the tremulous hope dawning in her face and, taking advantage of her momentary uncertainty, he grasped her wrists and pulled her towards him.

'Didn't he tell you I love you?' he demanded, taking her arms behind his back and staring down into eyes grown misty with longing. 'I do, you know. That's why I was such a fool. I was afraid…'

'Afraid?' she whispered, and, realising he didn't have to imprison her any longer, Matthew cupped her face in his hands.

'Yeah, afraid,' he breathed, bestowing a kiss at the corner of her mouth. 'Afraid I'd made a mistake. Afraid you didn't feel the same way.'

Helen moved her head. 'But you knew—'

'What did I know?' he countered, running a line of kisses along her jawline before finding her mouth again. 'That I was the first man who'd touched you? That I'd taken advantage of your—?'

'Don't.' She raised her hand and pressed a finger against his lips. 'You didn't take advantage of me. I—I wanted you just as much as you wanted me.'

'And now?'

'Now?' She looked doubtful.

'How do you feel now? Are you going to put me out of my misery?'

'Oh, Matt.' He felt her hands slip beneath his shirt and spread damply against his spine. 'If—if you want me, I—I'm here.'

His eyes darkened. 'For how long?'

She coloured. 'I don't know what you mean.'

Matthew's thumbs brushed her lips. 'Are we talking weeks, here, or months—or a lifetime commitment?'

He felt her tremble. 'As—as long as you want me, I suppose.'

'That so?' His fingers slid into her hair. 'Well, Miss—Graham? Gregory? Whatever the hell your name is, you just got yourself a life-sentence.'

It was the evening of that day before they really talked again. Some time after sundown, Helen stirred in the silken comfort of Matthew's huge bed to find he had turned on the lamps and was watching her with a decidedly possessive smile on his dark face.

'You must have been tired,' he remarked, dipping his head and stroking her bare shoulder with his tongue. 'I like watching you sleep.'

Helen coloured, and groped for the sheet, but he wouldn't let her cover herself. 'Don't ever hide yourself from me,' he whispered huskily. 'You're beautiful, and I'm never going to get tired of looking at you.'

Helen relaxed. 'Nor I you,' she admitted sweetly. 'Oh, Matt, I do love you.'

'Do you?' A dark brow arched. 'I'm so glad to hear it.'

She frowned. 'What do you mean?'

'Well, you didn't say that before,' he told her drily. 'I hoped, but…'

'Matt!' She got up on her elbows and looked down into his lazy face. 'You knew how I felt. I—I just don't find it that easy to—to say what I feel.'

'No?' His hand cupped her nape, under the glorious

tangle of her loosened hair. 'Well, let me see, what else can I do to help you?'

'You know what I mean,' she exclaimed hotly, and then, realising he was teasing her, she bent and nipped his lip with her teeth. 'Devil,' she said. 'You were never in any doubt.'

Matthew grinned. 'If I say I was, will you do that again?'

Helen shook her head. 'You're incorrigible.'

'Just insatiable,' he corrected her softly. 'For you.'

And for several minutes Helen couldn't answer him.

But when he eventually allowed her to prop herself above him again, she said, 'About Fleur—'

'To hell with Fleur,' he retorted feelingly. But at her troubled look he relented. 'The last we heard she was in Los Angeles. She'd apparently hooked up with some other poor guy.'

'No?'

'Yes.' He sighed. 'That was when I became convinced that she hadn't bothered to find out if you were OK.'

Helen grimaced. 'Well, I suppose that's something to thank her for,' she mused, but Matthew didn't look convinced.

'Mmm,' he said wryly. 'Well, at any rate, she shouldn't be bothering us again for some time. And once we've made her a grandmother, she's not going to find it easy to forgive us.'

Helen caught her breath. 'A grandmother,' she echoed, and Matthew drew her down to nuzzle her cheek.

'Well, maybe not immediately,' he said. 'There's the wedding to arrange first, and the honeymoon...'

Helen stared at him. 'Is that a proposal?'

'Unless you want me to get down on to my knees. I will, but not right now. You've tired me out.'

'You!' Helen punched his shoulder. 'I should refuse to accept it.'

'But you won't,' he teased, and then, with a trace of concern, 'Will you?'

'No,' she conceded ruefully, and with a triumphant groan Matthew rolled her on to her back and imprisoned her beneath him. 'Providing…'

'Providing?'

He stopped what he was doing to stare down at her, and she gave him a mischievous smile. 'Providing you'll ask your father to be your best man,' she finished, finding herself incapable of saying anything to burst his bubble of happiness, and he gave a hoot of laughter.

'Oh, yes,' he said, his thigh sliding between hers. 'My father will be more than willing to oblige. After all, someone's got to inherit Ryan's Bend, and he's been aching for a grandson for years.'

Miranda Lee is Australian, living near Sydney. Born and raised in the bush, she was boarding-school educated and briefly pursued a classical music career before moving to Sydney and embracing the world of computers. Happily married, with three daughters, she began writing when family commitments kept her at home. She likes to create stories that are believable, modern, fast-paced and sexy. Her interests include reading meaty sagas, doing word puzzles, gambling and going to the movies.

RENDEZVOUS WITH REVENGE

by

MIRANDA LEE

conference. Now, if you don't mind, I still have a few letters to dictate here for Miss Richmond to type up before she leaves.'

Abby's eyebrows rose in a sardonic arch. Six months she'd worked for Ethan Grant and he still called her 'Miss Richmond'. Not that she really cared. It suited her fine to keep the disgustingly handsome orthopaedic surgeon at a safe distance. Romance was not on her agenda this year.

Or any other year, came the added bitter thought. She'd had enough of romance to last her a lifetime!

Still, his cold indifference to her as a living, breathing human being did niggle a little occasionally. He'd never asked her one single question about herself during the last six months. Not one.

Abby smiled ruefully as she recalled their first meeting. He'd been sitting behind his desk with his head down when Sylvia had ushered her in for an introduction.

Apparently, he'd given his sister a free hand in hiring someone to take over from her on a Friday—Sylvia having decided that after years of slavery to Ethan as both his housekeeper and full-time receptionist she wanted Fridays off. Her dear brother's only instruction had been that she was to train her Friday replacement thoroughly so that there would be no hiccups in her absence.

Abby wasn't sure what she'd expected after having met Sylvia. Someone older, she supposed. And less... striking. Sylvia was around fifty, plump, pale and rather plain. So when Ethan Grant had lifted his darkly handsome head and set his startlingly blue eyes on her, she'd blinked her shock for a few seconds.

Her involuntary surprise at his unexpected good looks, plus his age—late thirties at the most—had not gone unnoticed, a scornful coldness sweeping over those arrogantly handsome features, setting their chiselled beauty into a forbidding concrete.

'How do you do, Miss Richmond,' he'd said with a frozen formality which had never changed, not once in six months.

Abby found his chilly aloofness almost amusing at times. What had he thought during those first moments of their meeting? That she'd been bowled over by his brooding sex appeal? Did he believe that she might be harbouring a hidden passion for him, and that if he gave her an inch she would take more than a mile?

God, it would take more than tall, dark and handsome to bewitch her these days. Her experience with Dillon had taught her well. Oh, yes, the dear doctor had made her silly female heart flutter for a split second, but that was all. She'd quickly learnt to control any further involuntary sexual responses when she looked at him; just as she'd quickly learnt what kind of man lay behind his smouldering good looks.

He was a machine, not a man. A cold-blooded, cold-hearted robot who worked eighteen-hour days, operating at not one or two, but *three* hospitals. He even operated on a Saturday occasionally, if his lists for that week were too long to be fitted in to his Monday, Wednesday and Friday morning operating schedules.

Abby sometimes wondered why his patients set such store by him. It had to be because of his skill, not his bedside manner. He had consultations every Friday afternoon while she was there, giving her plenty of opportunity to study his personality, and she'd never seen him so much as smile at a patient. He would come out of his rooms and call each successive one in with that same sphinx-like expression on his face.

They were just cases to him, Abby accepted finally, not people. She wouldn't mind betting that he had never become emotionally involved with a single person he'd operated on.

Obviously, he never became emotionally involved with *anyone*, from what she'd just heard.

'There's no use bullying me about it, Sylvia,' he was saying in a vaguely bored tone. 'I'm not going and that's final.'

'Then more fool you! Any other man would just find someone else to take.'

'Such as whom?'

'Oh, I don't know.' Sylvia was beginning to sound very irritable. 'You could hire yourself one of those escorts, I suppose.'

'Don't be ridiculous. One of my closest colleagues will be there with his wife. Do you honestly think I would show up with an amateur call-girl on my arm?'

'How would they ever know?'

'*I'd* know,' he bit out.

'Are you telling me you've finally developed scruples where women and sex are concerned? Frankly, I think it's a perfectly splendid idea, and perfectly suited to your requirements. For the right fee you'd get exactly what you want from a woman and no more,' Sylvia threw at him tartly. 'You certainly wouldn't have to worry about her having designs on you afterwards either. You'd know right from the start that she was only screwing you for your money!'

Abby's eyebrows shot up ceilingwards. Sylvia must really be mad to resort to such an unladylike expression. Still, it was rather good to hear Sylvia get the better of her pain of a brother for once. Clearly he was rendered speechless by her acid barbs, if the sudden silence was anything to go by.

'Aren't you going to say anything more, Ethan?' Sylvia demanded after a short while. 'Don't you dare just ignore me. I won't have it, do you hear?'

'And I won't have you telling me how to run my private life,' her brother returned in an ominously cold voice. 'Now, go home and leave me be. I have work to do.'

Abby knew that tone of voice. And clearly so did Sylvia, who emerged from the room looking defeated. Closing the door distractedly behind her, she began walking slowly across the empty waiting room with a genuinely troubled look on her face. She seemed totally unaware of Abby's presence behind the desk, so deep in thought was she.

Abby's clearing her throat brought her head up with a startled gasp. 'Oh, my goodness, Abby! I forgot you were still here.'

'Would you like a cup of tea, Sylvia?' Abby offered. 'You seem a little…upset.'

Sylvia sighed. 'No, thanks, but thanks for offering. You're a sweet girl. I'd better go home and get dinner started. It's time you went home too, isn't it? It's after five.'

'Dr Grant hasn't finished dictating today's letters. I'll have to stay back till I've typed them up. You know how particular he is about that.'

'What a slave-driver that man is! Make sure you put down the overtime.'

'Oh, I will; don't you worry.'

Sylvia gave her a sharp glance. 'Are you having money problems, Abby?'

'I'm always having money problems.' The money she

earned from her one day here plus her weekend waitressing job was just enough to make ends meet, with
nothing left over for emergencies or luxuries.

'No luck getting a permanent position yet?'

'Unfortunately no.' Despite spending every spare second and cent having her résumé photocopied and sending it off in answer to every suitable job advertisement.
The local unemployment office was getting sick of the
sight of her, as well.

'I don't understand that at all. I would have thought
some big flashy company would have snapped up a
good-looking girl like you for their front desk.'

Abby just shrugged. She didn't want to tell Sylvia the
probable reason that her application was passed over
most of the time. They obviously took one look at where
she'd taken her secretarial course and immediately put
her résumé aside.

Sylvia had never asked for a written or detailed application, naïvely hiring Abby on just a telephone call
and one short personal interview, blindly believing her
when she'd said she'd been overseas on a working holiday for a few years and had no recent employment history in Australia.

Abby had not liked lying to her—she'd taken to
Sylvia straight away—but poverty did rather make one
desperate. She took some comfort from the fact that the
glowing personal reference she'd been able to supply
had been the genuine article and not a forgery. Dear
Miss Blanchford…Abby was so grateful to her.

'I *did* get one interview earlier this week,' she admitted, cringing inside as she recalled the smarmy manner
of the man who'd interviewed her. No way would she
take *that* job, even if it was offered to her.

'Oh? Who with?'

'A small car-repair company in Alexandria.'

Sylvia's nose wrinkled. 'Surely you could do better than that.'

'I was hoping to, but times are tough.'

'I'll ask Ethan to find out if any doctor he knows requires a full-time receptionist,' Sylvia said kindly. 'Not that I want you to go. I'm really going to miss you. Ethan will too. He just doesn't know what a gem we found in you. You're always so willing to work back. Most pretty young things would be out of here like a shot on a Friday night.'

'I'm not that young, Sylvia.'

'Which is another thing I don't understand—how you got to be twenty-five years old without some lucky man snapping you up as well.'

'I guess I'm just not the type men snap up,' Abby said, smiling wryly as she glanced up at Sylvia. Her smile faded when she found that Ethan had come out of his rooms and was standing in the middle of the waiting room watching her, a drily cynical amusement in his cold blue eyes.

You're right there, darling, they seemed to say. You're the type men take to bed, not to the altar.

Resentment at his ongoing and unjustified assessment of her character sent her nostrils flaring and her heart thudding angrily. Who in hell did he think he was, judging her like that, and on such superficial evidence?

Abby was well aware that she hadn't been behind the door when God gave out looks. But she'd never been a flaunter of her various feminine attributes, or a flirt. And she had only had one lover in her life!

Admittedly she'd dressed and acted a bit more provocatively during her months as Dillon's girlfriend—he'd liked her in tight tops and short skirts and skimpy bikinis, and she'd been too besotted to deny him any-thing. He hadn't minded other men looking at her either, had seemed to enjoy their wanting what he had.

But nowadays she played down her sex appeal, using no make-up and wearing her long honey-brown hair in a simple plait most of the time. She never highlighted her full mouth with lipstick and did her best to keep her smiles to a minimum after her sleazy landlord had told her that her cool grey eyes took on a 'come hither' spar-kle whenever she smiled.

'Is there something I can do for you, Doctor?' she asked, congratulating herself on the coolly delivered question.

He arched a cooler eyebrow back at her. 'Just three letters to type, thank you, Miss Richmond. After that, you can go home.'

Sylvia made an exasperated sound. 'For goodness' sake, when are you two going to start calling each other by your first names?'

When hell freezes over, Abby thought tartly.

'Miss Richmond would not appreciate my being fam-iliar with her—would you, Miss Richmond?'

Their eyes clashed and Abby saw the mockery in his. She decided that two could play that game. 'I think a certain decorum is called for during surgery hours. Of course, if Dr Grant wants me to call him Ethan after hours, then he only has to say so.' Her steely gaze was drily challenging, but it didn't faze the robot one bit.

'I think we'll keep the status quo for now,' he coun-tered without turning a hair. 'Shouldn't you be off, Sylvia? It's getting late.'

Exasperation was written all over his sister. 'One day, Ethan,' she muttered as she stalked out, banging the door behind her.

Abby hoped that she'd be around to see this unlikely comeuppance. But she doubted it. Ethan Grant couldn't be emotionally hurt because he didn't *feel*.

Or did he?

Sylvia's earlier accusation that he was still getting over some woman named Vanessa popped back into Abby's head. She stared at him, wondering if that could explain his attitude towards her. Had he been jilted once by some pretty young woman? Was she still embittered years later?

Abby could appreciate how that might happen. She herself knew that it would be many years before she got over what Dillon had done to her. But she'd never attributed such sensitivity to the male sex, and especially not to a man like Ethan Grant, who didn't seem to have a sensitive bone in his body.

'Do I have a pimple on my nose, Miss Richmond?' Ethan Grant asked archly. 'You're staring at me.'

'Sorry, Doctor. I wasn't really staring at you. I was off in another world.'

'Not a pleasant one, by the look on your face.'

'No,' she agreed drily. Memories of Dillon and what he'd done never inspired her to do the Highland Fling.

'You're not the most communicative female, are you?' he said, a flash of irritation crossing his normally impassive face. 'Here. Make sure you post all the letters on your way home,' he said as he handed over the small tape recorder, then whirled to stride back into his room, his white coat flapping rather angrily around his legs.

Abby stared after him with rounded eyes, aware that she'd just seen Ethan Grant not quite his usual, coolly composed self.

What had disturbed his equilibrium? she puzzled. His earlier argument with Sylvia? Surely not his discovering that his latest ladyfriend wanted more of him than the occasional dinner date. He'd been coldly contemptuous about that.

No, it had been something to do with *her*. Probably her staring at him. He hadn't liked that one bit. He also hadn't liked her not revealing what lay behind her preoccupation.

Well, that's too bad, Abby thought caustically as she settled down behind her computer to begin typing up the letters.

She hadn't typed more than a heading when a bitter smile tugged at her mouth. God, she could just imagine Ethan Grant's reaction if she'd told him she was thinking about her bastard of an ex-boyfriend, and how *his* betrayal had sent her to prison for four years—four long, hard, soul-destroying years.

Abby didn't think that what had happened to the dear doctor via the hands of that Vanessa woman would match what Dillon had put her through. If anyone had the right to be bitter and wary about the opposite sex, it was Abigail Rose-Maree Richmond!

CHAPTER TWO

ABBY was just beginning the second letter when she remembered the *other* letter—the one she'd forgotten to give to Ethan.

All the mail had been delivered extra late that day, *after* Dr Grant had started seeing patients. Not that he ever opened the mail himself, unless it was marked 'Confidential' or 'Private'.

Such an occurrence was rare. Most letters sent to the surgery were either cheques for unpaid accounts, general enquiries from other doctors, or advertising mail from various pharmaceutical and medical companies. But there was one letter that Friday which Abby thought the doctor might want to see personally.

It was from the Bungarla private hotel where the medical conference was being held—a notice about a last-minute change of lecturer. It seemed that one of the Sydney surgeons listed to lecture was unavailable, and was being replaced by world-famous neurosurgeon Dr Philip Ballistrat.

Abby appreciated that Ethan probably wouldn't care less about it, now that he'd decided not to go, but since she wasn't supposed to know about that she thought she'd better take it in to him.

Sighing, she pressed pause on the tape recorder, picked up the envelope in question and rose to make her way across the waiting room floor. She stopped in front of the closed door, glancing down to check that all the

16

buttons on her white blouse were safely done up before smoothing the pleated black skirt down over her hips.

Abby didn't want a repeat of the unfortunate incident a couple of weeks back when, unbeknownst to her, one of the small pearl buttons on her blouse had popped open, giving anyone who had looked at her chest at an angle an eyeful of lace-encased breasts.

'It seems one of your buttons has lost its battle against your womanly shape, Miss Richmond,' Ethan had pointed out in a softly mocking voice as he'd bent to pick up his next patient's file from the tray beside her. 'Perhaps larger buttons are called for in future? Or even a bigger sized blouse?'

Abby had been thankful that he'd turned away before her embarrassment had time to blossom into a full-blown blush. Which it had—her mortification increased by the way her breasts had immediately seemed to swell further, straining against her bra and her blouse, making her fumbling attempt to do up the tiny button all the more difficult.

It was the only time Ethan Grant had managed to get under her skin—sexually speaking—and she wasn't about to let it happen again. So Abby was disturbed to find that when she knocked on the door, her hand was shaking. There was also an instant gathering of butterflies in the pit of her stomach.

Her scowl reflected her feelings. To have Ethan Grant reduce her to nervy state was irritating in the extreme.

'Do come in, Miss Richmond,' came the laconic invitation.

Gritting her teeth, Abby opened the door and went in, calmed by the knowledge that her private agitation was just that. Private. The man seated behind his desk would never guess from her calm demeanour and cool gaze that she was anything but totally indifferent, both to his personage and his looks.

'Yes, what is it?' he asked peremptorily on glancing up.

She stepped forward and deposited the envelope on the leather-topped desk. 'A letter for you, Doctor. It's from the people running the conference next week, letting you know about a last-minute change of lecturer. I thought you might like to have a look at it but I forgot to give it to you earlier. Sorry.'

He picked up the envelope and tossed it straight into the waste-paper basket in the corner. 'I've decided not to go to that,' he said brusquely.

The movement of light and shadow across his face showed dark rings of exhaustion under his beautiful blue eyes, and despite knowing that it was all self-inflicted Abby felt marginally sorry for him.

'What a pity,' she said, deciding to do her bit to get the damned fool to go. Love him or hate him, he was a good doctor and he really did need a break. 'They've been able to get Dr Philip Ballistrat in place of one of the lesser lights,' she said encouragingly. 'I would have thought you'd like to hear him talk. He's very famous, isn't he?'

Abby was taken aback by Ethan's response to her news. He remained frozen in his seat for several seconds, his normally phlegmatic blue eyes betraying...what? Surprise? Astonishment? Surely not shock! What was so shocking about what she'd just told him?

Abby was even more taken aback when any surprise was swiftly replaced by an icy smile which sent an oddly erotic shiver running down her spine.

'Well, well, well,' he drawled. 'Who would have believed that? You're quite right, Miss Richmond. I certainly wouldn't like to miss the opportunity of hearing such a renowned surgeon.'

He swivelled round in his black leather chair, slid over to the corner, lifted the envelope back out of the basket then slid back again. 'Thank you for bringing it to my attention. You've no idea how disappointed I would have been to have found out afterwards he'd been there and I'd missed him.'

'So you're going after all?' she asked hopefully, thinking how happy Sylvia would be.

'Wouldn't miss it for the world.'

Abby almost clapped her pleasure.

'That's some smile, Miss Richmond. I take it you won't mind my being absent next Friday?'

Was it his sardonic remark, or the intensity of his gaze on her mouth which rattled her? Whatever, her smile faded immediately, although her heart began pounding behind her ribs and she found herself staring back at *his* mouth and wondering how it would feel upon hers.

Abby could hardly believe her train of thought. Lord, she didn't even *like* the man. Yet here she was, fantasising about his making love to her.

Self-disgust made her stiffen inside. She straightened to her full five feet nine inches and delivered a cool look across the desk. 'It makes no difference to me, Dr Grant, whether you're here or not.'

His laugh was as cold as his eyes. 'No. I can see that. Which is just as well, I suppose. That way you'll be able to give the proposition I'm about to make a totally un-biased consideration.'

'P-proposition? What proposition?'

'Don't look so alarmed, Miss Richmond. I'm not about to ask you to do anything immoral or criminal. I am, however, in an awkward situation where this conference-cum-holiday is concerned. It's for couples, you see, and the ladyfriend I was going to take can't make it.'

Abby was taken aback by the smooth delivery of the lie. Funny. As much as she didn't like Ethan Grant, she'd never thought of him as a liar. It just showed that one should never underestimate the deviousness of the male sex.

'That was the main reason I'd decided not to go,' he continued coolly. 'Because it would be embarrassing and awkward to show up alone. Actually, my sweet sister suggested I hire a professional escort instead, but I'm sure you can appreciate that's not to my taste. However, it occurred to me just now that perhaps I could persuade *you* to accompany me.

'For a price, of course,' he added, before Abby could do more than blink her shock. 'I don't expect you to do it for nothing. Sylvia mentioned once that you work as a waitress on the weekend. I would naturally compensate you for any lost wages, with quite a bonus thrown in. So what do you say, Miss Richmond? Do you think you might be interested?'

What do I say?

Abby stared at him while she battled to control her simmering fury. I'd say not for all the tea in China, you presumptuous, patronising bastard. I'd say stick it in your ear. I'd say up yours. I wouldn't spend one hour alone with you, let alone three days and three nights!

'I'm sorry, I can't,' was what she actually said, congratulating herself on her silkily smooth voice.

'The boyfriend would object, I take it?'

'No. I don't have a boyfriend,' she said.

'Surprising,' he drawled. 'Why, then?'

'I wasn't able to work last weekend because of a

tummy bug. If I let my employer at the café down again this weekend I'll lose my job there, and I simply can't afford that.' She couldn't afford to lose *this* job either, which was why she was being so diplomatic. She'd have just loved to tell the dear doctor exactly what he could do with his proposition.

'How much do you earn in one weekend?'

'Why?'

He sighed. 'Just answer the question, please, Miss Richmond.'

'One hundred and twenty dollars, plus tips.'

'I see. How long would it take for you to get another similar job, if you lost that one?'

'What? Oh, I…I couldn't say exactly. Sometimes you can be lucky, but it could take weeks and weeks.'

'Three months tops, would you say?'

'Y-yes.' What was he getting at? Why didn't he just let the matter drop? She wasn't going to say yes, no matter how much he offered her.

He picked up a small calculator lying on his desk. 'Thirteen weeks times one-twenty equals one thousand, five hundred and sixty dollars,' he calculated aloud. 'I would assume a girl like you would get plenty of tips, so I'll up it to two thousand dollars—up front and in advance. What do you say to that, Abby? Not bad pay for three days' work. More than enough to make ends meet till you get another job.'

His use of her first name did not escape Abby, and it sealed his fate even more than his demeaning offer. 'I'm sorry, but I must refuse again, Dr Grant. I'm simply not a good enough actress for the part. I think Sylvia's right. I think you should hire yourself a professional.'

'But I don't want a professional, Abby,' he returned coolly. 'I want you.'

She just stared at him, her mouth going dry. My God, if she didn't know him better, she might think that he really meant that.

'Maybe I should clarify that last statement,' he went on drily, a single eyebrow lifting at her obvious surprise. 'The reason I said I wanted you specifically is because I know that underneath your oh, so cool politeness you can't stand a bar of me. I have no wish to have to fire you afterwards because you've stupidly fallen in love with me. On top of that, I would imagine that in the right clothes you could be quite lovely. Yes...' His eyes drifted down from her face to the swell of her breasts. '*Quite* lovely.'

Abby didn't know which part of his speech infuriated her the most. Certainly the condescending and lukewarm '*quite* lovely' kept going round and round in her head. My God, if she set her mind to it, she could knock this supercilious devil's eyes out!

'Aren't you afraid my underlying dislike might show through?' she asked through gritted teeth.

'No. I have great faith in the acting ability of women. Besides, I never take out females who fawn all over me. Of course, under the circumstances, I will only expect you to pretend to be a friend, not my live-in lover. Consequently I will change the booking to twin rooms.'

Abby only just managed to hide her contempt. So Evelyn had been expected to sleep with him during this little jaunt, play the part of his wife without ever expecting to get the part for real.

Charming.

For all Dillon's subsequent betrayal, he'd at least been prepared to pull out all the stops in winning her heart before expecting her to become his lover. Nothing had been too much trouble—flowers, chocolates, candlelit dinners. He'd swept her off to bed with sweet words ringing in her ears and promises of forever. Whereas Ethan Grant promised his women nothing…except a cold-blooded, machine-like performance between the sheets.

Why, then, did Abby find herself suddenly wanting to experience that machine-like performance? Why, for pity's sake? It went against everything she'd ever believed about herself.

Heat rushed into her cheeks at the appalling thoughts which sprang into her mind.

'I'm sorry,' she said, flustered now. 'It…it's quite out of the question. I simply can't.'

'There's no such word as can't,' he bit out. 'So what's the problem, then? I would have thought two thousand dollars would have smoothed over any antagonism you felt towards me. Believe it or not, I can be quite personable company when I want to be. Look, don't say no straight away. Think it over and give me a ring at home on Sunday night around eight. Sylvia will be out, so you needn't worry about any awkwardness there.'

Abby decided that it would be much easier to refuse for the second and last time over the telephone. It was hard to sound convincing when one was blushing and stammering. And when underneath one was insanely tempted to say yes. My God, she must be going mad!

'All right,' she agreed shakily.

When the beginnings of a smug smile pulled at her employer's disdainful mouth, Abby's heart immediately stopped its stupid fluttering. He believed she'd say yes, that the money he'd offered would override any qualms she might have.

Abby's heart hardened further as she recognised that

he might even suspect that underneath her surface hostility she was sexually attracted to him. This last suspicion closed the door on the subject. Nothing on earth would ever make her say yes now. Nothing!

CHAPTER THREE

NOTHING, as it turned out, except fate, and an old lady's heartbreak.

The first nail in Abby's coffin came the next day, when she quit her waitressing job after the boss pawed at her bottom one time too many. Then, on that same Saturday night, some rotten thug broke in and burgled Miss Blanchford's room. The poor old thing was so distressed that Abby spent the whole of Sunday trying to comfort her.

'It'll be all right, Miss Blanchford,' Abby soothed, after the police had finally left at around four in the afternoon. They were sitting in Miss Blanchford's room, which was the biggest and best in the ancient old boarding house, its large window overlooking the rather ramshackle front garden. Unfortunately, it had been this same window which had given the thief easy entry into the downstairs room.

Miss Blanchford shook her head as two big tears trickled down her wrinkled cheeks. 'All gone,' she said with a strangled sob. 'Five years' savings. All gone.'

Abby bit her bottom lip to stop herself from crying as well. The poor old thing. But, oh…if only she'd put her money in the bank, instead of in a biscuit tin under her bed.

The police thought the thief was probably someone who'd once lived in the same boarding house and had learnt about Miss Blanchford's distrust of banks—not an uncommon thing with survivors of the great Depression.

25

Unfortunately, the police also thought there was little hope of finding the perpetrator and recovering the money, although they hadn't said as much to Miss Blanchford. Abby had insisted on that. The poor old love was upset enough as it was.

The real tragedy was that the money had been to buy an electric wheelchair. Miss Blanchford was suffering a degenerative muscular disease which was making it harder and harder for her to get around in her hand-propelled chair.

'What am I going to do, Abby?' the old lady cried. 'I don't want to go into one of those government nursing homes. But soon I won't be able to manage on my own. If I don't have my independence, I'd rather be dead.'

'Now you stop talking like that,' Abby reprimanded, but gently. 'The police'll get your money back for you; don't you worry.'

'No, they won't. It's gone. I'm a silly old fool for keeping it in that tin.'

'Now stop that. It won't help, crying over spilt milk. I have this gut feeling your money will show up. Give them a few days.' Abby had a gut feeling all right. Her stomach was already churning with the acceptance of what she was going to do to get Miss Blanchford that money.

'The man was coming to show me a chair next Wednesday. He said it was one of the best second-hand electric chairs he'd come across. And only three thousand dollars. New ones cost a lot more, you know.'

'Yes, I know,' Abby said, her thoughts whirling along with her stomach. If Ethan Grant was willing to pay two thousand for her company, might he pay more? Three thousand, perhaps? 'Up front and in advance', he'd promised. If he agreed to her counter-proposal, she'd be able to give Miss Blanchford the money before Wednesday.

Of course, she would tell her that the police had recovered the money. Her old ballet teacher was very proud and would never accept charity. On top of that, she might ask Abby some sticky questions about where the money had come from.

'Come now, Miss Blanchford,' Abby urged. 'Dry your tears. The woman who put me through my paces at the bar would not succumb to self-pity. Neither would she despair so quickly. Give the police a chance. And promise me you won't cancel that man coming on Wednesday.'

'All right, Abby.' The old lady found a watery smile from somewhere. 'Whatever would I do without you?'

'You'd do just fine, like always,' Abby reassured her old friend. Privately, however, she wasn't so sure. The once seemingly indestructible old lady was looking very frail today.

'I still can't get over my good fortune in your coming to live here. You're so good to me, Abby. Reading to me and playing cards with me. You're not going to move out after you get a full-time job, are you? I know this is not the nicest place in the world...'

Nice! It was a dump—the old house crumbling around them. But it was cheap, and only a short train ride from the city centre. She'd been given the address by a cellmate, and had hoped that she wouldn't need it. She'd hoped to be able to live at home.

But when she'd arrived at the house the day she'd been let out of prison six months earlier, there had been a message from her father saying that she was not welcome there, though he'd magnanimously said that she could take her personal belongings. She'd been so upset,

however, that she'd left the house without taking anything, relying instead on the clothes she'd brought from
prison.

The decrepit old boarding house had come as a bit of
a shock to begin with, but not as much of a shock as
the inhabitant of the downstairs front room.

Miss Blanchford had taught Abby ballet from the age
of three till Abby had been shipped off to a private
boarding school during her twelfth year. She hadn't seen
her dance teacher since then, but had never forgotten her,
having always admired her staunch sense of self-
discipline. She probably had Miss Blanchford to thank
for instilling in her enough strength of character to sustain her during her dark days in prison.

It seemed that Miss Blanchford had never forgotten
Abby either, her face lighting up with pleasure once she
recognised her old pupil. She and Abby had talked for
ages, and Abby had told her everything that had happened to her in the intervening years. It had been wonderful to find a sympathetic ear and a shoulder to cry
on.

Miss Blanchford's friendship meant the world to
Abby, and she could not bear to see the old lady so
unhappy. She vowed to do whatever was necessary to
get her the money she needed for that wheelchair. She
leant forward and patted the old lady's knees. They felt
very thin and bony through the crocheted rug.

'Now, don't you go worrying,' she said softly. 'If I
ever move then you'll come with me. And we're going
to get you that wheelchair, come hell or high water!'

At eight that evening, Abby set about putting her
mouth where her vows were. She walked down to the
telephone booth on the corner and dialled Ethan Grant's
home number. It killed her to lower her pride this way,

but, given that there was no viable alternative, Abby resolved to do it with style—priority number one being that her lordly employer never twig onto her unfortunate weakness in finding him attractive.

'Ethan Grant speaking,' he answered coolly, and another of those erotic shivers rippled down Abby's spine. Damn, but he did have an incredibly sensual voice, once one was attuned to it.

'Abigail Richmond here, Dr Grant,' she said as soon as she'd gathered herself.

'Ah yes, Miss Richmond. I've been expecting your call.'

Abby hoped that her counter-proposal would wipe some of the smugness out of that sexy damned voice.

'I've thought about your offer, Dr Grant,' she said in a marvellously matter-of-fact tone, 'and I've decided I should be able to accommodate you...' She paused just long enough for his male ego to swell further before adding, 'For a price, that is.'

His sharply indrawn breath rasped down the line, followed by a few seconds of taut silence.

'I've already offered you two thousand dollars,' he resumed at last, not a trace of sexiness left in his voice. It was as cold as an arctic blizzard. 'I would have thought that more than sufficed for the job.'

'I'm sorry, but it doesn't.'

'I see,' he grated out, with a derisive edge added to the chilly reproach. 'How much would be enough, then?'

'Three thousand.'

'That's one thousand a day!'

'That's my price, Dr Grant. Take it or leave it.'

His laughter surprised then unnerved her. 'Oh, I'll take it, Miss Richmond, but only on one condition.'

'And what condition is that?'

'I don't have to change the room booking. Frankly, for reasons which I have no intention of explaining, I would prefer to pretend we were lovers, not just friends. Naturally I do not expect you to sleep in the same bed with me. I will make sure our room has a convertible sofa which will guarantee separate sleeping arrangements.'

'And if I say no?'

'Then you say no, and I'll make other arrangements.'

Abby only had to think of Miss Blanchford's despairing depression to know that she would never say no. But she detested Ethan Grant for manoeuvring her into a corner like this.

Still, there was no point in prolonging the agony. It would only add to her humiliation. Better to agree immediately, letting him think that she wasn't at all fazed by this change.

'All right,' she said with a superbly blithe offhandedness. 'I appreciate that for three thousand you can call the shots. But I want it all up front and in advance, as you promised.'

Once again, Ethan fell silent on the other end.

Had she surprised him? *Shocked* him, even?

Too bad. This was business—the business of healing an old lady's heart and giving her back a reason to live. She had no sympathy for Ethan Grant's feelings. Any man who offered money for a woman's company got what he deserved. Which was nothing.

'I'll send you the money by courier tomorrow,' he said in a faintly sneering tone. Clearly she hadn't surprised him at all, Abby realised. She'd acted exactly as he expected women of her ilk to act—like a mercenary-minded bitch!

'Cash, please,' she snapped, goaded into speaking

sharply by a fierce inner fury. Couldn't he see that *he* was the more contemptuous person, for offering her money in the first place?

'Naturally.'

Abby scooped in then let out a shuddering sigh. It was done and couldn't be undone. God, but she wished that she didn't feel so low. Anyone would think that she'd just hired herself out body and soul for life, instead of just her companionship for three miserable days.

'I suppose we should get down to details while we've got the opportunity,' he said abruptly. 'I don't want Sylvia to know anything. This is just between you and me. As far as my sister is concerned, I'll be going to this conference on my own. You must give me your word on that, Abby.'

Abby was thrown for a moment by this second use of her first name. Till she accepted that he could hardly keep calling her Miss Richmond. She wasn't about to argue about Sylvia not knowing either. Really, the whole situation was a tad tawdry.

And slightly mystifying.

She wondered why Ethan was so keen to have his colleagues believe his companion was his lover. Did he have a reputation as a stud to uphold? Or did he have some other secret reason for such a pretence?

Something—some feminine instinct—rang a warning bell at the back of her mind. There was more to this than met the eye…

But Abby could not allow herself to be swayed by worries and qualms of such an indefinite nature. Three thousand dollars beckoned. Three thousand very real, very vital dollars. Ethan's motivation for such a sham was his business. All she had to do was collect the money then play the appropriate part.

Maybe what she was really worrying about was how difficult playing that part might be. She hoped she wouldn't make a fool of herself and betray her own secret. Despite not liking Ethan Grant one little iota on a personality basis, she could not think about him any more without thinking of making love with him.

CHAPTER FOUR

'FIRST things first,' Ethan continued abruptly. 'Your clothes.'

'My clothes?' she repeated blankly, her mind still back on her perturbing weakness for the man.

'You do own something other than that black skirt and white blouse you wear every Friday, don't you?'

Abby thought of all the designer clothes hanging up in her wardrobe at home in Killara. They wouldn't really have dated, being timeless classical styles. She didn't doubt they would still be there either. She would have no trouble getting them if she went during the day, when her father was at the office.

'Actually, I have quite an extensive wardrobe,' she replied coolly, resenting both the criticism and scepticism built into his question.

'Yes, but what type of clothes?' he countered derisively. 'You must appreciate any lady friend of mine will be expected to be well dressed. Nothing cheap or flashy.'

'I am *never* cheap or flashy.'

'You're certainly not cheap, I'll give you that,' he muttered drily. 'And other than one wayward button, you haven't been flashy either. So far,' he added cynically. 'But I wouldn't like any nasty little surprises once we get down to the hotel. Which reminds me—there's nothing in your past or present which would preclude you taking this job, is there?'

One very good reason catapulted into Abby's mind and she gulped. Surely there wouldn't be anyone at this

33

conference who knew about her trial or her sentence? It
had not been in any of the papers. Her father hadn't been
prepared to help her with a decent lawyer, but he *had*
used his influence to suppress any publicity.

'Such as what?' she asked, guilt making her sharp.

'God only knows. You haven't graced the centrefold
of any of the better known men's magazines, have you?
Or any of the lesser ones, for that matter. I'm well aware
that Sylvia hired you without checking into your background too extensively. I didn't come down in the last
shower, Abby. When a girl's hard up for money and has
a figure as good as yours, she might be talked into doing
things not too savoury.'

Any guilt disappeared as Abby almost blew a gasket.
Not too *savoury*! What in hell did he think she was doing
now, going away with *him*? Lord, who did he think he
was, looking down his nose at her when *he* was the one
paying for her dubious companionship? As for her figure... She was fed up with him equating her lush curves
with loose morals.

'I've never done a thing I'm ashamed of, Dr Grant,'
she said with cold dignity. Till now, that is, she added
silently. 'Believe me when I say I will do you proud as
your...er...girlfriend. You won't have cause to complain.'

'Mmm. That's to be seen, isn't it? By the way, can
you play tennis at all?'

'Yes, but I...'

'You don't have to be proficient,' he cut in dismissively. 'Adequate will do. I suppose it's too much to ask if
you can play golf as well?'

His patronising tone made Abby seethe. She'd only
been going to say that she didn't have a racket.

If I ever get him on a tennis-court or a golf-course…she vowed blackly. Thank you, Father, for all those holidays filled with never-ending lessons. You did do something for me after all.

'Actually, I do play golf. A little,' she added, not wanting to give the enemy advance warning.

'You've surprised me, Miss Richmond. I would have thought your talents lay elsewhere than on the sporting field.'

Abby decided to ignore that remark. He would keep. 'I wish you'd make up your mind what you're going to call me,' she said waspishly. 'One minute it's Abby, and then we're back to Miss Richmond.'

'You're quite right. But I don't feel altogether comfortable calling you Abby. Shall we compromise and make it Abigail?'

'Whatever you wish. You're the boss. Just so long as I know where I stand and what to expect. Speaking of what to expect, *I'm* not going to get any nasty little surprises when we get to the hotel, am I?'

The silence on the line was electric for a few seconds. Abby had no doubts now that Ethan had some hidden agenda at this conference, and it was beginning to niggle her.

'Meaning?' he asked coldly.

Meaning what are you up to, you conniving devil? she wanted to say. What is making you pay three thousand dollars to have me there as your pretend lover?

'Meaning you wouldn't be the first man I've come across who was a wolf in gentleman's clothing,' she tossed back instead. 'I don't want to have to fight you off every night.'

He laughed drily. 'How beautifully blunt you can be, Abigail. I rather admire it. Actually, I rather admire *you*. You are a girl of rare spirit and a quite tantalisingly

enigmatic character. On top of that, you've never resorted to the manipulative ploys an attractive female in
your position might be tempted to use. But, no…you
don't have to worry about fighting me off. Rape has
never appealed to me, and seducing you is not part of
my plan.'

'What plan?' Abby just *had* to say, not believing his
back-handed compliments for one moment. He despised
her for some reason, and had never bothered to hide that
fact. Maybe he despised *all* females with a bust size over
AA?

'That, my dear Abigail,' he drawled, 'is none of your
business.'

And that, my dear Doctor, is an evasion.

But she didn't say it. It really wasn't a wise course of
action to persist, not if she wanted that three thousand
dollars.

'Fair enough, Doctor. You can keep your little secret.'

'Ethan.'

'What?'

'Call me Ethan.'

'Oh…oh, yes, I suppose I'll have to. I hope I'll remember.'

'Have a practice right now, then. Say yes, Ethan. No,
Ethan. Three bags full, Ethan.'

'Don't be ridiculous.'

'*Say it,*' he bit out.

Abby quivered deep inside at his darkly forceful tone.

'Y-yes, Ethan,' she started hesitantly. Then, 'No,
Ethan,' much more firmly, followed by, 'Three bags full,
Ethan,' in a dry, challenging tone.

'See?' he scorned. 'You didn't have any trouble at all.
Though perhaps you could practise putting a little more
warmth into my name between now and Friday. Say it

the way you just did in the presence of others and they'll think you want to kill me, not kiss me.'

Well, they'd be wrong, she thought ruefully. She wanted to do both. Kill him *and* kiss him. Damn, but she was actually enjoying sparring with him this way. It had a decidedly sexual edge to it. Abby was hotly aware that her pulse had started racing and that her cheeks were quite flushed with an unbidden excitement. Thank the Lord they were on the phone and he couldn't see her.

'I'll see what I can do,' she said, surprised by her cool tone. Heavens, she was a much better actress than she'd realised. Who knew? Maybe she might just be able to pull this fiasco off without getting her fingers burnt. If she started getting too hot and bothered over the sexy surgeon, she would simply remember Dillon. Thinking of that bastard always had a chilling effect. If that failed, she would concentrate on a simple survival. Now that she'd lost her weekend job, she needed her Friday job more than ever.

'Tell me the agenda for Friday,' she said in a businesslike tone. 'What do you want me to do?'

'We're supposed to arrive at Bungarla some time between three and five. I'm still operating on the Friday morning, and I do have a patient who's travelling down from the country to see me that day as well. I told her to meet me at my rooms at one.'

'Do you want me to come in as usual, then?'

'No. That's not necessary. Be at the surgery by one-thirty. I should be finished by then. I'm told the trip down to Bungarla shouldn't take any more than two hours.'

'What do you think I should wear for the trip down?'

'Something casual, but smart. It'll be pretty cool down that way of an evening in the autumn, so pop in a jacket

as well. And don't forget to pack suitable clothes for
tennis and golf. Oh, and throw in a swimsuit. According
to the brochure they sent, there's a heated pool.'

'Yes, boss.'

'Don't be cheeky.'

She'd be more than cheeky if she went swimming
wearing the bikini Dillon had picked out for her five
years ago. Abby had gone up a size since then, especially in her bust. It must have been all that lovely fatty
prison food. Or the free doughnuts and cappuccinos
she'd been stuffing herself with every weekend at the
café, so that she didn't have to spend so much money
on food.

She would literally have to starve herself between now
and Friday if she wanted her old clothes to fit her properly, but at least she'd already made a good start. She
hadn't eaten a darned thing all day!

'Abigail?'

'Yes?'

'Oh, nothing. Is there anything else you want to ask?'

'Do you have my address to send the money to tomorrow?'

His sigh sounded irritable. 'I'm glad you've still got
your priorities right. Yes, I have your address. You'll
have the money, in cash, by three at the latest. Is that
satisfactory?'

'Quite.'

'And I'll expect my money's worth in return.'

'You'll get what you paid for. And nothing more.'

'I'm glad to hear that, Abigail,' he drawled. 'Because
that's exactly what I am paying for. Nothing more. No
complications and no consequences. See you Friday.
And don't be late!' he snapped, then hung up.

Abby glared down into the dead receiver, her heart

thudding angrily. At least, she hoped that it was with anger. Friday seemed a long way off, but it would come round all too quickly, she feared.

It did, dawning cool and sunny, a beautiful autumn day. The week, which usually dragged when she spent it searching fruitlessly for a full-time job, had simply flown. Any spare minute had been taken up with alterations to her clothes. Hems had been taken up or down, and seams let out where possible.

'Tell me again the name of the place you're off to, dear?' Miss Blanchford asked as she watched Abby packing the freshly washed and pressed garments.

'Bungarla,' she replied, smiling as the old lady manoeuvred the chair closer with a small movement of the joy-stick-style steering. In just two short days she'd become a real expert, whizzing up and down the hallway and rarely bumping into anyone any more. Seeing her so happy made the sacrifice of the coming weekend worthwhile. 'It's a private hotel just outside of Bowral.'

'And what exactly is it you have to do there?'

Abby swallowed. 'Just secretarial work. Dr Grant wants me to take notes on all the lectures he'll be attending.' No way could she tell the old darling the truth. She would simply die, then demand that Abby give Ethan back the money and not go. Which would be a little difficult when it was already in the wheelchair company's bank account.

'And you need all these lovely clothes just for that?' came her frowning enquiry.

Abby tried not to look guilty. She laughed, and hoped that it didn't sound too false. 'No, of course not. There will be some socialising in the evenings. You wouldn't want me to look dowdy in front of all those high-flying doctors and their wives, would you?'

'You could never look dowdy, Abby.' Sharp grey eyes latched on to the heightened colour gathering in Abby's cheeks. 'This is all on the up and up, dear, isn't it? I mean…this boss of yours…he's not the type to expect you to be anything more than his secretary, is he?'

'Good heavens, no! Dr Grant's not like that at all.'

'I thought you told me he was very handsome. And quite young.'

'Well, yes, he is.'

'In that case he's like that, believe me, dear. I've been around long enough to know that all handsome young men are like that. Unless he's queer, of course. He's not queer, is he?'

'No,' Abby choked out. 'No, I'm sure he's not. But there's no need for you to worry. He doesn't fancy me at all. Certainly not in that way.' Which was just as well, given her unbidden excitement over the coming weekend.

'What makes you say that? Why wouldn't he fancy you? You're a very fanciable girl. And you're going to look stunning in that dress you have there.'

Abby stared down at the coffee-coloured lace gown that she was carefully folding into the case. 'I might not wear this one. It's a little tight.'

Actually, most of the clothes she'd collected from home last Monday had been a little tight to begin with. She'd been largely able to correct this problem by letting out seams, but that had been impossible with the lace dress—all the seams being overlocked, with not a centimetre left to spare. She was only bringing the dress because she thought she might fit into it by the last evening—if she swam up and down the pool Ethan had mentioned for a hundred or so laps every day. The colour did look well on her, and it was a dress she'd always felt good in.

Good?

Her conscience pricked and Abby had to admit that that particular dress had never exactly made her feel good. Sexy was closer to the mark. On the one occasion she'd worn it for Dillon he hadn't been able to wait to tear it off her at the end of the night.

She wondered what Ethan would say if and when he saw her in that particular dress, with her hair done up, full make-up on and her diamond and pearl choker around her throat. Seducing her might not be part of his original plan, but it might just come into his mind…if she put it there.

'Abby…'

Abby started, then glanced up from her suitcase, aware that her pulse was racing uncomfortably. What wicked thoughts that man put into her mind! 'Yes?' she said a little shakily.

'You're not in love with Dr Grant, are you?' Miss Blanchford asked worriedly.

'Lord, no!' Maybe a little in lust, she conceded with considerable understatement. But not in love. No way. The very idea was appalling!

'Telephone for you, Abby!' someone called along the hallway. 'Hop to it. Chap says he's only got a minute.'

Abby couldn't think who it could possibly be. No one ever rang her here. She didn't think she'd ever given the number to anyone. Her only friends since getting out of prison were Miss Blanchford and the other boarders.

She was hurrying along to where the 'in only' telephone sat on a solid table near the front door when she realised that she'd given Sylvia this number, which meant that Ethan would know it as well.

Her stomach tightened as she picked up the receiver, and her hello was taut.

'Ethan here, Abigail. I'm in between operations, so can't spare long.'

'What is it? What's wrong?' Her heart was already sinking at the thought that he was calling the whole thing off. Abby found her dismay highly disturbing, because it wasn't the money she was worrying about all of a sudden but the thought that she would not, after all, get the opportunity to display herself for Ethan in that damned dress!

'Nothing's wrong,' he returned crisply. 'But I was concerned over how you were going to get into town carrying luggage. I know you usually take the train and walk the couple of blocks from Martin Place when coming to work.'

'How on earth do you know that?' she asked, taken back.

His laugh was droll. 'You've no idea the amount of useless information Sylvia relays to me about her precious Miss Richmond. I assume your cash fee arrived without any mishap last Monday?'

'What? Oh, yes, thank you.'

'Then use some of it to take a taxi.'

'But I can't!'

'What do you mean, you can't?' he demanded impatiently. 'Good God, don't tell me you've already spent it all? The whole three thousand?'

'Afraid so,' she admitted, her lips twitching. In a way it *was* funny, the false things he kept thinking about her. Now she was not only a mercenary gold-digger, but a wicked spendthrift as well.

He muttered something under his breath which turned her amusement to annoyance. She hadn't quite picked up the exact expression he'd used, but it hadn't sounded at all complimentary.

'I won't be late,' she snapped. 'I don't have that much luggage. Only one suitcase.'

'I told you I wanted you to be well dressed!'

'I *will* be well dressed. *Very.*'

'Courtesy of my three thousand dollars, I dare say,' he growled. 'Still, I shouldn't complain. You only get what you pay for in this world. I wanted a good-looking, well-groomed woman on my arm this weekend and they never come cheap. But I'm also paying for no hitches, so do me a favour and catch a taxi anyway. Do you have enough money for the fare if I faithfully promise to reimburse every single cent when you get here?' he asked caustically.

'Yes.' Just.

'Then do that. See you no later than one-thirty.'

He hung up on her again, leaving Abby disturbed and frowning. All thoughts of coffee-coloured dresses and seduction had slipped from her mind, replaced by a renewed curiosity over what this weekend was really all about. What on earth was Ethan up to that he didn't care how much he paid to get what he wanted?

Her resigned sigh reflected the reality of the situation. Ethan was not about to tell her, even if she asked him straight out. He was paying for *non*-involvement.

And isn't that what you want too? she asked herself. *Non*-involvement. This ridiculous one-sided sexual attraction is best ignored, not fuelled by wearing sexy dresses and thinking sexy thoughts.

The coffee-coloured number, Abby decided sensibly, would stay safely behind.

But when she got back to her room, Miss Blanchford had finished packing for her, and the lace dress was already under several layers of clothes. With the old lady's intuitive grey eyes upon her, she was not about to wrench the offending garment from the depths of the case, though she staunchly vowed not to wear the darned thing. She didn't trust herself in it.

Just do what you've been paid to do, Abby, love, came the voice of reason as she snapped the case shut. Nothing more. Nothing less.

If she did that, and minded her own business, then the only real danger Abby could see was that she might say or do something which would lose her her one remaining job—which would be disastrous for her present depressing financial balance of fifty-five whole dollars in her bank account, plus approximately thirty dollars in her purse.

Well, you'll just have to make sure you don't say or do anything stupid, came her stern self-advice. Stay cool, calm and collected. Don't resort to too much sarcasm, however provoked. And don't, for pity's sake, start drooling over the man—even if he stands before you stark naked in all his masculine glory.

Abby's stomach clenched down hard at this last thought. Of course, she had no real idea how Ethan Grant would look naked. Maybe he was all pale and flabby underneath his clothes. Maybe his broad-shouldered, slim-hipped, flat-stomached shape was all an illusion, created by the superbly tailored suits he always wore.

And maybe pigs might fly, Abby decided ruefully. Ethan worked too damned hard to be flabby. As for being pale…the man had a naturally olive skin, his colouring as dark as a gypsy.

No, he would look gorgeous naked. Of that she was sure. Gorgeous and sexy and all man.

'Haven't you forgotten something?' Miss Blanchford asked Abby as she swung the tan leather suitcase off the bed.

'Have I? What?'

'This,' the old lady said, and produced from her lap the most beautiful perfume dispenser Abby had ever seen. It was made of rose cut glass, and had a pink satin puffer with a silver tassel hanging from it.

'Oh, Miss Blanchford!' Abby exclaimed, tears pricking her eyes as the old lady pressed it into her hand.

'It's full of Chanel No. 5. A man-friend gave it to me a couple of years back, but the exotic scent didn't seem to suit an old spinster like me. However, I think on you, my dear, it might just turn a few gentlemen's heads.'

Abby was both touched and tortured by the gift. For she knew that there was only one man's head she would want to turn this weekend. Yet his was the last one she could afford to!

CHAPTER FIVE

THE taxi driver let Abby off outside the tall building which housed Ethan's rooms, dumping her case on the pavement before speeding off into the heavy city traffic. The fare had come to twenty-two dollars, which left her precisely eight dollars and a few cents in her purse.

Abby sighed, then glanced at her watch. Only ten past one. Taking a deep, steadying breath, she picked up her suitcase and forged through the revolving glass doors into the foyer. Her stomach still began to churn as she made her way across the coolly tiled floor and over to the bank of lifts. She dropped the heavy suitcase, hitched her matching tan leather carry-all further up her shoulder, and pressed the 'up' button.

The doors opened immediately on an empty lift. Abby picked up her case and was about to step inside when something halted her.

It was a voice in her head.

Don't go, it said. Run!

Run? But how could she? She'd been paid—up front and in advance. Ethan knew her address. And she was almost broke. There was nowhere to run to.

The rather irrational fear subsided as Abby rode the lift up to the second floor. Really, what on earth was there to be afraid of, other than her own silly sexual feelings for the man?

It wasn't as though Ethan lusted after *her*. It was a one-way thing, and easily hidden. Lord, she'd hidden it for nearly six months, hadn't she? She would simply go on doing more of the same for the next few days.

Of course, she couldn't help being a bit nervous about the coming weekend away itself. It had been some years since Abby had mixed socially with the type of people who would be at this conference. Still, she *had* been well brought up, with all the advantages excessive wealth could provide, and she didn't think that she would embarrass herself or Ethan.

Her education had been excellent, with the right grammar, manners and etiquette being ground into her from the earliest days. Not even four years in prison had tarnished that style and elegance which seemed unconsciously to cling to girls of her background and upbringing, though she'd certainly learnt to stand up for herself, and to speak bluntly when necessary—not always in the most ladylike language.

She could well understand Ethan's ambivalence where her character was concerned. Most of the time she was the polished, refined creature her many nannies and teachers had created, but occasionally the tough survivor she'd had to become in prison would emerge, bringing out a feral cat-like creature, who could snap and snarl with the best of them.

Abby took some comfort from this new 'survivor' aspect of her personality. She could always rely upon it to protect her—emotionally as well as physically. It called a spade a spade and made her see things as they really were, shielding her from that other idealistic and romantic fool who had once resided within herself—the one who'd fallen madly and blindly in love with a handsome creep like Dillon; the one who'd always steadfastly believed that she had to be in love with a man to enjoy sex with him.

Abby the survivor now saw that sexual attraction need not have anything to do with love. It was an animal thing. Involuntary and primeval. An instinctive chemistry which just happened when one was confronted by an exceptionally attractive member of the opposite sex.

Scientists called it natural selection of the species. A female animal was always compelled to mate with the strongest and best looking male of her kind, so that the offspring would be the strongest and best looking too, giving them the best chance of survival.

Abby knew full well that what she felt for Ethan Grant had nothing to do with love and everything to do with natural selection of the species.

She emerged from the lift and walked slowly along the long corridor, reassured by her thoughts. She was still fifteen minutes early, so there was no need to hurry.

The door to Ethan's surgery was open, but the waiting room was empty. When Abby heard muffled sounds coming from Ethan's consultation room, she dropped her case and carry-all near the door and wandered over past the reception desk and into the small tearoom behind. She could do with a cuppa; her crash diet this week was beginning to take its toll.

Still, she'd certainly dropped a few pounds, and with those minor alterations most of her clothes of five years ago fitted her well enough.

There was one item, however, which still worried her—the treacherously brief black bikini lurking at the bottom of her luggage. Definitely not a garment to be worn in male company now that her bust had gone from a B-cup to a C, her bottom following accordingly. She wasn't fat, but she was definitely on the voluptuous side. She'd have bought herself a new one-piece costume if she'd been able to afford it.

Abby finished making herself the tea and sat down at the reception desk to drink it, her thoughts returning to what had happened when she'd gone home last Monday morning to collect her clothes.

Her father had not been there, of course. When was he ever at home? And the housekeeper had been new. It had taken Abby a while to convince her of who she was and that she'd come to get her clothes, which fortunately had still been in her room.

Not that she'd expected them to be gone. Her father had never bothered to throw away her mother's things when she'd left him, why would he throw away a mere daughter's? That would have been like admitting that he was affected in some way by their behaviour.

Abby had taken away two suitcases full, not wanting to stay long enough to sort through them. She'd also thrown in some of her better pieces of jewellery—both to wear this weekend, then perhaps to sell at some future date, if she ever needed to.

It had been a depressing morning. Just thinking about it depressed her.

Abby was sitting there, feeling quite down, when the door to Ethan's room opened and a woman carrying a small child emerged. Both were crying—the child irritably, the woman with soft, heart-rending sobs.

Moved by their distress, Abby was about to rise and offer to help when Ethan appeared by their side. He didn't notice Abby, his concentration all on the woman and child.

'Come now, little Chrissie,' he murmured, gently lifting the tiny girl into his arms. 'You're upsetting your mummy with those tears.' He kissed the chubby cheeks and jiggled her up and down. 'I'm sorry Doctor's fingers were so cold. Next time I'll warm them up on a heater.

How about that? And here's something for being such a big, brave girl.'

Abby watched, fascinated, as Ethan reached into the pocket of his white coat and produced a lollipop in bright, swirling pink colours.

'Here, let me help with this naughty wrapping,' he said, peeling off the cellophane and popping the sweet into Chrissie's waiting mouth. The child snuggled up to him, contentedly sucking, one arm tight around her doctor's neck.

The whole scene astounded Abby. Was this the same doctor she'd seen at work every Friday afternoon? This kind, gentle, compassionate person? Where was the brusque, autocratic manner, the coldly remote eyes? Truly, this was a genuine case of Dr Jekyll and Mr Hyde.

'Please don't be upset, Mrs Williams,' he was saying. 'The situation is far from serious at this early stage.'

'I know, Doctor, but I…I can't help it.'

Ethan put his free arm around the woman's still shaking shoulders. 'I know, I know,' he said softly. 'You're Chrissie's mother and you love her so.'

The woman lifted her face and Abby could see the intensity of emotion emanating from those red-rimmed eyes. A vice closed around her chest as she bore witness to the strength of this mother's love. She would move mountains for her daughter. Fight tigers. Ford flooded streams. She would never abandon her child. *Never*.

Abby tore her gaze away.

'Come back in six months' time,' she heard Ethan tell the woman. 'And we'll arrange a fresh set of X-rays for comparison.'

'I'll do that, Doctor. And don't worry, I won't forget those exercises you showed me. I won't miss a day.'

'I'm sure you won't, Mrs Williams.'

Abby's eyes were still dropped wretchedly to her half-empty teacup when dark-trousered legs materialised beside the desk.

'I didn't know you'd arrived,' Ethan said. 'I didn't see you there.'

Abby hoped the face she lifted to him had been wiped of all the pain she'd just felt. Perhaps not, since he frowned back down at her with what looked like compassion in his normally hard eyes.

'Are you all right?' he asked.

His unexpected concern caught at her still raw heart, and suddenly she felt like crying too. She stared up at him with wide eyes, wondering if he would put a comforting arm around *her* shoulders if she dissolved into tears. Would he take her in his arms like he had that child, let her nestle into the warm expanse of his chest?

Abby knew the answer even before she pulled herself together. Never in a million years.

'Just felt a little faint there for a moment,' she excused herself, though it wasn't far from the truth. She picked up the cup. 'I'll be fine after I get some sugar into me.'

By the time she rose, empty teacup in her hand, she was totally composed, and Ethan was right back to normal. 'Don't forget to take the taxi fare out of the petty cash tin,' he said curtly, and spun away from her, already in the throes of discarding his white coat as he strode across the waiting room floor and back into his surgery.

'Mr Hyde again, I see,' she muttered as she recovered her twenty-two dollars as ordered, then busied herself washing up the cup and saucer. She returned to Reception just as Ethan emerged from his room, looking more disgustingly handsome than ever in a dark grey suit, white shirt and blue tie—the exact blue of his eyes.

His gaze was coolly assessing as it flicked over her

own appearance. 'That outfit's a distinct improvement on that hideous black skirt,' he said drily. 'And I like your hair up that way. Very classy.'

'So glad you approve.' Abby knew full well that she looked good in the camel-coloured mohair shift which subtly outlined her hour-glass figure. Five years ago, with Dillon, she'd always hitched the hem up to mid-thigh by adding a gold chain belt. Today she had opted to let the garment hang to its more sedate length just above the knee, and the only gold gracing her body was a gold-linked necklace to fill the boat neckline and matching gold earrings in her ears.

The set had been a present for her nineteenth birthday, sent to her by her long-absent mother from somewhere in Europe. Most of Abby's jewellery was guilt presents from her mother. They held no great sentiment for her but at least they were the real thing. Real gold. Real pearls. Real diamonds. Ethan would not be able to accuse her of decking herself out in cheap or flashy jewellery.

'How on earth you manage to get all of your hair up in that particular style, I have no idea,' he said, almost scowling at her French roll. 'You haven't had it cut, have you?'

Abby was taken aback by his suddenly accusing tone. Why should he care if she'd had her hair cut?

'No,' she replied, struggling to remain calm. But stay calm, she would. By hook or by crook. It was the only way she would get through this long, long weekend. By not allowing anything that Ethan said or did to disturb her equilibrium. 'I've had plenty of practice at putting my hair up.' When she had worked in the prison laundry putting up long hair had been essential.

'It's very long, isn't it?' Ethan commented, still frowning.

'Yes.'

'You ever wear it down?'

'Only to bed,' came her crisp reply. Abby was no fool. Men liked long hair on women, especially when worn down. It was considered sexy.

She hadn't grown it for that reason. She'd simply not cared enough to have her already shoulder-length mane cut while in prison, then hadn't had the money to have it properly cut when she came out. Actually, it was very cheap to maintain long.

'In that case, I should have the pleasure of seeing it,' Ethan drawled, before walking over to pick up her case. His glance, when he straightened, was as provocative as his remark. His eyes were narrow and assessing, as though he was picturing what she would look like in bed with her hair spread on the pillow.

His pillow.

Abby quickly counted to ten before deciding that she was probably imagining things. That old natural selection was at work again, making her feel things and think things which had no basis in reality, only in her overheated imagination.

Calm, she ordered herself.

Calm refused to come.

'I'll take that,' she said sharply when he went to pick up the carry-all which contained her money, make-up and hair things.

'Be my guest. Are you ready to go? You don't want to visit the ladies' first?'

'That might be a good idea. Won't be a sec.'

Abby stared at herself in the mirror above the basin after she'd washed her hands. There was no calming the faint flush which ran across her high cheekbones, or the sparkle in her eyes. It was to be thanked that a casual observer would not see the way her heart was thudding heavily within her chest, though her breasts were rising and falling in a panting rhythm underneath the soft wool of her dress.

'You're excited, aren't you?' she accused her reflection out loud. 'Not nervous. Excited. That's where the danger lies, you fool, within your own silly self. Oh, be careful, Abby. Be very careful...'

Without thinking, she licked suddenly dry lips before she left the washroom, leaving them shiny and moist— and far, far more inviting than she realised.

CHAPTER SIX

'WHAT was wrong with that little girl?' Abby asked abruptly, in order to break the awkward silence which seemed to have developed.

They'd only been on their way a few minutes but it felt like an eternity to Abby. She was much too aware of Ethan, had been from the moment he'd taken her down to the darkened basement car park and personally handed her into the passenger seat of his BMW. She had quivered at his touch, her fears of blindly responding to this man well and truly founded.

Her question puzzled him for a moment. 'Oh, you mean Chrissie. She has a scoliosis of the spine. A curve…to the left. About seventeen degrees.'

'That sounds serious.'

'Maybe. Maybe not. She's only fourteen months old. Some correct themselves with exercise and time. Some, unfortunately, do not.'

'What sort of exercises?'

'Simple things, really. Always holding her the one way. Making sure she sleeps on the same side—in Chrissie's case, the left. Making sure her spine is always well supported. None of those soft-backed strollers. I've also recommended hanging her upside down by the ankles twice a day for as long as she can stand it. The parents could make a game of it.'

'What about a brace?'

'Not yet. Maybe, if there's no improvement in six

months, I might consider it. Children hate them so—
especially little girls.'

'You were…very kind to her.'

'I have a soft spot for pretty little girls.'

'You were sweet to the mother too. And she wasn't
at all little, or pretty.'

He slanted her a wry look. 'Not what you've come to
expect from me, by the tone in your voice.'

'Well, I…um…'

'A surgeon can't afford to become emotionally involved with his patients. Not if he might have to operate
on them. If he did, he might become nervous and make
a mistake. I broke a professional rule today. I allowed
that mother's distress to get to me. But I'm fairly sure
I'll never have to operate on that little girl, so I should
be safe.'

Safe from what, Ethan? Abby wondered. Safe from
making a mistake, or safe from feeling anything that
might turn you from a machine back into a man?

'I still couldn't do your job,' she murmured.

'It has its compensations.'

The lights ahead turned red and the dark blue BMW
glided to a halt, its expensive engine purring quietly as
it idled.

Like what? Abby mused. Working eighteen hours a
day, six days a week? Not having enough time for any
kind of relationship with the opposite sex except spas-
modic and strictly sexual ones?

Or was he talking about money—enough to buy the
latest model BMW without having to think twice?

The lights turned green and the powerful car surged
forward.

'Nice car,' she remarked.

'It does the job.'

His indifferent tone surprised her. Men who didn't care about cars usually didn't care about money. Her father adored cars, the more flashy and expensive the better. Dillon had been just as keen.

'It's also leased,' Ethan added. 'I get a new one every two years. I'm not into cars all that much, but women seem to like being driven around in a decent model. Besides, Sylvia says I have a responsibility to my patients to drive a reliable vehicle, and not to be stranded in the middle of the harbour tunnel one day when I'm supposed to be in Theatre. Frankly, I think she's more concerned about my making it home for dinner on time. She gets really hot under the collar when I'm late.'

'She only has your best interests at heart,' Abby pointed out, cross with Ethan for not seeing how lucky he was to have such a caring and concerned sister.

His sigh was irritable. 'Yes, I know that, but she's like an old mother hen sometimes.'

'I think she's very nice. One of the nicest ladies I've ever met.'

He glanced sideways at her. 'Do you, now? She thinks the same about you. It's amazing how quickly you women make up your minds about each other without anything concrete to base your opinions on.'

'Liking a person is rather instinctive, don't you think?' Abby said archly.

He threw her a pensive glance. 'First impressions can be deceiving,' he muttered, then swung his attention back to the road. 'Traffic's heavy, as usual. Damn, but I hate driving in the city.'

Abby frowned. Had he been referring to her when he'd said that? Had he changed his mind about her character, now that he'd had a bit more to do with her? She didn't really like him thinking that she was a mercenary little piece, but it was safer that he did.

Abby decided it best to steer his opinion right back in that direction. 'While we've got the opportunity to talk, Ethan,' she said matter-of-factly, 'Perhaps you should fill me in on exactly how you expect me to act towards you over the next few days. You said you don't like women fawning all over you—which suits me fine—but we can't go around acting towards each other like we normally do. People will think it strange.'

'What do you mean, "Like we normally do"?'

'Oh, come on, Ethan, do be honest. We rub each other up the wrong way, have done since day one. The office fairly vibrates with our mutual antagonism every Friday afternoon.'

'It does, doesn't it?' he said, sounding drily amused.

'Lord knows why you asked me to come with you to this conference in the first place,' she went on. 'You must have been really desperate. And you know darned well *I* only agreed for the money.'

There! She'd really spelt it out for him, hopefully putting them back to the status quo and their original underlying hostility. He'd started being far too nice to her for her peace of mind. Heck, she already fancied the devil. The last thing she wanted was to like him as well.

'I certainly hope so,' he said drily. 'As to my being really desperate, I thought I explained my reasons for asking you quite clearly. Your basic…er…antagonism towards me is a plus. I'm tired of women wanting more of me than I'm prepared to give. You, my dear Abigail, have admitted you want nothing but my money. I find that surprisingly refreshing and relaxing. Frankly, I didn't realise till this moment how much I might enjoy hiring a woman as my companion. It does free one from all sorts of tensions and pressures. I might give some thought to doing it again some time.

'Not with me, you won't,' she snapped.

'Really? Why not? You still like money, don't you? You certainly spent my three grand quickly enough.'

Abby took a deep, steadying breath, letting it out slowly. 'You're a cold-blooded bastard, do you know that?'

Another set of red lights brought them to a halt, and Abby found that her heart was racing a lot faster than the idling engine. She held her breath when Ethan turned to lock his chillingly amused eyes with hers, before letting them slide slowly down to her suddenly quivering mouth.

'Not always,' he drawled.

'Most of the time,' she retorted, struggling to stop her thoughts from turning sexual again. 'And you're a dreadful cynic about women.'

His chuckle was dark. 'Only some women, my dear Abigail. Not all of them. I reserve my so-called cynicism for the type of woman who uses the gifts God gave her in the ruthless pursuit of money and material gain.'

'I suppose you've included *me* in that category, just because I accepted your offer.'

'You didn't *accept* my offer, Abigail. You made me a very cold-blooded counter-offer—one which showed your true colours, wouldn't you agree?'

'No, I wouldn't agree. But I, like you, see no need to explain myself to you. You're my employer, not my husband or lover. I had reasons for asking for that specific amount of money—reasons which I'm not ashamed of.'

'Ah, let me guess. You have an invalid grandmother who desperately needs an operation which happens to cost exactly three thousand dollars.'

Abby knew that she should be outraged by his sarcasm. But for some weird reason she found it funny. Her laughter first surprised, then seemed to tickle his fancy, which was not what she'd intended.

'You are a wicked girl, Abigail Richmond,' he said, slanting her a rueful smile. 'I think I could get to like you.'

'You mean, if you didn't despise me so much.'

He laughed. 'You sound like you don't mind.'

'I don't. I'm counting on it.'

'Really? Why's that?'

'It makes me safe.'

'Safe? Oh, you mean from my jumping on you in the room tonight. Don't worry,' he said, a dark edge creeping back into his voice. 'Jumping on you will be the last thing on my mind once we get to Bungarla.'

Abby stared over at him. She'd been trying to forget about his ulterior motive for asking her to accompany him to this conference. Now her earlier doubts and qualms came back with a vengeance. What on earth was he up to?

'You…er…still haven't told me how you want me to act towards you when we get there,' she reminded him, hoping to fish out some other information at the same time. 'I mean…if you want your colleagues to think we're lovers, then a certain amount of public intimacy and affection will be called for, won't it? For one thing, what should I call you?'

'Ethan,' came his flat reply. 'I told you…no fawning. Look, just follow my lead in public, be your natural charming self, and try not to look revolted if I take your hand or put my arm around your waist.'

Revolted? Abby suspected that she might just tremble all over from a perverse pleasure.

'I doubt if I'll go so far as to kiss you,' he went on, 'but I'm sure, if I do, you can close your eyes and think of your three thousand dollars.'

'I'll do that,' she said with seeming nonchalance, whilst inside almost panicking. God, what a mess she'd got herself into!

'No more chit-chat for a while,' he ordered peremptorily. 'I need to concentrate on where we're going. I'm not all that familiar with these roads.'

Once again they drew up at some traffic lights, a perplexing intersection on the western outskirts of the city. Ethan finally negotiated the right road and soon they were on the expressway south. Within another hour they would be in Bowral. And then Bungarla.

Abby knew Bowral, a small country town a hundred kilometres or so south of Sydney. She'd travelled there once on a school excursion to see the tulip festival they held every spring. It was rather a quaint place, dotted with tall English trees, antiques shops and stately country homes—some of them very large, with equally large rambling gardens.

Bungarla had originally been one such home, according to the brochure which had been sent to Ethan and which Sylvia had left lying around on her desk. It showed a grand two-storeyed mansion set in the middle of a huge manicured lawn. The rectangular façade of the house might have been plain, except for a white-columned porch and a spectacular set of semicircular steps.

The rest of the photos inside the brochure showed a well-cared-for, well-appointed private hotel with an elegant, old-fashioned decor which looked both charming and comfortable. A newer, U-shaped motel-style wing had been added behind the main house, and here the guests were accommodated in lavish style—the original home containing the conference rooms plus the dining rooms and general living areas.

The heated pool Ethan had spoken of was in a separate building near the tennis-courts. The eighteen-hole golf-course lay at the end of a short walk through the back garden.

Under other circumstances Abby would have been really looking forward to her stay there. The meals were sure to be marvellous and it would be wonderful to be pampered for a change. But she knew that it would not be easy to relax while pretending to be something she wasn't and worrying all the time about when Ethan might kiss her, or something equally hazardous. It was one thing to hide this unwanted attraction in the cool climate of the office, where they were employer and employee. Quite another in the strained atmosphere of a pretend relationship and a shared hotel room.

Abby scooped in a shaky breath, turning her head towards the passenger window as she slowly let it out. She would have to keep her wits about her if she meant to survive this situation totally unscathed. Either way, she could see that her Friday job might have to go. Come next week, she would double her efforts in finding a full-time job, thereby eventually removing Ethan Grant from her life.

Abby sighed at the involuntary feeling of loss this last thought evoked. It just showed how lonely her life had become if she was going to miss Ethan Grant. Or was it Sylvia she'd miss most? Sylvia with her no-nonsense ways and kind heart. Yes, that was more like it.

When Abby had first come out of prison and been literally thrown out on the streets she'd vowed to show her father—and the world—that she could make it on her own, that she was not the spoilt, selfish young rich bitch the judge and jury had believed her to be.

She had planned to secure herself a good secretarial job, find a nice little flat to live in, make some real friends who liked her for herself, and eventually marry some decent man who would give her the large family she'd always wanted. She'd hated being an only child.

But in the six months so far she hadn't even achieved that first goal. And her only friend outside work was an old lady she'd known from her childhood. The world was a much tougher and harder place than her privileged and cosseted upbringing had prepared her for.

But she wasn't about to give up. No way. She was going to make it, or die trying. Who knew? Maybe she *would* find a doctor who wanted a full-time receptionist down at this convention, as she'd told Miss Blanchford. There was no harm in doing a bit of canvassing on the side, was there?

At last they were whizzing past Campbelltown, the houses gradually diminishing on either side and the rolling hills looking browner and browner. Abby had heard about the crippling drought on the news, but this was the first time she'd seen the evidence of it for herself. She stared up into the bright blue sky and prayed silently for some rain.

Though on second thoughts, God, she added wryly, not for the next couple of days. I'd still like to get this patronising devil next to me out onto a golf-course or a tennis-court and whip his butt!

Shortly before three-thirty they made it to Bowral, the silence between them having stretched to close on an hour.

Abby might have been able to relax if Ethan hadn't grown increasingly tense with each mile. There was a stiff, strained attitude about his shoulders, and his eyes were fixed unwaveringly on the road ahead. Maybe he was always like that when he drove long distances, but Abby began to suspect that he was not looking forward to the conference with any real pleasure.

She tried not to be curious about this, but it was difficult. Try as she might, Abby could not discount the concern that she was a pawn in some plan which was not quite lily-white. Ethan had claimed that he was not asking her to do anything criminal or immoral, but what of himself? Was *he* going to do something criminal or immoral?

A shiver ran down Abby's spine. Curiosity killed the cat, don't forget, she warned herself, and steadfastly pushed the worrying thoughts to the back of her mind.

Once through Bowral, Ethan consulted his handdrawn map then swung the BMW down a narrow, treelined road. 'The entrance to Bungarla is supposed to be down here on the left aways,' he muttered. 'Between two large oak trees. Keep an eye out for me, would you?'

'All right,' Abby said. 'There,' she pointed out ten seconds later. 'That must be it.'

In front of one of the huge trees was a discreet sign on an ornamental iron postbox which said simply 'BUNGARLA'.

The driveway was long, winding through extensive gardens and gradually rising to higher ground where the house stood in all its white grandeur. As they made their way slowly along the gravel road Abby realised that it was an even larger and more impressive place than the photos had led her to expect.

'I meant to ask you earlier, Ethan,' she said hurriedly before they arrived. 'Do you want to admit to my working for you?'

'Why not? It would explain how we met.'

'Yes, but you—'

'I'm not a snob, Abigail,' he broke in curtly. 'You can admit to waitressing too, if you like. I don't want you to feel you have to lie, other than about your relationship with me.'

'Actually, I'm not waitressing any more. I…er…lost my job there.'

He lanced her with a sharply frowning look. 'What happened? Did you ask for this weekend off?'

'No. The boss thought paying me my pathetic salary entitled him to further services.'

One of Ethan's eyebrows arched, his expression wry. 'One of the hazards of being so damned sexy-looking, I suppose. Did he fire you or did you quit?'

'Quit,' she said succinctly, a little rattled by Ethan's comment. Did he find her sexy?

'Mmm. I'd better be on my best behaviour, then,' he muttered as he slid the car to a halt at the base of the front steps. 'I don't want you quitting on me. Not during the next few days, that is.'

His sudden return to silence, plus his rigid staring straight ahead made Abby follow his narrow-eyed gaze. A black Jaguar was already parked in front of them, and a couple were alighting. A grey-haired paunchy man and a most elegant blonde woman. Startlingly blonde, in fact, her shortish hair fluffed out around her head.

When the man came round to take the woman's hand to guide her up the steps, she curled her arm through his instead, stroking his arm with her other hand as she did so. The man bestowed an indulgent smile down at her and began guiding her up the steps.

Abby snuck a sideways glance at Ethan as he continued to glare at the couple, his blue eyes ablaze, his hands gripping the steering wheel with grinding intensity. Was it hatred that burnt in his eyes? And, if so, for which one?

'Do you know those people?' she asked, forgetting her earlier resolve not to be curious. It was no use. She simply had to know what was going on.

Ethan took a deep breath, letting it out slowly as he uncurled his white-knuckled fingers from the steering wheel. 'Yes,' he admitted coldly. 'I do.'

'Oh? Who are they? Colleagues?'

'Not exactly. The man is Dr Phillip Ballistrat. The woman's his wife. His *second* wife. I'm surprised you didn't recognise them. They used to be in the papers quite a bit. Of course, that was ten years ago, when you were little more than a child.'

Abby frowned, a vague recollection of some scandal teasing her brain for a few seconds before bursting back into headlines in her memory.

'Oh, yes, I remember now!' she exclaimed. 'He was over here in Australia to do some operations, and while he was here he left his wife to take up with a blonde nurse young enough to be his daughter. The gossip rags had a field-day for ages. So he married her in the end, did he?'

'Naturally. You don't think home-wrecking bitches like that settle for less than a ring on their finger, do you?'

Abby felt the beginnings of a niggle about this woman, this blonde whom Ethan called a home-wrecking bitch with such vitriolic contempt. 'You knew her back then?' she asked nonchalantly.

'Actually, I did,' he returned just as nonchalantly, all emotion now wiped from his face and voice. 'She was a theatre nurse at the hospital where I did my residency.'

Abby wasn't fooled. The exquisite Mrs Ballistrat had to be *her*—the girl who'd once jilted him, that Vanessa person. Nothing else made any sense.

'Her name was Vanessa something or other, wasn't it?' she asked with feigned innocence, wanting to settle the matter in her mind once and for all.

'Yes,' Ethan admitted coldly.

'I thought as much,' Abby murmured.

So this was why Ethan had come. Out of a morbid curiosity. And this was why he'd brought *her*. As a salve to his ego. He wanted to see the woman he'd once loved, but under no circumstances would he want her to think he was still pining for her. So he'd hired Abby to parade on his arm as his current live-in lover. Male pride at its most destructive.

Exasperation towards the man sitting beside her swept through Abby. Why didn't he just let it go? Hell, she never wanted to see Dillon again, would not go one inch out of her way to cross his path a second time.

Perhaps because if I did see him again, Abby thought savagely, I might be tempted to kill the bastard!

Abby's eyes flew to Ethan's. Lord, he wouldn't do anything like that, would he? He hadn't come down here to exact some sort of violent revenge, had he?

The gentle and compassionate Dr Jekyll she'd seen in action this morning wouldn't have, Abby conceded. But what about Mr Hyde? The coldly embittered and heart-less machine who also lived in Ethan's body, and who came out whenever exposed to the type of woman he had nothing but contempt for.

'I think we should get out,' Ethan said coolly. 'Henry's just pulled up behind us, and any minute now we're going to be descended upon.'

CHAPTER SEVEN

ABBY grabbed Ethan's sleeve before he could alight. 'Who's Henry?'

'A valued colleague, so be nice to him. But not too nice,' he added drily. 'My ladyfriends not only do not fawn over me, they do not fawn over other men.'

I'll bet they don't, Abby thought ruefully as she let Ethan go and waited for him to open her door. They wouldn't dare. Not that they'd be inclined to fawn over another man when with Ethan, she accepted. No other man would measure up. Physically, at least.

Abby wondered what exactly had happened between Ethan and Vanessa which had embittered Ethan so. She couldn't imagine any woman passing him over for the portly man she'd just seen. Even ten years ago, Dr Philip Ballistrat wouldn't have been any oil painting.

Of course, a nurse might have been very impressed by the famous neurosurgeon on more levels than the physical. Success was supposed to be a powerful aphrodisiac.

Abby suspected, however, that the doctor's appeal for Vanessa had lain more in the money which had come with his success. Ethan's contempt for mercenary women had to have some basis somewhere, and it seemed only logical to lay this firmly at the feet of a two-timing girlfriend with more ambition than loyalty.

Abby could think of nothing that this Vanessa could have done, however, that would inspire Ethan to a violent revenge ten years after the event. That kind of reaction to a jilting—or whatever had happened—came swiftly, not donkey's years later.

No. Ethan wasn't about to do murder. Not in Abby's considered opinion. It was probably more a matter of showing his old flame that he didn't give a damn about her or what she'd done to him. He was now successful in his own right, had plenty of money, friends and women.

Abby was still mulling over these conclusions when Ethan opened the passenger door. Distracted, she swung her long legs out onto the step without thinking, her dress riding up sufficiently to give Ethan a good view of her nicely shaped knees and slender thighs.

He looked too, one eyebrow arching at the sight. By the time Abby noticed what he was staring at, it was too late to do anything about it without losing her much valued composure.

'I almost have some pity for that other boss of yours, Abigail,' he said drily. 'You're a temptation, all right.'

Abby locked cool eyes with his mockingly admiring gaze before rising gracefully to her feet, her chin tipped back indignantly. 'Really?' She pushed the long, tight sleeves of her dress up to her elbows in an unconsciously defiant gesture. 'I find absolutely no pity for pawing creeps. How would you like it if a woman kept grabbing you on the *derrière*?'

His smile was wry. 'I suppose that depends on the woman.'

'Oh? What happened to your dislike of women fawning all over you?'

'Fawning in public and pawing in private are two entirely different things.'

'Well, don't worry, I won't be doing either!' she huffed, the hypocrisy behind her statement bringing a rush of heat to her cheeks. Damn, but she wished that he was as ugly as sin. Instead, even the most sardonic of smiles added a dazzling sex appeal to his already handsome face, the movement of his mouth bringing attention to the perfection of his flashing white teeth.

'Ethan, old man,' a loud, rollicking voice interrupted them. 'You made it after all.'

Abby welcomed the distraction, grateful when Ethan turned away from staring at her flushed face.

'I said I was coming, Henry,' he replied evenly.

Henry was a large, craggy-faced man, with a shock of thick, wavy white hair and a florid complexion. His wife, who was hovering at his shoulder, was a petite woman with bright dark eyes, short brown hair and a trim figure encased in cream trousers and a cream and brown striped top. She looked about fifteen years younger than her husband—thirty-five to his fiftyish, Abby guessed.

'I know,' Henry went on, 'but I wasn't convinced. I'm well acquainted with your tendency to opt out of these dos on the flimsiest excuse. I was sure you were going to say you couldn't find anyone to bring. *Again*.

'But you certainly have this time, haven't you?' he added, winking at Abby and ogling her figure with such uninhibited delight that she couldn't find it in her to be offended. 'So where have you been hiding this delicious creature, and when are you going to introduce me?'

'Henry, behave yourself,' his wife ordered from his side, though not with any great urgency or distress. Clearly she was used to her husband's flirtatious behaviour.

'Forgive my husband,' she directed at Abby. 'He can't help himself when confronted with a beautiful young woman. Thank the Lord he's a gastrologist and not a gynaecologist. Ethan, perhaps if you could do the honours with the introductions, we might be able to proceed inside. It's quite cool out here and my jacket's packed away.'

'Whatever you say, Ann. I'm easy,' Ethan said equably, giving Abby a glimpse of yet another side of his character which she'd previously been unacquainted with. A stunningly relaxed easy-going side. It seemed he had more personalities lurking inside him than just Dr Jekyll and Mr Hyde.

'Abigail, this lecher is Dr Henry Maclean,' he continued, in the same marvellously charming and casual manner, 'the most overrated stomach man in practice today. But a damned good golf player. And this is Ann, his long-suffering spouse and mother of his two equally long-suffering sons.'

'Three, Ethan,' Ann reprimanded, rolling her eyes at him. 'We had a third boy a couple of years back. You were one of the godparents.'

'Good Lord, was I? It must have slipped my mind. Sorry.'

'These slips of memory are a symptom of being a workaholic, Abigail,' Ann told her. 'There again, if you're dating Ethan, I dare say you already know he's chained to his operating table.'

'Only too well,' Abby answered, adopting a droll tone in keeping with the mood of the group. 'If I didn't work for him, I'd never see him.' And wasn't that the truth!

Ann's neatly shaped dark brows lifted skywards. 'You work for Ethan? What as, for heaven's sake? I know you can't be a nurse, or Henry would have already raved *ad nauseum*.'

'Actually, I'm Sylvia's stand-in receptionist on a

Friday. But not for much longer, I hope. I'm looking for a full-time receptionist's job.'

'Good Lord, you mean that?' Henry exclaimed excitedly. 'You're hired! I'll fire my other girl on the spot the moment we get back to Sydney.'

'Over my dead body,' Ethan drawled. 'Abigail's going to work full-time for me.'

Abby turned rounded eyes upon him. He couldn't be serious. This had to be part of the pretence. But why, for heaven's sake?

'I've been thinking about sending Sylvia on a much deserved world cruise for ages,' he continued casually, 'and I think the right time has just arrived. So what do you say, Abigail? Do you think you could stand me on a five-day-a-week basis as well as at weekends?'

'Of course she could,' Ann snorted. 'Men ask such stupid questions sometimes, don't they?'

'All the time,' Abby agreed, in defiance of his springing this upon her. 'Ethan knows I'm his for the hiring,' she added with a bold glance. 'If the price is right.'

He seemed startled for a second, before a slow and very knowing smile pulled at his sensual mouth. Abby found herself staring at that mouth again and thinking all sorts of appalling things, only a porter's arrival saving her from another mortifying blush. She looked swiftly away, feeling totally irritated with herself. Talk about saying stupid things. She'd just opened her mouth and put her foot right in it.

'Let's go, Abby,' Ann said, and slid an arm through hers. 'The men can organise the luggage. You don't mind me calling you Abby, do you?'

'Not at all. I prefer it.'

'You know, Abby,' Ann said as she began leading her

up the never-ending steps, 'I'm so pleased to see Ethan dating a nice young woman like yourself, and not one of those chilly pieces of porcelain he usually displays on his arm. Although I have to tell you I was surprised to find out you work for him. He's never even looked sideways at any of the nurses at the hospital. Or so Henry tells me, and he'd know.

'He doesn't miss a trick, that man. Henry says Ethan has this thing about not mixing business with pleasure. Not that Ethan leaves much time for pleasure anyway. As Henry says, it's a miracle he agreed to come here at all. But I suppose we have you to thank for that,' she finished, smiling over at her.

'I think you could safely say that's true,' Abby replied carefully while smiling back at Ann.

The woman was clearly a gossip, but not a malicious one. Abby rather liked her. She liked Henry too, despite his open leering. There was something sweet and endearing about both of them. They were also pleasantly down-to-earth, with not a trace of snobbery about them. Her estimation of Ethan's basic character went up a notch with his choice of friends.

'So how did you manage to get past that professional reserve of his?' Ann enquired.

Abby remembered what Ethan had said about being natural and sticking as close to the truth as possible. 'I don't know.' She shrugged nonchalantly. 'I certainly didn't try to. To be frank, when I first met Ethan I didn't like him one bit. I don't think he liked me much either.'

'Fiddlesticks! I'll bet he was instantly smitten but just didn't want to break his precious rule. So how long were you working for him before he asked you out?'

'Er…quite a few months.'

'How long have you been going out together? It can't

have been very long. He brought some hideous Evelyn woman to a dinner party of ours a few weeks back.'

'Hideous in what way?' Abby countered, cleverly by-passing a direct answer to the other awkward question about how long they'd been dating.

'Oh, I don't mean hideous-looking. She was very beautiful in a coldly sophisticated fashion. But you could see that she kept sizing up Ethan like an antiques collector with a prized piece in her sights. I was terrified he was going to bring her down here this weekend. You've no idea how relieved and delighted I was to see you.'

Abby laughed. 'You'll be giving me a swelled head if you don't stop.'

'No, not you, Abby. I can see you're a girl with her feet on the ground and her heart in the right place. You like Ethan for himself, I'll bet, not his bank balance.'

Abby battled not to blush or look guilty as the men joined them on the top step, the wry expression in Ethan's cold blue eyes making it perfectly clear that he'd heard that last remark.

'Inside, my love,' Henry ordered cheerily as he re-claimed his wife's elbow.

'She wouldn't have said that if she knew the truth,' Ethan rasped in Abby's ear as he guided her along in the other couple's wake.

'Maybe Ann has more insight into the truth than you give her credit for,' Abby countered, stung by both Ethan's cynicism and the effect his touch was having on her. 'Not that *you* can talk,' she whispered. 'You lied just now about hiring me full-time. I'll bet you just didn't want me working for Henry.'

'Too true. But I wasn't lying. I do want you working

for me full-time in the future. I have plans for you, Abigail, my love.'

'And you think I'll just fall in with them?'

'But of course you will,' he returned with silky smugness. 'If the price is right.'

Their turn to approach the busy reception desk put an end to their provocative sparring, by which time Abby's delicious defiance had begun to give way to a churning nervousness. Ethan *was* attracted to her, she realised as she stood there next to him. She could feel the heat beneath his bruising fingertips, had heard the ruthlessly sexual intent behind his declaration that he had plans for her.

Suddenly she knew what those plans were. He wanted her, not just as his receptionist, but as his lover. His bought and paid-for lover. His mistress, in other words.

Abby should have been outraged by the prospect of such an indecent proposal. Instead she was terrified of what her answer would be, if and when he made that proposal.

Ethan was given two sets of keys to their room and a uniformed porter carried their luggage ahead of them along a high-ceilinged wood-panelled corridor, through a sun-lit doorway, then along a covered garden walkway which led to the motel-style wing. A minute later they were alone in the spacious and quite luxuriously furnished suite. Abby glanced agitatedly around, her eyes landing on the bed to her immediate left.

It was king-sized and covered in a forest-green quilted bedspread, and a huge gilt-edged mirror hung with erotic placement over the darkly polished bedhead. Abby gulped, her nervous gaze searching for and finding what she hoped was a sofa-bed in the sitting area across the way. It looked too elegant to be a convertible, covered in a silky green and maroon striped material.

A large bowl of fruit sat on the coffee-table in front of it, along with a complimentary bottle of champagne and two fluted crystal glasses.

'Anyone would think we were here on our honeymoon,' Ethan commented drily as he walked over and picked up the bottle. 'At least it's a good brand.' He shoved it back in the ice-bucket and moved on to stare through the plushly curtained window, his face instantly becoming shuttered, as though he wasn't looking at the garden beyond at all.

'Why *are* we here, Ethan?' Abby asked abruptly.

He turned to face her, his far-away expression immediately replaced by his usual stony countenance and hard blue eyes. Mr Hyde was firmly in residence again.

'Pardon me if I repeat that that is none of your business,' he drawled. His tone was typical of the Ethan she'd come to dislike so intensely. Coldly arrogant and ruthlessly insensitive to her feelings.

When he behaved like this, Abby ached to give him a big kick. Since this reaction wasn't practical, she'd found over the last few months that acting with blithe indifference towards his black moods worked almost as well.

'Fair enough.' She shrugged. 'But if you want me to become your full-time receptionist I suggest you start treating me with a little more manners. I can bear your boorish behaviour one day a week, but I certainly could not stand it for five. And *no* amount of money would sway me on this.'

She lifted her nose in snooty defiance of his belief that he could corrupt her with cash. Little did he know that any corruption would have nothing to do with his bank balance but something far more basic, and totally free.

He glared back at her, the muscles flexing along his jaw, a furious glitter bringing a momentary fire to his normally cold gaze.

I've really got under his skin this time, she realised with some surprise. Good! I need to get this relationship right back to square one, which means bristling with mutual antagonism.

'I'll treat you exactly as you deserve to be treated,' he flung at her.

'In that case, I suggest you start smartening up your act, because I deserve a hell of a lot better than you've been dishing out.'

His visible shock was almost laughable, but *he* was the one who finally threw back his head and laughed. 'You have a hide as thick as an elephant, do you know that? Very well, I will play the gentleman with you, if that's what you wish.'

He strode over and took her hand, lifting it to his lips before she could object. She knew his kiss was mocking, but still it stirred her blood more than it had any right to. She stiffened under the surprising warmth of his lips, and he glanced up at her from underneath derisive dark brows.

'Not to your taste?' he taunted.

She said nothing, merely removed her hand from his before she burst into flames before his very eyes. Damn, but if this was what a kiss on the hand could do, imagine what would happen if he really kissed her!

Ethan shrugged. 'Well, you can't say I didn't try. So what were you and Ann talking about on the steps, before Henry and I joined you?' he asked abruptly. 'Don't hedge, now. I want the truth.'

Abby was happy with the change of subject, but not happy with Ethan's continued closeness. Whirling, she walked over and sat down on the side of the bed. 'Nothing of vital interest. Ann was saying how delighted she was to find you'd brought someone really sweet like me, instead of that hideous Evelyn person you took to their dinner party recently.' She batted her eyelashes at him and crossed her legs, swinging them idly to and fro.

Ethan stared, first at her legs, then at her face. 'So how do you do it, Abigail?' he asked, cold derision in his voice. 'How do you pull the wool over people's eyes so quickly and so completely? First Sylvia. Now Ann and Henry. Oh, yes, Henry as well. He virtually said the same thing while we were organising the luggage and cars.'

An indignant anger seethed deep inside Abby but she refused to surrender to it. 'Maybe I'm a conjurer,' she returned airily. 'Or a witch. Yes, that's it.' Her smile was one of wicked mischief. 'I'm a witch. I put spells on people when I want them to like me. Watch out, Ethan, or I might put a spell on you.' Dear heaven, but he did bring out the worst in her!

'There isn't a woman on earth who could make me like her against my will,' he sneered. 'My days of being blinded by beauty are well and truly over.'

'Then what were you doing with the beautiful Evelyn?'

'What do you *think* I was doing with her?'

It sent a chill through Abby that Ethan would ruthlessly take a woman he didn't care for to bed, simply because she had a beautiful body. Strange…only a couple of days ago she'd fantasised about his doing the same thing to her and had found the idea perversely exciting.

She still found it exciting, but repulsive at the same time. How could one want something, yet be repelled by it?

'Yuk,' she said, and meant it.

'Watch out I don't put a spell on *you*, lovely Abigail,' he said darkly. 'I have a penchant for seducing beautiful women, and, believe me, I'm invariably successful when I put my mind to it.'

'Ah, but not with me, Ethan. My days of being blinded by beauty are well and truly over as well.'

'Are you complimenting me?' he drawled, unnerving her when his hands lifted to begin undoing his tie.

'No, I'm warning you not to waste your time.'

His eyes searched her face, noting, perhaps, its high colour and glittering eyes. 'I'm not so sure it *would* be a waste of time.'

'Touch me and I won't stay.'

'Do that and you'll lose your job. The only one you have left, I gather.'

Abby could only stare at him, truly shocked that he would stoop to such low tactics. And oddly disappointed. Yet she shouldn't have been. Hadn't she always known that he was an unfeeling and ruthless bastard?

Shock and disappointment quickly gave way to a blind outrage. 'God, but I despise you,' she spat, jumping to her feet and glaring her fury at him. 'Who do you think you are, threatening me like this? And who do you think you are, offering me money to come here with you, then thinking badly of me because I accepted? I'd actually *tell* you the real reason I made that counter-offer if I thought you'd believe me. But you won't. You like justifying your demeaning proposition by thinking I'm some kind of amateur whore.'

She was quivering with emotion as she stalked towards him. 'You can stick your pathetic job on

Fridays. Plus your so-called *plans* for me. I'm sick and tired of you looking down your nose at me. Though why in hell should you? What have I ever done to make you think what you obviously think?'

She was close to him now. *Too* close. She could actually smell the tang of his expensive aftershave, see the sudden blaze in his eyes, feeling the heat of his own anger.

'I'm leaving,' she told him defiantly. 'And there isn't anything you can do about it.'

He glared at her, and for a split second she was sure he was going to grab her. Grab her and kiss her and seduce her, as he'd threatened a minute ago.

Her eyes widened as the seconds ticked away and she began willing him to do just that. Her head whirled as she struggled to gain control over her appalling thoughts and dangerously excited body.

What was it about this man that aroused such a primitive sexuality within her? Thinking of Dillon didn't help, for what she'd felt for Dillon had been nothing like this at all! There was nothing romantic or idealistic about her feelings for Ethan. It was just sex at its most basic. Raw and tempestuous, and totally without conscience.

Suddenly he spun away, striding across the room and picking up her suitcase. But instead of throwing it at her he tossed it onto the bed and snapped it open.

'Don't be so bloody melodramatic,' he ground out harshly. 'I've never thought of you as an amateur whore, and I don't give a damn why you asked me for that amount of money. I accept I was out of line just now, and I humbly apologise. Believe me when I say it won't happen again. Refuse my offer of a full-time job if you detest my company that much. Quit your Friday job as well. But you're not quitting *this* job. I've paid you to be my pretend lover for the duration of this conference, and my pretend lover you are going to be. Do I make myself clear?'

She nodded weakly as reality returned, all her pent-up emotion and tension abruptly draining out of her. Ethan was so right. Her own threat to leave *had* been melodramatic. And quite impractical. She didn't even have enough money with her to get back to Sydney on her own. No, she was locked in, and she had to see these three days through, no matter what.

'Now, I suggest you unpack and start getting ready for cocktails and dinner,' he ordered curtly. 'It's already after four, and if I know women, you'll need all of the next two hours to be totally satisfied with how you look.'

CHAPTER EIGHT

ETHAN was in the shower when the telephone rang. Abby turned from where she was putting the finishing touches to her hair, securing the sash of the complimentary cream bathrobe as she walked over to pick up the receiver from the bedside chest. Without thinking, she said the words she always said when answering Ethan's telephone.

'Dr Grant's room.'

Dead silence down the line.

'Dr Grant's room,' she repeated. 'Hello, is anyone there?'

'*Abby*?' came the startled query. 'That is you, isn't it?'

Abby's hand flew to her mouth. Dear God. Sylvia.

What to do? Hang up, or change her voice suddenly and pretend to be the housemaid?

'Abby, say something,' Sylvia demanded sharply. 'I know it's you, so there's no use hanging up or pretending it isn't.'

Abby sighed. She'd given Ethan her word that she wouldn't tell Sylvia about their arrangement, but she could hardly have anticipated this. Lying seemed stupid at this stage.

'Yes, Sylvia, it's me,' she said, resignation in her voice.

'What on earth are you doing down there...at Bungarla...in Ethan's room?'

'Being a good little employee,' Abby replied ruefully.

For the time being, that was. Abby now accepted that she could never work for Ethan ever again after this. The thought depressed her unbearably, but it had to be.

'I'm sorry, but I...I don't understand.'

'You only have yourself to blame, Sylvia. You put the idea into Ethan's head.'

'What idea?'

'Hiring a female escort for the conference. Last Friday night, after you left, he offered to pay me to come with him and I agreed.'

'He did? You *did*?'

Abby smiled wryly at Sylvia's startled bewilderment. 'You don't have to sound so shocked, Sylvia. It's merely a business arrangement. Nothing to get all het up about.'

'But you're in his *room*!'

'We have separate sleeping arrangements,' she said firmly, glancing at the sofa which she'd been relieved to find *did* unfold into a second bed. God knows what she'd have done if it hadn't.

'I see,' Sylvia said slowly. 'Yes, I see. At least, I hope so.'

'There's no hanky-panky going on, if that's what you're thinking.'

'More's the pity.'

Abby was taken aback by both the remark and its dry tone. 'What on earth do you mean by that?'

'Is Ethan there with you now?'

'He's in the shower. We're going down for pre-dinner drinks at six.' Just thirty minutes away. Abby wasn't looking forward to it.

'Then I must speak quickly. Ethan never spends long in the shower. He would also kill me if he knew I was about to tell you this, but I've been so worried since

coming into the office this afternoon and finding that
letter on Ethan's desk.'

Abby had a pretty good idea of what letter Sylvia was
talking about, but decided not to let on. As much as
Abby had tried not to be curious about Ethan's past relationship with the Ballistrats, she was. So she was eager
to hear what Sylvia had to say about the matter.

'Lord, but this is difficult,' Sylvia muttered. 'I'll just
have to be blunt. Look, about ten years ago, when Ethan
was a resident, he fell in love with a nurse—a gorgeous-
looking blonde named Vanessa. They moved in together
and were going to be married. In fact the wedding was
only a couple of weeks away when she ran off with
another doctor—a famous visiting neurosurgeon named
Dr Philip Ballistrat. You must have heard of him. Maybe
you even heard of the scandal at the time. The man was
married with a family. The wife was very vocal and
bitter.'

'Yes, I do recall the incident,' she murmured, feeling
a lot of sympathy for the youthful Ethan, but little for
him now. To be jilted like that was not nice, but the man
should have put it all behind him by now, not remained
bitter and twisted for all these years.

'Of course, nobody paid any attention to the young
doctor she left behind, but Ethan was devastated,' Sylvia
explained with sisterly understanding. 'Simply devastated. He was crazy about her, and she'd seemed to be
crazy about him. I worried for his sanity and his life for
a long time after she left. I thought he might go after
her and do something…well…something silly…

'But he didn't, thank God. Dr Ballistrat went overseas
to America, where he took up some post at a big fancy
clinic which charges huge fees. He's never been back to
Australia. Till now. He's going to be at the conference,

Abby. Lecturing. Which means *Vanessa's* going to be there too. I'm positive the only reason Ethan changed his mind about going was because of that, and I'm afraid of what he might do.'

'Ethan is not a violent man, Sylvia,' Abby assured the worried woman.

'No, I know he's not.'

'And this all happened *years* ago!' she exclaimed with some exasperation.

'Maybe so, but he's never forgotten or forgiven. I've always felt there was something about their break-up which Ethan never told me—something really wicked on her part, something totally unforgivable.'

'Such as what?'

'I don't know. All I know is that Ethan's up to something. Maybe he's not about to do murder, but what if he's planning to steal Vanessa back from Philip Ballistrat as a type of revenge? He was besotted with that woman once. Maybe he still is, in a way.'

Abby could hear the panic rising in Sylvia's voice. The woman was getting herself in a real tizzy. 'Now, why would he have gone to the trouble of hiring *me* to be by his side if his intention was wife-stealing?' she argued reasonably. 'No, Sylvia, I don't believe that for one moment. I think he just wants to see her again, that's all. But he didn't want *her* seeing *him* without an attractive young woman on his arm. He has his pride, you know. I don't believe Ethan's about to do anything stupid. He's just laying an old ghost to rest.'

'Oh, I do hope you're right and I'm wrong. I just have this awful feeling. I know you said your being with Ethan was just a business arrangement, but please, Abby, do your best to keep him right away from that woman, will you? She's poison where Ethan's concerned. And who knows? Now that he's older, and very successful, Vanessa might decide to give her ageing husband the flick and go for Ethan again. That's less likely to happen if the lovely girl by his side uses some of her previously understated attractions to distract him, don't you think?'

'What, exactly, are you proposing, Sylvia?' Abby asked slowly.

'You know exactly what I'm proposing, Abby,' came back the forthright remark. 'You're not that naïve. Frankly, when I first hired you I secretly hoped something might develop between you and Ethan. *And* I think he knew it, the stubborn, cantankerous devil! Why else would he have gone to so much trouble to keep you at a safe distance? All that "Miss Richmond" rubbish didn't fool me one bit.

'And you're just as bad,' she swept on before Abby could open her mouth. 'I know that underneath everything you find Ethan attractive. What woman wouldn't? So don't bother to deny it. All I'm suggesting is that now you're in a more intimate situation don't do anything to stop nature taking its natural course. You might even give it a helping hand, so to speak.'

'Ethan doesn't like women who fawn all over him,' she said drily.

'Then don't fawn. Flirt.'

'Flirt?'

'Yes. Believe me, Vanessa will. She's the expert of experts when it comes to flirting. Wait till you see her in action.'

Abby was in no hurry to see Vanessa at all, let alone flirting with Ethan. The very thought made her insides go all tight. Surely Ethan wouldn't have anything to do with a woman like that again. Surely not!

The shower water being switched off made her jump.

'Ethan's finished in the shower, Sylvia,' she whispered hurriedly. 'I think, if you don't want him knowing about this conversation, you'd better hang up. I also won't mention you rang.'

'You'll do what I asked, then?'

Abby swallowed. 'I…I'll do my best.'

'Oh, thank you, thank you. I've been sick with worry.'

'I'm not going to sleep with him, Sylvia. That's asking too much.'

'Only do what you feel comfortable with, dear,' Ethan's sister said rather smugly, and hung up.

Abby grimaced as she replaced the receiver and hurried back to where she'd been doing her hair.

Lord, what a pickle! Hired by the brother to be a pretend lover, then urged by the sister to become a real one—neither of them knowing how she actually felt about the man. If it wasn't so damned dangerous a situation, it would be funny!

Abby wanted to help Sylvia out, but really it was impossible. If she started flirting with Ethan after the way she'd just carried on, he'd wonder what on earth was happening. Either that, or he'd cynically think that she was after more money for extra-curricular activities, and would probably take her up in what she seemed to be offering.

Abby didn't believe that her cold-hearted boss was in anyway smitten with her, but he was a man, after all. And a man who didn't have too many qualms about where he got his sex—which might include with his silly receptionist!

That was all very well for him. He could obviously bed a woman he didn't love without turning a hair. As much as Abby had toughened up during her four-year stint in prison, she didn't think she was tough enough to make love with Ethan and walk away afterwards totally unscathed.

It was the first time Abby had conceded that she might feel a fraction more for Ethan than just lust. Only a fraction, mind. But it was enough to worry the hell out of her. She'd been brutally used by one man in her life and she wasn't about to set herself up to be used by another.

So she wisely decided not to make even the slightest flirtatious move till she saw the lie of the land for herself. For all she knew, it might not be necessary for her to 'distract' Ethan in any way at all. Vanessa might take one look at him and not give him a second glance, and vice versa.

The bathroom door opened and Ethan walked out, naked except for a large fluffy cream towel looped casually around his waist. His black hair was still wet from the shower, and a few wayward locks flopped rakishly across his high forehead. The dark curls in the centre of his chest were also still damp, tight little swirls of glistening hair which screamed out to have a woman's fingers slide sensually through them.

Abby did her best not to stare, her heart sinking all the while. Vanessa would definitely take a second glance. She was taking more than two herself.

'Was that the telephone just now?' he asked abruptly.

She swallowed and lifted her eyes back to his face, praying that nothing showed in her expression or demeanour to betray her X-rated thoughts. 'No,' she lied fairly smoothly.

'Must have been next door,' he muttered, scooping the now dripping locks back from his forehead with both hands, the action highlighting muscles in his chest and arms which hadn't come from lifting a scalpel. Either he worked out regularly with weights, or he'd been born with a physique most men had to sweat long hours for.

'Won't be long,' he added, then strode back into the bathroom without looking at her again.

Abby let out a shuddering sigh. 'Take all the time you like, Ethan,' she murmured. 'I'm in no hurry.'

But it seemed Ethan *was*, for less than five minutes later he emerged from the bathroom a second time. Thankfully he was fully dressed this time, though he still looked devastatingly attractive in elegant black trousers and an open-necked burgundy-coloured shirt which had fullish sleeves. He was combing his hair as he walked, trying to put some order into his still wet black waves.

'I think I should have had a haircut before I came,' he grumbled.

Abby disagreed. Longish, his hair was wildly attractive and compellingly touchable. Combined with his naturally olive complexion and that shirt, his overall look tonight was gypsyish and sinfully sexy.

When he glanced up to find her standing stock-still and staring at him, she adopted a casually thoughtful expression, as though she was studying his hair at his behest. 'Actually, it suits you long,' she said carelessly.

'I see you've put *your* hair up again,' he returned.

Abby shrugged, though the thought crossed her mind that if things looked really bad where the awful Vanessa was concerned, she might leave it down a couple of times. From experience, leaving her hair down invariably drew male attention, and Ethan had already expressed a desire to see it down. Such a gesture would be more subtle than openly flirting with him.

'You *are* going to be ready in time, aren't you?' he demanded brusquely, scowling at her still robed body.

'I only have to slip into my clothes.' And put my

lipstick on, plus my perfume, not to mention my jewellery, she added silently.

'Then do so. I promised Henry I would collect them right on six.'

He was tense, Abby saw. Very tense. Because of Vanessa, no doubt. Presumably he hoped to see her during the cocktail hour, when people tended to mingle.

Abby extracted her chosen clothes from where she'd hung them in the wardrobe, scooped up the velvet case which contained her pearls and hurried into the bathroom.

She took only two minutes to slip into the classically tailored blue suit and cream satin camisole, another thirty seconds to apply the coral lipstick which matched the coral nail polish she'd painted on earlier, then another few seconds to spray a conservative amount of Miss Blanchford's Chanel No. 5 behind her ears and on her wrists. Abby finally dropped the long single rope of pearls over her neck, then clipped the pearl drops to her lobes.

Sylvia would be pleased, she thought wryly as she surveyed her reflection, aware that the outfit looked more provocative on her than she recalled it looking five years ago. Those few extra inches on her figure again.

The camisole was not overly low-cut, but its shoelace straps precluded her wearing a bra. The pearl necklace had settled into the shadowed valley between her unfettered breasts, bringing attention to the beginnings of a cleavage. Cheap and flashy she was not, but there was no denying it was an eyecatching outfit.

Abby frowned at the tightness of the straight skirt around her hips and bottom, wishing she'd had more time to lose just a little more weight. Thank heaven the jacket reached down a fair way, and also covered her suspiciously erect nipples.

Sighing at her silly self, she pulled a few extra strands of hair out of the loose chignon to curl around her face and neck, thinking that they might soften the image she presented. But she ended up looking even more sexy, as though she'd been kissing her lover and he'd tangled his hands in her hair.

God! She almost stamped her foot in frustration.

An impatient tap on the door had her yanking it open and striding out, defiant eyes flying to Ethan.

'I'm almost ready,' she snapped. 'I only have to slip into my shoes. It's only five to six, you know.' She jammed her stockinged feet into cream court shoes with finely pointed heels. A year or two ago they would have been hopelessly out of fashion, but the style had come back in, thank heavens.

'There. I'm done. Do I pass?' she asked, striking a model's pose for him. She knew she was being a bit of a bitch, but fear of making a fool of herself had drawn her nerves tight.

Ethan's gaze was irritatingly unreadable as he looked her up and down. 'You'll do,' he said, then strolled over to inspect the pearl necklace more closely. 'They look real.' He picked up the end and dangled it from his middle finger.

'They are,' she retorted, piqued by his attitude. He could have said something nice instead of being nasty. '*Everything* about me is real.'

His eyes turned sardonic as they moved over her breasts. 'Impressive,' came his droll remark before he dropped the pearls back into place, seemingly making a point of not actually touching her. 'So is your wardrobe, by the look of things. My three thousand might have covered the clothes, not to mention the undoubtedly expensive perfume which is wafting from your delectable body, but I'd say it would be struggling to stretch to the price of those pearls. So tell me, Abigail…where does a casually employed working girl get the money to buy real pearls?'

'Not from my pathetic salaries, I can assure you,' she countered scornfully. A minute ago she might have told him the truth, but not now. Why give him the opportunity to hold her in more contempt by not believing her. 'They were gifts,' she said offhandedly.

'From men?'

'No. Just one man.' It wasn't even a lie. Her father had paid for all her clothes, and her mother's gifts had really been bought with her father's money as well.

'Ah. So that's the answer to what you were doing before you came to work for me. You had a sugar-daddy. I suppose he's the one who paid for you to go overseas as well. Sylvia says you've travelled extensively over the past few years.'

'That's right.'

'How old was he, this man who showered you with gifts and trips?'

'How old?' she retorted, swallowing.

'It's a simple question, Abigail. How old was this man?'

Abby gulped again. She hadn't meant this petty little word-game of hers to go this far. 'That's none of your business,' she tossed back, and went to walk past him.

His hand shot out and grabbed her upper arm, swinging her round. 'How old?' he rasped down into her face.

The pain shooting through her arm brought another spurt of defiant anger. 'A lot older than you,' she spat at him. 'And a hell of a lot richer!'

He let her go, his blue eyes like chips of ice.

'I can't believe how disappointed in you I am,' he drawled. 'There I was, thinking I might have misjudged you.'

'Really? Well, I'm not disappointed in you, Ethan,' she returned frostily. 'Because I never misjudged *you*.'

'Meaning?'

'I don't think we have time for a deep and meaningful chat about our respective weaknesses, do you? But be assured, my relationship with this man was based on love, not lust.'

'You mean he loved you?' Ethan said derisively.

'No, I mean *I* loved *him*. As it turned out, he didn't love me at all.'

Ethan was obviously taken aback. His frown betrayed surprise, then a dark thoughtfulness. 'But you don't love him any more.'

'I wish I didn't.'

'Are you saying you still *do*?' Ethan sounded angry with her.

She could see his point, but how did one stop loving a parent? She even loved her mother—her silly, feckless, selfish mother. 'I dare say I'll always love him,' she confessed, her heart turning over.

'But that's stupid,' he snapped. 'The man used you, can't you see that?'

Abby found a measure of relief for poor Sylvia's concern in Ethan's words. If that was his way of thinking then he clearly no longer loved Vanessa. Unless it was a case of do as I say, not as I do. Men had a tendency to hypocrisy in matters of love and sex.

'I can see more than you give me credit for, Ethan,' she bit out. 'Now, no more talk about the past, please. It's gone and should stay gone. It's also gone six, and Henry and Ann will be waiting. Shall we go?'

CHAPTER NINE

ANN was looking pretty in pink silk, with Henry quite suave in a polo-necked jumper and tweedish smoking jacket. The two couples were moving along the covered walkway which led from the motel-style units back to the main building of the hotel when Ethan startled Abby by sliding an arm around her waist.

'For appearances' sake,' he whispered wryly into her ear as he pulled her close.

Abby stiffened beneath his touch. God, but she could actually feel the heat of his palm right through her jacket and skirt. Or was it her own sudden heat she was feeling, the heat of a burning sexual awareness? Whatever, she quivered inside when his fingers splayed over the curve of her hip, thrilling to the way they applied a masterful pressure as he steered her through the doorway into the hotel.

She'd always admired Ethan's hands, with their long, elegant fingers and economically graceful movements. But she'd never guessed how strong they were. How strong *he* was. Seeing him semi-naked had shown her an Ethan other than the coolly professional surgeon she encountered every Friday afternoon. The memory sent more heat through her body, travelling with speed around her veins to every tiny capillary, making her feel hot all over.

'This way,' Henry said, directing them to the hallway which would bring them back to the front lobby. 'Reception actually gave me a map of the hotel with all the rooms marked for all the various functions, so we poor, unintelligent medicos don't get lost. Did they give you one, Ethan?'

'Probably. They gave me a whole pile of stuff which I threw on the coffee-table. I haven't really had time to look at it yet.'

'Oh? What on earth have you two been doing for the past two hours, old chap?'

Abby felt Ethan's fingers freeze on her flesh.

'None of your business, Henry,' he said evenly.

'Henry,' Ann warned.

'All right, all right. I'll be good. Truly, I'm sure Abby wasn't offended. You weren't, were you, Abby love?'

'Not at all,' Abby admitted, despite her cheeks feeling awfully hot.

'There. I knew she wouldn't be. Not like that Madam Muck you brought to dinner a month or so ago, Ethan.'

'Oh, God!' Ann exclaimed exasperatedly. 'Do shut up, Henry, before you put your other foot in your mouth as well.'

Henry genuinely looked perplexed. 'What did I say that was so wrong?'

'Abby doesn't want to hear about Ethan's other women,' Ann snapped.

'It's all right, Henry,' Abby reassured him. 'I know all about Ethan's other women—Evelyn included. Ethan and I are very open with each other, aren't we, darling?'

The 'darling' just slipped out before she could stop it. Ethan arched a cold eyebrow down at her, at the same time digging his fingertips into her hip. His smile was quite frightening, if one was accustomed to its chilling undertones.

'Too true,' he agreed in a low, silkily menacing voice.

'There's nothing I don't know about Abigail, here. Absolutely nothing.'

Abby resisted pulling a face at him. God, but he was a cynical bastard. Why she wanted him so much she had no idea. 'Oh, I wouldn't go that far, darling,' she countered, finding sweet revenge in not dropping the endearment. 'A woman wouldn't be a woman if she didn't have some little secrets.' And mine are real whoppers! she thought.

For a split second Abby felt a frisson of fear that someone here might know about her stay in prison. But she quickly dismissed it again as highly unlikely. She couldn't see too many surgeons showing up with ex-cons as wives or even girlfriends.

'Secrets are not the sole prerogative of women,' Henry announced heartily. 'I know a few doctors who practically lead a double life when it comes to their pursuit of the opposite sex! Up the stairs here, folks. Cocktails are being served on the first floor.'

'Don't look at me, Ann,' Ethan defended himself. 'I'm too damned busy to bother with juggling women. One woman at a time is more than enough for me. Especially one like Abigail. She's such a loving little thing, aren't you, darling?'

When Abby automatically glanced up at this mocking return of the endearment, he stunned her by bending down and kissing her on the lips.

It was over almost before it began, a mere brushing of mouth against mouth. But oh, how it sent her heart a-thudding and her eyes a-widening. She stared up at him as his head lifted, knowing that if he ever chose to leave those lips on hers for longer than two miserable seconds, she would be in deep, deep trouble.

His blue eyes narrowed as he frowned back down into

her stunned face. Was he reading her troubled and very vulnerable mind? Already planning a ruthless seduction, perhaps?

The possibility was perversely delicious to think about, but Abby knew that such a reality would be a disaster. She knew who would be the one who ended up getting hurt, and it wouldn't be Mr Hyde.

'Enough of that for now,' Ann interrupted. 'There's just so much spontaneous passion I can stand on an empty stomach. I'll let you continue canoodling after I've had a couple of G and Ts.'

'We'll await your permission with bated breath,' Ethan said with another rueful glance down at Abby. 'Lead on, Henry. I think I could do with a drink myself.'

Me, too, Abby agreed. Alcohol had a tendency to make her aggressive and sarcastic, not at all the mellow you-can-do-anything-you-like-with-me type of female most men hoped for when they plied their partner with drink. Dillon had taken some time to realise that he did much better with chocolates and compliments than wine.

Not that Abby seriously thought that Ethan was interested in getting her drunk, or in seducing her. He was just being his usual supercilious self, trying to niggle her. It was a continuation of the coldly competitive game of one-upmanship they'd played with each other right from the first day.

'Straight ahead,' Henry directed, ushering Ann towards the open doorway directly opposite the top of the stairs.

The first room they entered contained a large centrally located bar and a polished wooden rectangular construction with a black leather top and a myriad of matching stools anchored to the red carpet on steel poles. The rest of the large room was filled with groupings of armchairs and tables, most of which were occupied. A smoke haze filled the air, which caused Ann immediately to wrinkle her nose.

'Clearly this is the smoking section,' she said. 'But I see an archway over there and clear air in the distance. Come on. Let's find our pure lungs a more suitable breathing place for the next hour.'

Abby couldn't help but notice the way Ethan looked around as they followed Ann and Henry through the smoke-filled room, his searching gaze checking out every group of people, including those sitting and standing at the bar. Was he looking for Vanessa? she wondered. And felt an irritating pang of jealousy.

Several of the men greeted him by name, their women companions invariably looking him up and down—all with interest, some with outright hunger. Abby found herself glaring back at these with open hostility. She even linked arms with him at one stage, staking her pretend possession. It brought a sour glance from Ethan and a muttered, 'Don't overdo it.'

'You started it,' she returned airily. 'You should never have kissed me like that. I was overcome.'

'I did notice you were stunned into silence for a second or two.'

'Shock does rather have that effect on one.'

'Hopefully, next time I kiss you you won't look quite so much like a stunned mullet.'

'*Next* time?' she repeated, her stomach flipping over at the thought.

'Having established your highly affectionate nature, it seems only natural that I would act differently with you from my usual distant self.'

'Stop whispering you two,' Ann said, glancing over her shoulder at them. Her gaze moved momentarily beyond Ethan and Abby, her eyes suddenly flinging wide. She stopped walking, tugging on Henry's sleeve as she did so. 'It's her, Henry,' she gasped. 'The hussy! She's just walked in. And alone too. Don't turn round, Ethan. Pretend you're talking to me while I surreptitiously watch.'

Ethan didn't turn round, but his spine had gone instantly ramrod-straight, the hand on Abby's hip freezing. Abby risked a peek over her shoulder. The hussy Ann was referring to was Vanessa Ballistrat, all right, looking exquisitely feminine in oyster pearl chiffon.

'I presume you're referring to Mrs Ballistrat,' Abby said in a superbly bland voice.

'Don't tell me you know of her, Abby? Why, you're much too young to remember the scandal when it happened.'

'Actually, I do remember it. Quite well. I was at boarding school at the time, and my girlfriends and I used to devour all the women's magazines. I even remember her first name. It was Vanessa. But I like hussy much better. It suits her. She hasn't changed all that much, physically speaking, has she?' she remarked, with another glance over her shoulder at the blonde, who'd already been claimed by a male admirer.

'I'd say she was *better* looking, if anything,' Ann remarked sourly. 'And still obviously irresistible to men.'

Ethan stayed standing like a statue, his face grim, his fingers now like ice. Abby tried to feel sympathy for him. Instead, all she felt was a fierce frustration, and more curiosity than ever.

'Did you and Henry know her personally back then, Ann?' she went on, determined to bring as much out in the open as she dared. 'Ethan tells me she used to work at the hospital where he was a resident.'

'Is that so?' Henry commented interestedly. 'Would that I had been so lucky, but I worked in Canberra around that time. What was she like, Ethan?'

'Irresistible to men,' Ethan said drily.

Henry laughed. 'Not you too, old chap. I heard from an American doctor I know that she takes scalps wherever she goes. When we read that letter, cock-crowing about this conference having ensnared old Ballistrat as a lecturer, Ann and I were curious to see for ourselves exactly what he risked his career for. I must say that even from this distance she packs quite a punch. Marilyn Monroe reincarnated, with a touch of Marlene Dietrich thrown in for good measure. Mmm, yes...ve—ry nice indeed.'

Ethan at last turned to see for himself, his hand falling away from Abby's hip as he did so. She should have felt relieved by this. Instead, she felt oddly bereft. Abandoned. Rejected. She wanted his hand back on her flesh, wanted the intimacy—however slight—sustained.

She stared up at him, troubled by the emotion racing through her, hating the time he was taking in surveying his old flame.

Whilst Ethan's face remained fairly impassive, Abby thought she glimpsed a tightening around his mouth and a darkening in his eyes as he watched the woman. By the time he turned back to face them, she found that she was holding her breath.

'You're right, Ann,' he drawled, his tone bored. 'She *is* better looking. But I doubt she's changed in other ways. Let's go and get ourselves a drink. My throat's as dry as the Simpson Desert.' Taking Abby's arm, he urged her forward, forcing his friends to move on.

Abby slanted him a quick look, but there was nothing

for her to see now. Clearly Ethan was a master at hiding his feelings once he put his mind to it.

Did he still want Vanessa? she agonised. Had he taken one look and been swamped by renewed desire for her beautiful face and body? They'd been lovers once, had *lived* together, for pity's sake! She had probably made love like a sex goddess, knowing exactly what Ethan had wanted and needed to make him happy. Sylvia had said he'd been devastated when she'd left him, her power over him so strong that he'd almost gone mad with losing her. He might hate her, but he still wanted her. Abby felt sure of it.

God, but she'd never felt so jealous of a woman in all her life! It was a telling moment, and one which Abby struggled to explain to herself—unfortunately not with a satisfactory answer. All she knew was that she was going to do everything possible to keep that bitch away from Ethan.

The second lounge was smaller, quieter and very comfy, with a couple of waiters circling the room and offering drinks and hors d'oeuvres to the occupants.

They settled into a corner, Ethan drawing Abby down with him into a deep two-seater against the wall and Ann and Henry pulling up armchairs, forming a U-shaped group which didn't prevent anyone from looking around the room or through the wide archway into the bar beyond. Abby wondered if Ethan had chosen the spot for that reason, so he could keep an eye on Vanessa. It seemed likely, considering this was why he had come.

Once everyone was seated, one of the hovering waiters immediately offered them a large selection of drinks from an oval silver tray. Abby took a glass of champagne, Ann a dry sherry, Henry a beer and Ethan a Scotch and water.

'I wonder where her doting husband is tonight?' Henry resumed, obviously not willing to let the subject of Vanessa drop. Hard to do when she was in full view, standing with a group just through the archway.

A group of *men*, Abby noted ruefully. She had her hand on one of the men's arms and was smiling up at him as though what he was saying was simply riveting.

'Perhaps he isn't feeling well,' Ethan said, and curled his free arm around Abby's shoulders. She glanced up at him before producing what she hoped was her best 'come hither' smile. Anything to stop him looking at that woman. He blinked for a moment, then smiled back, a slow, sardonic curve which might have seemed seductively warm to anyone who only knew Dr Jekyll and not Mr Hyde.

'You'll keep,' he murmured in so low a voice that only she could hear, his lips pressed against her hair.

'What do you mean, Ethan?' Henry persisted. 'What do you know that I don't know about Ballistrat?'

'I don't know how much you know, Henry, but rumour has it he has some form of arthritis in his fingers and can't operate any more. That's why he's been reduced to the lecture tour circuit. They say he has money troubles and is drinking like a fish as well. Maybe he's not here for cocktails because he doesn't dare—in case he has a hangover tomorrow.'

Abby absorbed all this information with growing concern. Ethan had certainly gone to a lot of trouble to find out about Dr Ballistrat. She was sure that he hadn't known any of this last Friday, when that letter had arrived. Sylvia could be right about Ethan planning some sort of revenge. Not necessarily violent, but maybe just as vindictive. The objective of that revenge didn't seem

to be Vanessa, however, but the man who'd stolen her
from him.

'I wouldn't take too many bets on that marriage last-
ing, then,' Henry said. 'Women like Blondie like the
good things in life. And I wouldn't rank being poor in
that category.'

Too true, Abby thought caustically.

'Well, well,' Henry said with gleeful anticipation.
'Our luck's in. She's coming this way. You might be
able to introduce us, Ethan. Why don't you wave her
over?'

Abby watched the hussy enter the room with the man
whose arm she'd been clinging to. Immediately she felt
not only inferior in the beauty stakes, but a great big
clumsy horse by comparison.

The woman didn't walk, she floated—the chiffon skirt
swirling sensuously about her slender legs. She was really quite tiny, with a pocket Venus figure, a creamy,
unlined complexion and the shiniest blonde hair Abby
had ever seen. The colour of whipped cream, it curved
around her face in soft waves, its glossy paleness a perfect foil for her eyes which were large and limpid and
blue. *Very* blue. The bluest of blue lagoons against the
whitest of white sand.

Abby could well imagine any man drowning in them.

They all watched her approach, every single one of
them, with various expressions written on their faces.
Henry with goggled-eyed admiration; Ann with avid curiosity; Abby with envy and Ethan with far too studied
an indifference, Abby thought. He didn't fool her one
bit. She could feel his tension through the arm around
her shoulders.

Vanessa didn't appear to notice them watching her,

keeping her big blue eyes glued to the man she was with, seemingly wrapped in what he was saying.

Abby recognised the act for what it was. An act. The beautiful Mrs Ballistrat wasn't at all interested in what her companion was saying. What she cared about was the admiration she was getting in return. Abby had known the type before. Women who thrived on male attention, could not live without it. Her own mother had been one.

Suddenly Vanessa laughed, a caressing feminine sound which held promise of the sweetest of natures.

'What an actress!' Ann muttered disgruntledly, obviously thinking the same thoughts as Abby.

Henry chuckled. 'Who cares? She can turn those big baby blues on me any time she likes.'

'Over my dead body,' Ann snorted.

'I wouldn't say that too loudly, if I were you, Ann,' Ethan remarked, a sardonic edge to his voice. 'Women like Vanessa would not stop at murder to get any man they wanted.'

'I believe you,' Ann returned sourly.

'Hush up, you two,' Henry muttered. 'She's coming over here.'

Which she was, having dispensed with her companion, who stood staring longingly after her, looking both adoring and crushed. But he was no longer wanted—hadn't been from the moment the hussy had spotted Ethan out of the corner of her eye.

She floated towards their corner, her gaze clamped to Ethan's face. She didn't seem at all surprised to see him there, though a degree of apprehension did cloud her beautiful blue eyes as she drew closer, as though she was unsure of her welcome. Her wariness grew as she drew to a slightly nervous halt in front of him, a red-nailed and very feminine hand fluttering up to her throat.

'Hello, Ethan,' she said softly. 'It's been a long time. *Too* long,' she added, her melodic voice carrying real regret.

'You're looking remarkably well, Vanessa,' Ethan returned with surprising charm. 'Would you care to join us for a drink?'

Ann looked daggers at him, Abby noted, but he ignored her. I'd like to kill him myself, she thought mutinously. True to form, Henry was delighted, jumping to his feet immediately. 'I'll pull up a chair for you.'

Vanessa beamed at him. 'Oh, thank you. What a nice man you are,' she added sweetly, as he slid a chair into the gap between his and Ann's, completing a cosy little circle.

Vanessa sank gracefully into it, the chiffon skirt making a swishing sound as she delicately crossed her legs. Her eyes immediately returned to Ethan's, as though they held some secret magnet for her. 'I was so surprised when I saw your name on the register, Ethan,' she said, smiling her pleasure. 'Not that I should have been. You always said you'd become a top orthopaedic surgeon. I'll bet you're good.'

'I like to think I am,' Ethan returned modestly.

'He's more than good,' Henry inserted. 'He's the best bone man in Australia, even if he is the rudest. Since Ethan's forgotten his manners, we'll introduce ourselves. Dr Henry Maclean at your service, Mrs Ballistrat.'

'Oh, do call me Vanessa,' she said, leaning over and touching him lightly on the wrist. 'I can't abide formality.' With the leaning forward, her high and impossibly perfect breasts formed a deep cleavage within the low V-neckline of her dress.

Henry only just managed not to gawk. 'You won't get any arguments from me on that score,' he said, his florid face gaining some more redness.

'And I'm Ann Maclean,' Ann said coldly. 'Henry's wife.'

'How do you do, Mrs Maclean?' came the equally cool reply. Clearly formality still applied to wives.

Abby waited for those big blue eyes to turn to her, which they eventually did, but only after lingering on Ethan again for a few more moments. Abby couldn't catch Ethan's reaction without being obvious.

'And I dare say this sweet young thing is Mrs Ethan Grant?' she suggested.

Abby cringed at the description, and the woman's saccharine tone.

'Not as yet, Vanessa,' Ethan returned, before Abby could think of a suitably cutting retort. 'But that's to be remedied shortly. I know we said we'd keep it a secret for a while yet, darling,' he murmured, giving Abby an affectionate squeeze, 'but what's the point? I asked Abby to marry me this afternoon and she bravely said yes.'

CHAPTER TEN

ABBY suspected that her eyes must have shown shock, but she doubted anyone saw it, Ethan immediately obliterating her face from view as his mouth swooped.

Shock quickly changed to resentment as he forced his will upon her lips, but resentment proved a poor weapon against the mad desire which was lurking deep within her treacherous body. How could she possibly keep her lips primly shut when Ethan's tongue was demanding entry? It was what she'd dreamt about, what she'd fantasised over.

So she opened her mouth and let him kiss her—*really* kiss her.

It was once again only a brief kiss. Even so, for those few savage seconds everything else ceased to exist. Where they were. Henry and Ann. Even the dreaded Vanessa.

Ethan's tongue surged deep into her mouth, tracing a swiftly erotic path around her own tongue, then up over the roof of her mouth. When it abruptly withdrew she almost moaned her disappointment, only then remembering where they were and who was watching.

Ann and Henry were smiling broadly at her blushing face, but Vanessa looked as if she was carved in stone. Abby still felt somewhat disorientated, but it did cross her muddled mind that Ethan's unexpected statement was part of his secret plan where that woman was concerned.

Had he been going to up her status all along? Or had

it been a spur-of-the-moment decision, based on Vanessa's reaction to him? If he thought his being engaged would discourage her, he was in for a surprise. The past showed that neither engagement ring nor wedding ring would stop the woman if she wanted someone.

And she wanted Ethan. Abby had no doubts about that any longer. But did he want her back?

Another thought struck, and Abby recoiled. Was she being used as a blind? Had Ethan planned on having an adulterous rendezvous with Vanessa all along? Maybe he did despise the woman, but still desperately desired her. Maybe her undoubted sexual prowess still haunted his dreams. Maybe the way he wanted to lay *this* ghost to rest was to lay her—literally…

Abby's eyes cleared to find Henry and Ann both congratulating them and castigating them for not telling them earlier.

'We weren't going to say anything till I could buy her a ring,' Ethan explained, hugging Abby to his side. Again. 'Aren't you going to congratulate us, Vanessa?'

'But of course,' she purred. 'I'm just surprised some lucky girl didn't snap you up long ago.'

'I doubt I've been suitable marriage material over the past ten years,' Ethan countered casually. 'You know what they say. All work and no play makes Jack a dull boy.'

'Not you, Ethan. You were never dull.'

'He surprised us too, Vanessa,' Henry chimed in. 'Even showing up here with Abby was a surprise. I didn't get a whiff of a serious romance from the sneaky devil, and I work with him three days a week.'

'Is that so?' The big blue eyes threw Abby a thoughtful glance.

Abby reacted automatically, her only objective to

wipe that speculative look right off Vanessa's too beautiful face.

'Ethan likes to keep his private life, private, don't you, darling?' she murmured, gazing at him adoringly before lifting her mouth and pressing a soft little kiss on the corner of his mouth. 'Actually, we've been crazy about each other since the first day we met six months ago, but we took our time in revealing our true feelings. But once we did, all that pent-up emotion just sort of exploded!'

'Oh, how romantic!' Ann sighed.

The waiter returning to offer fresh drinks came as a welcome distraction at that point. He was quickly followed by a waitress carrying a huge tray of hors d'oeuvres.

Vanessa wasn't at all happy with the selection of either, and asked Henry if he would mind getting her a dry martini from the bar. Much to Ann's chagrin, he hopped up immediately and dashed off to do the blonde's bidding. Vanessa was fairly gushing in her gratitude on his return, making a big fuss of Henry's 'gentlemanly' qualities and bestowing the most outrageous compliments about his 'dashing' clothes.

Poor Henry. He was her slave from that moment. It seemed that with Ethan's declaration of imminent matrimony, plus his open display of affection for the woman by his side, a piqued Vanessa had temporarily switched her charm in another direction.

Ann looked positively livid, Ethan fell cryptically silent, and Abby wished that she was back in Sydney. Lord, what a mess she had got herself into. Here she was, actually wishing that she *was* engaged to the infuriating and unfathomable man crushed up against her.

Yet she didn't love him. She didn't even *like* him. She

did, however, seem to care about what happened to him. God knows why! Maybe it had something to do with Sylvia, who was such a nice woman that one had to believe her brother must have some niceness in him somewhere too. Or maybe it was because she wanted an excuse to explore the very real pent-up emotion which had indeed been building up in her since she'd met the man.

Genuinely engaged people invariably made love these days, didn't they? When they shared a hotel room they didn't worry about whether the sofa unfolded into a second bed. They tumbled into the one double bed together, ripping off their clothes and urging their panting, naked bodies into one flesh without hesitation. The very thought of doing as much with Ethan sent her blood coursing hotly through her veins.

Abby shuddered as she recognised that her lust for Ethan was now in real danger of getting out of hand. She'd almost got to the stage where she didn't care about pride, or any of that self-respect rubbish. She wanted the man. Why couldn't she have him? What was to stop her?

He wouldn't knock her back.

Or would he? she frowned.

Maybe he would!

Now, that was one blow her pride could not take. To offer herself to Ethan Grant and have him reject her. The very thought made her feel nauseous. No, she could not—*would not*—put herself in such a humiliating position.

Another shudder rippled through her.

'Cold, darling?' Ethan murmured, wrapping his arm more tightly around her and pulling her even closer.

Abby gulped. My God, she'd be in his lap soon!

'No,' she denied, trying to extricate herself from his

steely hold but failing. 'Well, maybe a little,' she said, and lanced him with a warning glare.

His returning smile mocked her discomfort. He knew that she was hating being this close to him. What he didn't know, however, was that she was dangerously turned on, not repulsed at all.

'Drink up your wine,' he urged, a coldly amused gleam in his eyes. 'That should warm you up.'

'I doubt it,' she muttered, knowing the effect alcohol had on her.

'So tell me, Ethan,' Vanessa interrupted sweetly. 'How's your sister these days? Did she ever get married, or is she still happy just playing mother to you?'

Once again, Abby could feel the stiffening of Ethan's muscles.

'Sylvia's been a wonderful sister to me, Vanessa,' he praised, and Abby felt quite proud of him. 'I don't know what I would have done without her after our parents were killed. But no, she's never married. I don't think she's ever wanted to. She lives a full life—going to the theatre and ballet and playing bridge.'

'And does she approve of *you* marrying? Or will she be jealous of Abby?'

Ethan laughed. '*Jealous*? Sylvia simply adores Abby. Actually, I think she had this in mind when she first hired her.'

'Abby *works* for you?' Vanessa asked with a sour surprise.

'Didn't I say she did? Yes, Abby's my receptionist. I must say it makes work a pleasure to come in and see her lovely face over the desk every day.'

Abby almost choked on her drink. He really was laying it on a bit thick, the lying devil!

But she loved it. There was something wickedly pleasurable in the deception all of a sudden. Seeing Madame de Pompadour's perfect lips purse into a prim expression was worth any pretence, however dangerous.

'Oh, darling,' she murmured, cuddling into Ethan's side. 'You say such lovely things.'

'He *does*?' Henry chortled. 'Must be a different chap from the man who terrorises all the theatre nurses, in that case. He barks at them something rotten.'

'He never barked at *me*,' Vanessa murmured coyly.

'No man would bark at you, Vanessa,' said a doting Henry.

Ann rolled her eyes and called a waiter over for a third sherry. Clearly she was in dire need of another drink in the face of her husband's sickening display. Abby swallowed up her champagne and took another glass as well.

She had a feeling that she might need some alcohol-induced sarcasm later, if stupid bloody Henry asked Vanessa to join them for dinner. It would undoubtedly ruin her appetite, but hopefully not her tongue. Ethan might be the terror of the operating theatre, but *she* had been the terror of the prison laundry. If madam there thought she could get the better of Abby when it came to words, then she had another think coming!

As it turned out, Henry did ask her to join them for dinner, but—luckily for Vanessa—she had to decline. Apparently hubby was joining her for the actual meal, and they were expected to sit with the other lecturers. Abby almost felt disappointed that she wouldn't have the opportunity to sharpen her claws on the woman.

Ann, however, did not feel the same. 'Don't you ever, *ever* ask that bitch to join us again, Henry Maclean,' she hissed as soon as the woman was out of earshot.

Henry chortled, then leant over to give his wife a kiss on the cheek. 'I love it when you're jealous.'

'How you can be fooled by that man-eating tigress is beyond me!'

'I thought she was very engaging,' Henry huffed.

'So's the Venus fly-trap!' Ann spat.

And that was how it continued, all through dinner. Henry and Ann sparring, and Abby amused by Ann's tart remarks, which she privately agreed with.

Abby would have enjoyed the meal more if Ethan hadn't been so silent. The food was mouth-watering, the dining-room elegantly luxurious, the service splendid. It had been a long time since she'd eaten so well, and she forgot all about her intention to watch her weight, attacking each course with relish.

Afterwards, they sat over several cups of coffee for some time, till Ann started yawning.

'Tired, love?' Henry asked straight away.

'Rather. It's been a long day, what with driving the kids over to your mother's at God knows what hour this morning.'

'How about a nightcap at the bar, then we'll call it a night?' Henry suggested.

'All right,' Ann sighed.

Ethan happily agreed to Henry's suggestion. Abby had no objections either. But, as luck would have it, there was Vanessa, perched up at the bar on a stool, with another male admirer glued to her.

Where on earth was her husband? Abby fumed. Why didn't he lock her up and give all the poor, unsuspecting males in the world a break?

'Oh, dear,' Ann said when Vanessa swivelled round on the stool just in time to catch sight of their entry. The

smile she sent Ethan's way was inviting and seductive.
'She's like a cobweb. You can't brush her off.'

'Don't you mean a Black Widow spider?' Abby said,
unable to resist a barb of her own.

'You could be right, girls,' Henry said as he feasted
his eyes upon Vanessa's blatant show of leg. 'I reckon
once she's finished with a man, he'll be a spent force.
In the interests of matrimonial harmony, I think Ann and
I will have our nightcap back in our room.'

Abby glanced hopefully up at Ethan, waiting for him
to agree, but it seemed that scuttling off to his room was
not part of his plan for this weekend—whatever that plan
was. Abby was becoming increasingly irritated at being
left in the dark.

'Fair enough, Henry,' Ethan said. 'Off you go. See
you in the morning.'

Henry and Ann exchanged surprised glances before
shrugging and departing for their room, leaving Abby
feeling confused and dismayed. How could she keep
Ethan away from the hussy if he actively sought out her
company? Already he was guiding her over to the bar.
Worse, the man Vanessa had been talking to was walking away at the same time, leaving an empty stool beside
her.

'Mind if we join you for a nightcap?' Ethan said casually.

Her beautiful blue eyes flicked rather coldly over
Abby before warming upon her preferred subject. 'Not
at all,' she gushed. 'I was hoping you'd come over.'

Ethan guided Abby onto the empty stool, standing behind her with his hands curled rather possessively over
her shoulders. She tried to relax under his intimate touch
but found herself sitting stiffly, her face just as frozen.

Vanessa arched an eyebrow at her obvious discomfort,

then proceeded to exert every ounce of her considerable
charm on the man who'd once been her lover.

'I can't believe how marvellous you look, Ethan,' she
complimented him. 'Not that you weren't always a handsome man. But you look so fit as well. A lot of professional men let themselves go, which is such a shame—
don't you think so, dear?' she directed towards Abby, in
a simperingly insincere voice.

Unfortunately, Abby could hardly do anything but
agree.

'You've certainly looked after *yourself*, Vanessa,'
Ethan pointed out. 'You haven't aged a day.'

Her smile carried satisfaction. 'How kind of you to
say so. But you always were a flatterer, darling.'

'Not at all,' Ethan denied smoothly. 'I've always said
it as it is.'

'Yes...yes, so you have.' She gave him a wistful look,
full of longing. 'It really is lovely to see you again,
Ethan. I've thought of you so many times over the
years.'

'And I you, Vanessa.'

Abby's cheeks flamed with embarrassment and resentment. How dared Ethan conduct a nostalgic flirtation
with this woman in her presence? She felt the urge to
get up and walk out on both of them, but no sooner did
the thought come into her head than Ethan's fingers increased the pressure on her shoulders, virtually holding
her down on the stool by force.

Clearly he'd read her mind, and was reminding her to
keep doing what she'd been paid to do, not indulge in
hysterically emotional reactions.

But Abby couldn't seem to help it. Was it jealousy
rampaging through her veins? Or just injured pride? She
bitterly resented the feeling of being used, of being a

pawn pushed this way and that without having any say in or knowledge of what was going on.

The hovering barman finally asked what they'd like to drink, and Vanessa ordered a cognac.

'Ethan, you'll have a cognac too, won't you?' she said. 'I know how much you used to love it, but of course you couldn't always afford it in the old days, could you? You're a lucky girl, dear,' she directed towards Abby again. 'I dare say there's nothing Ethan can't afford nowadays. You'll be living in clover.'

'I really hadn't thought about our future lifestyle,' Abby said stiffly.

'Really?' Vanessa laughed—a soft, sardonic sound.

They all ended up having cognac, Abby swallowing hers with an angry swiftness. It burned a path down her throat and into her brain, sparking fiery rebellion into her system. She would have liked to tell the bitch where to go, but she knew that Ethan would be furious with her if she made a scene in public. Still, when Vanessa suggested a second round, Abby decided that she'd had enough.

'I don't think so,' she said sharply. 'I'm quite tired after our long drive down. I'd like to go to bed now, darling, if you don't mind?' And she sent a glaring glance over her shoulder up at Ethan.

His returning gaze was cool. 'No, of course not, darling. Besides, too much alcohol has a tendency to deaden the system—especially at bedtime. Can't have that, can we?' he drawled rather icily. 'Well, goodnight, Vanessa. No doubt we'll have the opportunity to chat about old times some more over the coming weekend.'

So saying, he took Abby's hand, his grasp tightening as he led her from the room.

'I thought I told you to take my lead,' he bit out on

the way down the stairs. 'In future, *I* will decide when we go to bed. I'm the boss, remember?'

By the time they reached the privacy of their room, she felt totally flustered and infuriated. She was suddenly very tired of playing this game, especially when she didn't know the rules.

She slammed the door behind her, glaring at Ethan's back as he strode over to open the mini-bar and pour himself a brandy. Abby only had to take one look at his body language to tell that nothing had changed between them. That kiss had meant nothing to him. *She* meant nothing to him. Nothing.

God, but it hurt, and the hurt was spurring her to say something. *Anything*!

'Deadening your system, Ethan?' she taunted.

He lanced her with a savage look. 'Just shut up, Abigail, *darling*. I've had quite enough for tonight.'

'And I've had *more* than enough!' she flung back at him, ripping off her earrings. 'What in hell did you think you were doing, saying we were engaged, then kissing me like that? That wasn't part of our deal.'

'Really? I would have thought the role of a fiancée much preferable for your reputation to being considered a mere lover, so what are you complaining about? Besides, you enjoyed that last kiss almost as much as I did. So is it more money that you want? Or more kisses? Or both?'

That did it. That really did it.

'Now, you listen here, you patronising, hypocritical prig! I won't even stoop to denying that I enjoyed your kiss, because yes, I did! I happen to be a normal woman, who likes good kissing on the whole, so don't take any satisfaction from that. But I *am* going to deny your on-going implication that I'm some kind of hard-nosed mercenary piece who can be bought and sold for the right price.

'I demanded the particular fee I did because a sweet old lady I know was burgled last weekend, with all her savings stolen. Just over three thousand dollars. She was going to buy a second-hand electric wheelchair with that money and I simply couldn't bear to see her heartbreak, so I rang you up—which I'd vowed I wouldn't, believe me—and accepted your peculiar and quite pathetic proposal.

'I'm prepared to honour my word and see this through to the bitter end, but I will not be sneered at and put down and used without so much as a by-your-leave. Do I make myself clear?'

He stared at her, long and hard. 'Are you telling me the truth? About that old lady?'

'Of course I'm telling you the truth! Why would I lie?'

All the breath rushed out of his lungs, his shoulders sagging. All of a sudden he looked so tired—tired and grim and almost bewildered, as though everything which had sustained him for so long no longer existed.

God, but her heart went out to him. Her foolish female heart.

She came up to him, touched him on the arm. He turned and she looked into his bleak blue eyes, aching to make things better for him, to soothe him. 'Oh, Ethan,' she cried softly. 'Let it go. Let *her* go.'

His shoulders immediately straightened, his eyes hardening as he glared down at her. 'You don't know what you're talking about, woman. Now, let *me* go.' He shrugged her hand off his arm and she staggered backwards, more hurt than she could ever have thought possible.

'God, don't look at me like that,' he ground out, his glare changing to a frustrated frown. 'All right, so I misjudged you and I'm sorry. I'm sorry about a whole lot of things. But this still isn't any of your business, Abigail, so just keep out of it. Now, go to bed and leave me be. You can use the bed. I'll sleep on the sofa when I'm good and ready.'

CHAPTER ELEVEN

THEY were late for breakfast; Ann and Henry were just leaving the dining room as they were entering.

'You look like you didn't get much sleep last night, old chap,' Henry teased Ethan. 'I could go overseas with those bags you're sporting under your eyes.'

Abby wouldn't have been quite so blunt, but Henry was right. Ethan looked as if he'd been out on the tiles all night.

She had no idea what time he'd eventually turned in, but he'd still been nursing a drink at midnight, sitting silently in an armchair in the dark. When Abby had woken this morning, after a rather restless sleep herself, he'd been sprawled on the sofa asleep, still in his clothes, having not even bothered to pull out the bed.

Oddly, the dark rings under his eyes were not unattractive on him. Ethan was one of those men on whom the dissipated ravaged look was irritatingly attractive—something she'd noticed more than once over the last six months.

'You know what it's like, Henry,' Ethan returned offhandedly. 'Strange beds and all that.'

Henry chuckled drily. 'Sure, sure. That's your story and you're going to stick to it. You'd better get yourself into breakfast or you'll be late for the first lecture.'

'How about a game of tennis this morning, Abby?' Ann asked. 'Henry's challenged me to a match after lunch, and I need to get into practice.'

'Love to,' she answered. She needed to work off the

calories that last night's dinner had already landed on her waistline. At the same time she might also work off some of the frustration she was feeling.

Ethan had showered and dressed in a brooding silence this morning, then snapped at her as they'd left the room that he hoped he could rely upon her to do what she'd been paid to do in future, and nothing more.

Abby had approached the dining room, and the day ahead, in a state of total confusion. Sylvia's pleas kept going round and round in her head. But, as she'd found out last night, it was impossible to keep Ethan away from Vanessa if he didn't want to be kept away.

'Meet me down at the tennis-courts at ten,' Ann called over her shoulder as she moved off down the stairs after a disappearing Henry.

'Will do,' Abby called back, then hurried after Ethan, who had already wandered into the dining room and was browsing along the breakfast buffet, plate in hand. Abby had just picked up her plate, and was trying to find something unfattening from the wide selection of food, when a murmuring sound made her glance round.

Vanessa had just swanned into the room on the arm of her puffy-faced, bleary-eyed husband, and was causing a stir of comments from those already seated.

There was plenty to comment on, Abby thought tartly—the woman's choice of a loose, shiny mauve trouser suit so resembling pyjamas that she looked as if she'd come to breakfast straight from bed. Her blonde hair had that tousled look which was incredibly sexy, and when she moved those too perfect, too firm, impossibly high breasts undulated under the silk, peaked nipples betraying their bra-less state.

Abby could hardly fail to notice that Ethan had also glanced around, and that his eyes were riveted to her just like all the other men's. She tried not to feel jealous, or worried, or even curious any more. But she failed miserably.

'She might be married to a neurosurgeon,' Abby muttered, 'but she's visited a few plastic surgeons in her day.'

Ethan slid her a drily amused look. 'Something *you* will certainly never need, my lovely Abigail, so don't be such a cat.'

Abby was startled by his compliment, till cynicism took over. 'And I thought you said you weren't a flatterer.'

'I'm not. You have the perfect female figure, and you know it.'

Abby flushed with both pleasure and surprise. She didn't know it all—her figure was far from perfect, she believed—but it thrilled her to think that Ethan thought it was.

Their eyes locked momentarily, and for the first time she was sure that she saw real desire lurking in those normally cool blue depths. It shook her. Maybe she'd been wrong last night about those kisses meaning nothing to him. Maybe he'd been as stirred by them as she had been.

'Don't just stand there, staring at me like that,' he snapped. 'You know damned well I've always found you a desirable woman. What normal man wouldn't? Now, hurry up and select some breakfast. Time is a-wasting.'

Abby was totally thrown by these new developments. He'd *always* desired her? It was an unsettling thought, and incredibly distracting. She found herself dithering terribly over what to eat, and in the end settled for orange juice, toast and coffee.

When they settled down at a table—unfortunately not

far enough away from the table Vanessa and her husband were occupying—her nerves were so stretched that she was unable to eat more than a few mouthfuls. Aside from the shock of Ethan's announcement, she didn't like the way the blonde bombshell had looked her over as she'd carried her tray to the table—those big blue eyes scoffingly dismissive as they swept over her clothes.

Underneath, Abby knew that her designer jeans and simple striped bodysuit were quite suitable for the occasion, but Vanessa's scornful regard still irked her.

'You're not eating much,' Ethan commented as he tucked into his plate of bacon and eggs, belying Abby's earlier assumption that he'd had a distressing night and was in a mood. Surely a man in a mood—or pining over his lost love—would not have such a good appetite.

'I'm not hungry.'

He put down his knife and fork and just looked at her. 'Are you angry with me for snapping at you, or for finding you desirable?'

When she declined to answer that, he shrugged. 'Look, I realise I've been a bit of a pig. I wish I could explain...'

'Why can't you?'

He stared at her again, then shook his head. 'I can't risk it.'

'Risk what?'

'My sanity.'

'I don't understand, Ethan.'

'Better you don't, I think,' he said darkly.

'Tell me one thing. Are you still in love with Vanessa Ballistrat?'

His gaze slid over to the blonde, then back at Abby. 'You *have* to be joking,' he said, but far too vehemently.

Hate was the other side of love, wasn't it? Or was he admitting to a strictly sexual obsession?

'Then what is it with you and her? What game are you playing, Ethan?'

'A game as old as time, my sweet.'

'And what game is that?'

'Drink your coffee, Abigail. And stop worrying about what doesn't concern you.'

'But it *does* concern me, Ethan.'

'Why? It has nothing to do with you.'

'But it does, don't you see? You've involved me in this far more than you said you would. For one thing, Henry and Ann think we're genuinely engaged. Have you thought what you're going to tell Sylvia once they relay the news to her? And they will. Ann is an inveterate gossip.'

Ethan frowned. 'I hadn't thought of that.'

'I think there's a lot of things you haven't thought of, Ethan.'

He glared at her, and she would have loved to know what he was thinking. His glare slowly became a troubled frown. 'Yes,' he said slowly. 'Yes, I'm beginning to see that…'

'You…you're not going to do anything violent, are you, Ethan?'

'To whom?'

A strangely sexual glitter came into his ruthless blue eyes and she shivered. For he was looking at *her* at that moment.

'To…to Vanessa, of course,' she said shakily. 'Or to her husband.'

'Now, why would I do that?'

'I'm no fool, Ethan. I can read between the lines. You

were lovers once, weren't you? And she jilted you when she ran off with Ballistrat.'

His face stiffened at her statement of the facts. His eyes grew tormented and her heart turned over at his obvious distress.

'Forget her, Ethan,' she urged. 'She's not worth it.'

His gaze slid slowly over to the woman who obviously still obsessed him, then back again. 'It's not that simple,' he said coldly.

'It *can* be.'

'No,' he denied. 'It can't. Now, finish your breakfast, Abigail, then go and play your tennis.'

She wanted to scream at him not to be so stupid or so blind. There were so many women in this world worth loving, but Vanessa Ballistrat was not one of them. But she could see that Ethan's mind and heart were closed to love. He was an embittered man who had come here seeking some kind of vengeance for Vanessa's betrayal of his love.

It worried Abby that he might still fall foul of that love again, that this clever, wicked woman might somehow ensnare his heart almost against his will. Her beauty and her womanly wiles were incredible, Abby could see. Not many men would stand a chance against her, once she set her sights on them.

Breakfast ended in a tense silence, with Abby glad to leave Ethan and be alone for a while in her room. She sat down on the side of the bed, her head whirling and her stomach churning.

What on earth was she going to do? How was she going to persuade Ethan that revenge was a self-destructive course, and not one which would lead to any happiness? Worse, how was she going to defuse that woman's potential power? She could not bear to think of that woman ever touching Ethan again, let alone kissing him. Or, God forbid, making love with him.

Maybe she should do what Sylvia had suggested. Seduce Ethan herself!

She wanted to. Dear God, she wanted to so much it had become a constant ache in her body. But she was afraid—afraid of getting emotionally involved with the man. Already she was being drawn deeper and deeper into his problems, wanting to solve them, wanting to protect him.

For her own sake she had to pull back, to distance herself from the situation. It really was none of her business, as Ethan had said more than once. And it was all getting out of hand!

Tennis was the answer. And swimming. And any other activity which would keep her busy, and tired, and away from Ethan.

Abby jumped up and stripped off her jeans and top in favour of her tennis gear—a very feminine lemon pleated skirt and matching T-shirt top, both edged in white. White socks and joggers completed the outfit, and Abby wrapped her hair into a tight knot on top of her head.

A glance in the mirror reassured her that she looked fine, though she still felt big compared with the petite and truly perfect Vanessa. Suddenly she couldn't wait to get onto the court and blast off a few of the offending inches.

There were four tennis-courts, clay-based and surrounded by tall rows of pines cleverly positioned to form a natural windbreak. The adjoining kiosk was well supplied with spare rackets, as well as several plastic tables and chairs for relaxing, and a refrigerator stocked with coolly refreshing non-alcoholic drinks.

'That's enough for me,' Abby said after their third set. She'd easily lost the first two before finding her own form and walloping Ann in the third. 'I'm shockingly unfit,' she said as they both collapsed into chairs with an iced mineral water.

'You don't look unfit,' Ann replied with an admiring glance. 'You have a fantastic figure.'

It was exactly what Abby needed to hear. She knew from experience that women did not flatter other women. 'That's sweet of you to say so, Ann, but I really could do with losing a few pounds. Some of my skirts are beginning to be a little tight.'

'I wouldn't worry too much about that, if I were you. Men don't mind tight skirts. They don't mind women with a few extra pounds on them either. Certainly not when they're as well distributed as yours.'

Ann leant forward suddenly, dropping her voice a little. 'Tell me to mind my own business if you want to, but did Ethan and Vanessa Ballistrat have something going once?'

'Perhaps. Perhaps not,' Abby returned, battling hard to keep her voice casual. 'Frankly, I don't really care if he did. I don't believe in a woman cross-questioning a man about his past love-life. The past is the past.'

'I agree, but it's foolish to put your head in the sand where a woman like that is concerned. I'd watch her, if I were you. I think she's after Ethan.'

Abby could not help the stricken look which crossed her face.

'Oh, dear. Perhaps I shouldn't have said anything. It's just that it's perfectly obvious you absolutely adore Ethan. The way you looked at him last night after he kissed you…'

Abby opened her mouth then shut it again, simply unable to speak at that moment.

'Men can be such fools sometimes,' Ann went on. 'And females like that Venus fly-trap can be so unscrupulous. If Dr Ballistrat is having money troubles, she won't stay with him. That's the way women like that work. If she and Ethan have already been lovers, and if she senses he still feels anything for her at all, it's only natural he'd be the one she might try to trap next. And, let's face it, she's got a lot of equipment for setting traps...'

Abby felt quite ill. Not because of the warning about Vanessa. She had already conceded the possibility of Ethan falling back into her clutches. No, Abby's distress came from Ann's words—'it's perfectly obvious you absolutely adore Ethan.'

I do, she realised, her head spinning. I adore him. And I want him like mad. Oh, God, I must love him. I thought I couldn't possibly, simply because I didn't like him, but my foolish female heart simply bypassed liking and went straight to love.

'Oh, my dear, please don't look like that,' Ann pleaded. 'I didn't mean to worry you. I'm terribly sorry. Please forget what I said. No sane man could prefer that woman to you.'

No sane man...

The words echoed in Abby's brain.

But Ethan wasn't sane where that woman was concerned. She'd festered in his brain for years, distorting his view of women, making him suffer a coldly cynical existence rather than trust another woman with his heart. Sylvia had recognised his madness. That was why she'd been so worried about his coming here, why she'd begged Abby to keep him away from Vanessa.

'Excuse me, but can either of you two ladies help us out? We'd like to play a set of doubles but there's only three of us.'

Abby looked up at the three eager-faced ladies and shook her head. 'I couldn't,' she murmured, still feeling shattered. 'You play, Ann.'

Ann groaned.

'Please,' the three women chorused.

'Oh, all right,' Ann sighed. 'But only one set.'

She left and Abby was alone. With a moan she put her elbows on the table and sank her head into her hands, her eyes closing.

How could I have allowed this to happen? Didn't Dillon teach me anything? God, am I going to spend the rest of my life falling in love with the wrong men?

I'll really have to quit working for him now, she accepted bleakly. I refuse to go on being some kind of martyr to my silly feelings. Hell, I despise women who love men who don't love them back. How self-destructive can you get?

'Have a headache, do we?'

Abby whipped her hands away just as Vanessa pulled out the chair Ann had not long vacated. The mauve silk outfit suggested that she hadn't come down to play tennis.

'No, no headache,' Abby returned coolly. 'Just tired. I've been playing tennis.'

'So I noticed earlier on. I was taking a stroll around the gardens. When I saw your friend returning for another game I came round in search of the missing Miss Richmond.'

'Really? Why?' Abby snapped.

'There's no need to be rude.'

'I think there's every reason to be rude.' Abby was

not going to pull any punches. She'd found in prison that when dealing with people like Vanessa politeness was interpreted as weakness, and tact as stupidity. 'I don't like you any more than you like me. I also know what you're up to, so don't feed me any of your manipulative lies. Say what you have to say, then get the hell out of my sight.'

'My, my, not so much the polite little lady after all, are we?'

'No, so don't you forget it.'

'Meaning what?'

'Meaning you come round batting your false eyelashes at Ethan any more, and I'll tear your equally false boobs off.'

She gasped and staggered not so gracefully to her feet. 'I'm going to tell Ethan you said that!'

'Go ahead. He'll laugh himself silly.'

Those blue eyes narrowed nastily as she quickly gathered herself. 'You don't know who you're dealing with.'

'I know exactly *what* I'm dealing with. An amoral, mercenary bitch.'

'You're going to be sorry you said that.'

'I doubt it.'

Abby was lashed by a look that would have shrivelled a lesser woman. She looked boldly back at her adversary and had the satisfaction of Vanessa being the first to look away and stalk off.

'You won't win,' Abby muttered under her breath. 'I don't care what I have to do. The man I love is not going to end up in your clutches again. No, siree!'

CHAPTER TWELVE

'I'M GOING back to my room,' Abby shouted out across the tennis-court, and Ann waved her approval.

Fifteen minutes later Abby was standing in the bathroom, biting her bottom lip as she grimaced at her reflection in the mirror. She had been staring at herself in horror for some time.

The black bikini was more outrageous than ever. She seemed to be spilling out everywhere. No matter how she tried to spread the gathered cups which inadequately encased her C-cup breasts, they always concertinaed back down into two narrow strips of material which only just covered her nipples.

The bottom half was just as bad—two skimpy triangles, joined at the sides with the flimsiest ties, and legs so high-cut that she'd almost had to shave herself bare to be presentable. God knows what the back view was like!

Sighing, she opened the bathroom door and backed up a bit, standing on tiptoe to get a longer view of her hips and legs in the waist-high vanity mirror. Gritting her teeth, she half turned and glanced over her shoulders at her behind. Dear heavens, the amount of creamy flesh on display was appalling.

'I could never wear this in public,' she muttered dispiritedly. And there she'd been thinking she could out-seduce Vanessa by prancing around the pool in front of Ethan in this.

'I agree.'

Abby squawked, whirling as her eyes darted around the room, her heart pounding. Ethan was lounging back in the armchair nearest the window, his arms outstretched, his ankles crossed. The sunlight was behind him, which cast his face into shadow, so she couldn't see either his features or his expression.

She went quite hot all over, at the same time wishing there was something at hand she could snatch up and cover herself with. 'I...I didn't hear you come in,' she stammered. 'And what do you mean, you agree?' she snapped, almost as an afterthought. 'I think I look pretty good!' Abby was never at her best when someone tried to put her down these days.

'You know damned well you don't look pretty good,' Ethan drawled. 'You look bloody fantastic.'

'Oh...'

Ethan rose slowly to his feet, his considerable height blocking out a good proportion of the light. 'But you're right about wearing it in public,' he said ruefully. 'I think you should keep it for my eyes only.'

Abby blinked, the atmosphere in the room suddenly charged with an electric sexual tension. She knew now, without seeing his eyes, that they were staring at her body, and not with disgust but with desire. It sent a thrill racing all through her—a dangerously exciting thrill. Her face flamed and her body followed suit.

When he started walking towards her she remained exactly where she was, her chin tipped almost defiantly upwards while her mind recklessly willed him on. Her heart began to hammer against her ribs as he drew nearer, but when his eyes came into view there was nothing of desire in them, only a coolly speculative regard.

Abby was utterly thrown.

'What...what are you doing here?' she asked shakily

when he stopped just in front of her. 'You should still be in conference for another half-hour.'

'I had a headache,' he explained, his eyes dropping to her breasts, which were rising and falling with betraying speed. 'I needed something for it.'

'Oh…'

'It's gone now,' he said, and quite calmly, even coldly, reached around behind her and untied her bra top, tossing it nonchalantly away.

Abby didn't say a word, merely stared at him in shock as a horrified elation raced through her. He bent and brushed his lips over hers while he played with her breasts, his hands gentle, yet oddly merciless. She sensed that they would not stop if she asked. *He* would not stop.

But she didn't want him to stop, did she? She loved the man and wanted him like crazy. Besides, this was the perfect way to defuse any sexual power Vanessa might hold over him.

Ethan was as she'd always suspected as a lover. Ruthless, and cold, and, yes, machine-like. Yet for all that…incredibly exciting. There was no hint of seduction in his movements, however, merely a steely resolve. No hint of making love to her, merely cold-blooded caresses designed to arouse her sufficiently to suit his dark purpose.

Perversely, Abby found that a real turn-on. It was so different from Dillon, who had dressed everything up with flowery words and false promises. How many times had Dillon said he loved her while he made love to her?

Lies. All lies.

There would be none of that from Ethan. He was only offering her sex, and even though she loved him, and might secretly hope for more, she admired his unspoken honesty. Oh, yes, she could cope with this type of love-making far better than Dillon's lies.

Cope? Oh, God…what an inadequate word for the feelings rampaging through her. She was already dizzy with desire, aching and yearning for more.

When his hands abandoned her throbbing breasts she groaned her disappointment, only to gasp when they slid smoothly down her sides to untie the ineffective bows on her hips. Simultaneously his mouth deepened his kiss, perhaps to keep her distracted while he stripped the scrap of material away.

Abby was beyond caring what his motives were, as long as he kept his mouth on hers and his hands on her flesh. She moaned softly under the relentless rhythm of his tongue, then moaned anew when one of his hands slipped between her thighs to set up another, far more relentless rhythm.

She could hardly believe the sensations, or the wanting. Her body strained against his knowing touch. She tensed. Then trembled.

He took her so close, so terrifyingly close, before he stopped and lay her throbbing, burning body back across the bed, coolly watching her mindless arousal drain away while he undressed with meticulous measured movements, placing each item of clothing neatly on a nearby chair.

Abby's heartbeat finally regained some normality, her brain and body galvanised by his cold control. Even when he was naked, with his stark erection flaunting his need, he seemed totally composed, joining her on the bed and setting about re-arousing her with a second session of calculating kisses and caresses till she was once again balancing on that razor's edge.

'Please don't stop,' she begged breathlessly. 'Oh, God...'

Only then did he spread her legs wide and move between them, bending her knees back to angle her body to fit perfectly to his.

Abby squeezed her eyes shut in anticipation of Ethan's body invading her, but when it came her eyes flung back open, so stunned was she by the feel of his flesh as it probed, then pushed inside her. He was much the same size as Dillon. Yet he felt so different.

It had to be *her* who was different, she finally realised. She was far more turned on than she'd ever been with Dillon, her body enclosing Ethan's with a greedy, grasping need which would never let him go till it had milked him dry.

Her head spun as he slid deeper and deeper inside her, and she moaned her ecstasy.

His penetration finally complete, he wrapped her legs high around his back then began surging into her, his body as relentless as his tongue and his hands had been.

He was inhuman, she thought despairingly, his face a mask of perfect concentration as he pumped robotically into her, not a flicker of emotion to disturb the symmetry of his classically handsome features. Yet *she* was swiftly beside herself, her head threshing from side to side, her hands clenching and unclenching as she tried to prolong the pleasure and stop herself coming.

The thought of him coldly watching her face convulse in the throes of a climax was suddenly anathema to her. She wanted him to come with her. She wanted him wild and unthinking, his own face all twisted with a raw, primitive ecstasy which he could only ever find with her. She could not bear his machine-like performance another moment. There was a living, breathing, passionate man somewhere beneath that cold, calculating faǫde, and she meant to find him.

Her actions were instinctive—her hands reaching up to run feverishly over his stiffly held shoulders, then up his corded neck towards his suddenly taut face muscles. His mouth gasped open when she began to trace his lips boldly with her fingers. She didn't hesitate, daringly inserting them into his mouth, sliding them back and forth along his wet tongue in an echo of what his body was doing inside hers.

'Ethan,' she moaned in her mad passion for him. 'Oh, Ethan…'

He froze for a second, then shuddered violently, a raw, animal sound punched from his lungs. He began sucking ravenously on her fingers and pounding her body in a mad frenzy of desire. Abby's already sensitised flesh immediately responded, and she rocketed to a climax with him, her fingers falling from his mouth when his back arched violently away from her. Her own mouth fell open and she gasped breath after ragged breath into her starving lungs.

Ethan swore, then collapsed onto the bed beside her, taking her with him so that she was lying sprawled across his chest. His hands felt furious as they cupped her face and lifted it from his still heaving chest, forcing her to look down at him and witness his torment.

'Why in hell did you do that?' he growled, gasping for breath between outbursts. 'I meant to protect us…or at least pull out… You shouldn't have done that… You should have stopped me… Hell, why didn't you?'

Stop him? Was he joking? She couldn't have stopped him even if she'd wanted to.

Abby expelled a long, quivering sigh. The heat of the moment was quickly giving way to a rotten reality. Still,

Abby had long since become a realist. She'd known what she was doing when she allowed Ethan to make love to her, known what to expect from him afterwards.

Nothing.

But it still hurt. God, when would she ever learn? 'It's all right, Ethan,' she managed in a relatively calm voice. 'If you're worried about my getting pregnant, then don't be. If you're worried about anything else, then don't be as well. I've never had unprotected sex before. I hope you can give me the same assurance.'

'Don't be ridiculous,' he said, staring at her as though she were mad. 'Of course I can.'

Abby almost laughed. She should have guessed that this was the first time Ethan had lost his much vaunted control and done something really rash. A type of triumph softened any hurt at his presumption that any risk would come from her.

'Are you absolutely *sure* you won't get pregnant?' he demanded hoarsely.

Abby didn't really want to discuss the issue. She'd always believed that a pregnancy which resulted from an act of love was not something which could be wiped away with a pill or an operation. And it *had* been an act of love. For her.

In truth, the risk was minimal this weekend, and would grow less with every passing day. She knew her body well and should have ovulated earlier in the week. Nine times out of ten, she would have. There were times, though, when her cycle could surprise her—usually when she was under stress.

She thought of all that had happened last weekend and made a silent prayer.

'There is no risk,' she said aloud. 'My period's due soon, and I'm disgustingly regular.'

'I can write you a prescription for a morning-after pill, if you'd like.'

'Oh, do shut up, Ethan. You're spoiling the moment.'

He stared at her. 'What moment?'

'You and me, abandoning our mutual hostility.'

He almost choked on the spot, then gave a harsh bark of laughter. 'I should have known sex with you would not be like sex with any other woman. Hell, it certainly wasn't. I've never known anything like it.'

'Should I be flattered by that remark?'

'No, complimented. As I said before, I don't believe in flattery. You're damned good in bed, you know that?'

'I'm not in bed. I'm on top of you.'

'Which is another perspective we must explore in the near future,' he said darkly.

'How near?'

Abby tried to feel shock at her eager voice but could not. Already she was addicted to his mouth, his touch, his body. It had never been like this for her before. With Dillon she hadn't always reached a climax, and when she had it had always taken ages. It had been less than ten minutes since Ethan had taken her bra off.

Already, she wanted him again. Ten minutes wasn't nearly enough. She wanted a whole lifetime of his love-making, dammit. But, failing that, she would take whatever she could get as often as she could get it. Keeping him away from Vanessa would be an added bonus.

'How about after lunch?' he suggested, rubbing one of his thumbs backwards and forwards across her puffy lips.

Her heart leapt even as she frowned. 'We're supposed to be playing tennis with Ann and Henry.'

'Leave it to me,' he said, before pulling her harshly

down onto his mouth and swiftly showing her that she would always be at his mercy. Always.

It was a telling and troubling thought, and one Abby promised herself that she would address when this weekend was over. Meanwhile she had neither the strength nor the will to resist him. He could command, and demand, and she knew that she would simply say yes.

Yes. Yes. Yes.

'Do you like making love in the afternoon?' he muttered thickly against her bruised mouth.

'Mmm,' was all she could manage. He'd idly begun to massage the small of her back and her buttocks, and it was sending her thoughts into a spin.

'And in the middle of the night?'

She made a small moan of assent. Dear God, he was actually swelling inside her again, filling her own still sensitised flesh for the second mind-blowing time within fifteen minutes. She hadn't known a man could do that. Dillon never had.

'And in the morning?'

'Yes,' she gasped.

'What about just before lunch?' He pushed her upright on him, gripping her hips and ruthlessly urging her to ride him.

'Yes,' she choked out, just before she closed her eyes and lost all control. Again.

CHAPTER THIRTEEN

ABBY poured herself another glass of wine, took a sip, then turned to walk over and peek through the drawn curtains at the setting sun.

'Pull the curtain back. I want a better look at you.'

She did as Ethan asked before glancing over her shoulder at him.

He was lying on the rumpled bed, a sheet dragged across his lower half, his head and shoulders propped up against a mountain of pillows. He was sipping a Scotch. He was also staring at her, his hard blue eyes glittering with a decidedly primitive desire.

Abby could not believe how quickly Ethan had stripped her of all inhibition where her body was concerned. She'd never been this comfortable before, walking around naked. Now she not only did so without shyness, she found the experience a turn-on.

What an incredible afternoon, she thought as she gazed at Ethan.

He'd made love to her swiftly and urgently on their return to the room after lunch, taking her up against the door, leaving her unsatisfied and wildly excited. Afterwards, he'd undressed them both and carried her into the shower, where he'd washed her in a most erotic fashion, keeping her aroused at the same time.

'No,' he'd ordered when she'd automatically reached for a robe afterwards. 'I want you naked. And your hair down.'

Which was exactly how she'd spent the rest of the

afternoon. Naked, with her hair down, and totally at his sexual disposal.

He'd finally let her come…after a long hour of exquisite torment, stunning her then by giving her climax after climax in quick succession. She was powerless against his expertise, especially that merciless mouth of his. He'd taken his time in using that last weapon against her. But when he had, he'd driven her mad.

She'd made love to him with her mouth in return— something Dillon had surprisingly never pressed for, but which she'd always been sure she would hate.

But she hadn't hated it at all. She'd felt a heady sense of power as she'd driven Ethan once again to lose control. When she'd stopped momentarily, to push her hair out of her eyes, he'd actually begged her to go on. God, but she'd revelled in his guttural pleas, exulted wildly in his mindless surrender to her ministrations. She couldn't wait to do it again.

'Henry didn't believe your migraine story for a moment, you know,' she said. This was their first real conversation all afternoon.

'Neither your excuse that you were tired and wanted to read,' he returned drily.

'No.'

'Has it occurred to you that what you told Henry and Ann about us has partly come true?'

Abby frowned. 'What did I say to them?'

'About our pent-up feelings exploding. I can't speak for you, but I know it was true in my case. I've been wanting to do this from the first moment I laid eyes on you.'

Abby was startled. 'Really?'

Now *he* was startled. 'You mean you didn't know? I

thought you saw it in my eyes the very first time I looked at you. You looked shocked at *something*.'

'I was surprised how young you were. And how handsome.'

'I wasn't at all surprised how good-looking *you* were,' he said drily. 'I had a feeling Sylvia would line up some delectable young thing to tempt me.'

Abby had to smile. 'And did I tempt you?'

His own smile was rueful. 'Excruciatingly so. I used to dread Fridays, yet I enjoyed them too, in a perverse way. You've no idea the thoughts that used to go through my head. It was all I could manage to keep a straight face.' He took another sip of his drink, his eyes turning speculative. 'So how *have* you felt about me all this while?'

'I hated you,' she confessed, despite seeing now that that hate had been the other side of love.

He laughed. But it was a bitter sound. 'Then don't stop, for God's sake. There's no future with me, Abigail. I'm poison to any woman. Frankly, I just can't bring myself to trust women, especially beautiful ones. I probably never will.'

She stared at his coldly bitter eyes, and knew that he was telling the truth. There would never be any future with him. Not a real one. She'd been silly to begin hoping for it.

'Don't worry,' she said. 'I won't go falling in love with you any time in the future.' Can't, she thought with wry irony, I've already done that.

'I didn't think you would. You and I are alike, my sweet. You've been hurt too. And you're tough. I like that. Of course, I don't want you hating my making love to you. I have plans for you where that's concerned.'

'Are you saying you want us to remain lovers when we go back to Sydney?'

'Yes, of course.'

Abby's heart contracted. 'What about my job on Fridays?'

'I didn't lie to Henry. I'm going to send Sylvia on an extended holiday. She deserves it. Work for me full-time as well. I see you're a girl with pride and that you wouldn't want me setting you up as some kind of kept woman. I'll pay you a good salary and I'll treat you well. I promise.'

Abby swallowed. He was dressing it up to sound respectable, but she knew exactly what he was asking. On the surface she might be his receptionist, but underneath…underneath, she would still be his mistress. He was trying to buy her body as surely as he might buy the lowest streetwalker. She wasn't sure if she could do that to herself. Yet she wasn't sure if she had the strength to say no.

'We'll see, Ethan,' was all she said for the moment, and took another sip of her drink, watching him closely over the rim of her glass. He wasn't a man to take a refusal lightly, even the possibility of one.

His eyes narrowed with ruthless resolve upon her. 'Come here.'

An unbidden quiver of excitement rippled down her spine and she obeyed, though not at any speed, her walk slow and seductive across the room. 'What do you want?' she asked as she stood beside the bed.

He reached up, curled his hand around a long lock of her hair and pulled her down onto the bed, the abrupt action sending her wine spilling all over his chest. 'You know what I want,' he grated out.

'Say it, then,' she whispered harshly, suddenly want-

ing some kind of revenge for his ruthless using of her.
'Say it,' she ordered him.

He said it.

She threw back the sheet and bent her mouth to where
the wine had spilled over his chest. She licked up the
droplets with calculating slowness, lingering over his
male nipples for an excruciatingly long time before
working her way ever so slowly downwards.

He was groaning long before she reached her ultimate
target.

'Wear this tonight,' Ethan ordered, pulling the coffee-
coloured lace dress out of the wardrobe and tossing it
across her still naked body.

'Say please,' she purred.

'Please.'

She laughed. 'You're the only man I've ever known
who could make the word "please" sound like an order
as well.'

He grabbed her wrist as she slid off the bed, and
pulled her to him, only the dress between their naked
bodies. 'And how many men *have* you known, darling
heart? Biblically speaking.'

His sudden black jealousy startled her.

She searched his eyes for what lay behind it, hoping
and praying but not at all confident. 'Would you believe
me if I said only one before you?'

Clearly it was a struggle for him to do so.

'Never mind,' she said drily. 'It doesn't matter, does
it?'

His face filled with torment. 'It shouldn't—but, damn
it all, it does!'

'Then *believe* me, Ethan,' she urged with a quiet desperation. 'Believe me.'

'I want to.'

'What's stopping you?'

'It just doesn't make sense. You're so beautiful and desirable. I can't stop wanting you. Many other men must have wanted you just as much,' he groaned, and bent to kiss her.

His dark passion sparked an equally dark passion within herself. She let the dress fall to the floor between them and slid her arms up around his neck, Ethan sucking in a sharp breath as she rubbed the still hardened tips of her breasts against his bare chest.

'And you're far too good at this,' he rasped against her mouth.

'In that case just shut up and enjoy, Ethan. I haven't asked you how many lovers you've had, have I?'

'No, but that's because you don't—' He broke off, his mouth twisting into an agonised grimace.

'Don't what?' she whispered, dying for him to kiss her again, to touch her. Why did he have to ask stupid questions at times like this?

'Never mind,' he growled, and, grabbing her by the waist, he picked her up and tossed her back onto the bed.

'You're a wonderful dancer,' Ethan praised in a husky whisper, his breath warm against her ear.

They'd dined with Henry and Ann earlier in the evening, then the four of them had come down to where there was dancing in the ballroom.

Abby took Ethan's compliment as the truth. There hadn't been much call for dancing in prison, although the girls had sometimes put the radio on and mucked around. But, hell, nine years of ballet, tap and modern had to count for something!

'You're a pretty good dancer yourself,' she said, thinking that it was as well she could execute the right steps without thinking. Concentration was impossible with her body moulded to Ethan's from chest to thigh.

'And you smell delicious,' he murmured. 'What's that perfume you've been wearing this weekend?'

'Chanel No. 5.'

'Another gift, I suppose. Women don't buy perfume like that for themselves. Now don't get huffy,' he went on swiftly when she stiffened under his taunt, 'I seem to have developed an irrational case of jealousy where you're concerned. I can only apologise for my own hypocrisy in expecting you not to have a past. Damn it all, mine's not too wonderful.'

Ethan's mention of a past made her think of her stay in prison for the first time this weekend. She wished that she could tell him about it, but knew that to do so would be a disaster.

'I picked the right dress for dancing, didn't I?' he chuckled, the hand in the small of her back exerting some more inward pressure as he whirled her round.

He was referring to her braless state, of course, as well as the figure-hugging nature of the gown. Abby had given in to his request to wear the dress, despite knowing that it would be extra tight and that the off-the-shoulder and daringly low neckline would mean she'd be half-naked underneath it. It had taken her ages to do up the back zipper, and a lot of breathing in.

Now the dress felt like a corset over her curves, the cool silk lining making her hotly aware of her erect nipples, especially when Ethan pressed her hard against him, as he was doing at this moment. Thank God the skirt flared out from the hips or she would not have been able to move, let alone dance.

'You're wicked, do you know that?' she whispered shakily.

'Then we're a good pair, aren't we?' he countered in a low, thickened voice. 'Do shut up, Abby. I want to savour the moment, not chat about it.'

Abby felt a momentary jab of dismay that she hadn't really managed to change his opinion about her. Of course, she had only herself to blame. She should never have invented that sugar-daddy lover. Once again, it crossed her mind to tell him the whole truth. But would he believe her?

She doubted it. All she would probably achieve was a cessation of their relationship, such as it was, plus the loss of her job. No, she wasn't about to risk either of those things. She loved Ethan too much to lose what little of him she had. Her desire to protect herself from future hurt was simply not as strong as her desire for the man. It was as simple as that.

So Abby closed her eyes, buried her face into his neck and savoured as well, revelling in the feel of his hard body pressed up against her and the promise of pleasure to come…when the dancing was over.

Ethan's muttered 'Good God' had her lifting her head and looking up at him.

'What is it?'

'Nothing for you to worry about.'

Abby's natural curiosity still had her glancing around the ballroom. She didn't have to look round for long. Madame Vanessa had just made an entrance, dressed in the most outrageous red satin gown Abby had ever seen. Halter-necked, it had a V-neckline in front plunging to her waist, which was cinched with a wide jewelled belt. There was no back to speak of, and the skirt was so tight that she could not possibly be wearing a stitch underneath.

Once again, Philip Ballistrat was nowhere in sight, and his adultery-seeking wife was immediately claimed for a dance by a male admirer. She went into his arms as if she belonged there, a seductive smile on her full red lips.

'At least she's wearing the right colour for a scarlet woman,' Abby said tartly.

'True.'

Ethan's agreement sparked some hope in Abby that his ex-flame had shown her true colours to him at last, thereby laying her ghost to rest once and for all.

'You…you don't care about her any more, do you, Ethan? I mean…she might be beautiful and sexy, but she's very shallow and superficial, you know.'

'Yes, I know.'

'Know that she's beautiful and sexy? Or that she's shallow and superficial?'

'Both.'

Jealousy had her pulling out of his arms a fraction, but he pulled her right back. 'Don't be silly,' he growled. 'She's not nearly as beautiful and sexy as you.'

'What about shallow and superficial?' she challenged archly. 'I hope you don't think I'm just as shallow and superficial!'

'I wish I did. But I have a feeling there are depths to you, Abigail, my love, which I haven't even begun to discover yet.' His lips moved over her hair and she shivered. 'You're such an enigmatic creature,' he murmured. 'A chameleon. I don't know what to make of you sometimes. But, frankly, I'm not keen to discover those other depths just yet. I might not like them. I just want to enjoy you for now.' He kissed her hair and pressed her even closer.

Abby wanted to cry. For he'd just spelled it out for her, hadn't he? Even with Vanessa out of the way, he didn't want *her* for anything more than sexual pleasure. It was as cut and dried as that.

She gazed with shattered eyes over Ethan's shoulder, hoping to distract herself from her emotional state by looking around the elegant ballroom. Her eyes were travelling from couple to couple when the glimpse of a face across the crowded room had her grinding to a shocked halt.

'What's wrong?' Ethan asked, pulling back and glancing down at her with a puzzled frown.

'I…er…I…nothing. A slight dizzy spell.'

'You're as white as a sheet. Do you want to sit down?'

'What? Yes…er…yes, I think I might. But not here. I'll go to the restroom. Perhaps a glass of water will help. No, don't come with me. I'll be fine.'

'If you're sure. I'll talk to Henry and Ann while you're gone. Take your time.'

Abby fled to the ladies' and hid in the toilet cubicle for a while, afraid to go back to the ballroom lest she find out that she was right, and that that face actually belonged to whom she thought it did. She finally emerged from the cubicle, only to find that same face staring back at her in the powder-room mirror.

'Abby!' the woman exclaimed.

Abby's heart sank. Of all the rotten luck. 'Hello, Dr Seymour,' she said, struggling to keep her voice calm. 'What on earth are you doing here?'

'Having a well-earned rest. I'm not here professionally. Just as a wife. My husband's a surgeon.'

'Oh…'

'And you, Abby? What are you doing here?'

She took a deep breath and hoped she'd covered her shock well. Who would have believed that the prison psychiatrist and counsellor would turn up at a surgeons' conference? It hadn't remotely occurred to Abby that doctors tended to marry doctors.

'I'm here with my fiancé,' she said. 'He's a doctor.' The moment the words were out of her mouth she wished she hadn't said them. She should have said that she was just here with a friend.

'Oh, who? Would I know him?'

Abby swallowed. She'd done it now. 'Dr Grant. Dr Ethan Grant.'

'The orthopaedic surgeon?'

'Yes, that's right.'

'I don't know him personally, but I've heard of him. He's an excellent doctor—and very handsome, if I've heard correctly.'

'I've been working as his receptionist,' Abby offered, feeling a little better that Ethan and Dr Seymour's husband weren't colleagues in any way.

'But how wonderful! I'm so happy for you, my dear. I didn't think you'd be able to put that other awful business behind you too easily, but it seems you've managed splendidly. It just shows what true love can do. It can restore trust and make life worthwhile again, can't it?'

'Yes,' Abby said weakly.

'I hope you'll be very happy, my dear. I always believed in your total innocence and it seems someone else does too. That must make up for your family's attitude. Or has your father finally come round?'

'No,' Abby said stiffly. 'No, he hasn't come round.'

'That's too bad. And what about your mother?'

'Nothing's changed on that score either.'

Dr Seymour gave a sad sigh. 'Never mind. You can't force someone to believe you. You have the love of a good man now, which must be some consolation. Be totally honest with him and I'm sure you'll be fine. Promise me you'll do that?'

Tears welled up in Abby's eyes and she valiantly blinked them away. 'I'll try. I…I must go,' she added tautly. 'Ethan will be wondering where I am.'

'Of course. Look after yourself, dear. I'm so glad to see you again. I've often thought of you.'

Abby almost ran back to the ballroom, her thoughts and emotions a-jumble. If she'd been able to, she would have kept on running—away from Dr Seymour and the heartbreaking memories she evoked, away from Ethan and the new heartbreak he was going to create for her.

But she knew that she couldn't. She loved him, and wanted him, and her hungry eyes were searching for him the moment she returned to the crowded room.

Those eyes opened wide when she found him, shock and dismay mingling to clamp her heart into a painful vice. For he was dancing with that scarlet-clad bitch, his arms wrapped tightly around her, his eyes clamped to hers as they swirled around the polished floor, their bodies and legs perfectly attuned. Abby felt sick as she watched them, sensing in that moment that here was something Ethan would never feel for her.

For this had once been true love, despite its bitter ending—an obsessive love which had left Ethan a hard shell of a man who used silly women like herself to satisfy his carnal lusts while secretly yearning for the one woman who'd meant something to him.

She paled as she watched them together. They were oblivious to the other couples dancing around them, oblivious of their surroundings, oblivious of Abby watching them with her heart bleeding and breaking into little pieces. She saw both of Ethan's hands move caressingly over Vanessa's bare back, saw her slender white arms slide seductively around his neck, saw her tip her lovely head under his chin.

She could watch no more, whirling and fleeing back to her room, banging the door shut behind her and throwing herself onto the bed before bursting into loud noisy sobs. She was still weeping wretchedly when Ethan walked in some time later.

'Why didn't you come back to the ballroom?' he demanded abruptly. 'And why are you crying?'

She dashed away her tears, rolled over and glared up at him, using anger as a survival weapon. 'Because!'

'Because why?'

'Because you're a bastard and I hate you!'

He sighed. 'You saw me dancing with Vanessa.'

Abby laughed. '*Dancing?* I wouldn't call what you two were doing dancing,' she sneered. 'You lied to me about still caring for that bitch. You've been using me, Ethan. Making love to *me* while you've been thinking about *her*. And you humiliated me tonight. If you recall, I'm supposed to be your fiancée. I hate and despise you.'

'We've already established that.'

'I won't ever be your lover again after this! Never ever.'

'Don't say that,' he groaned.

Abby stared at his suddenly bleak face and felt total confusion. What was she going to do with this man?

'Believe me when I say what you saw meant nothing,' he insisted fiercely. 'It was just something I had to do, a test I had to make. You're not a fool, Abby. You were right when you guessed there was something between Vanessa and myself once. But we were more than just lovers. We were engaged to be married. The wedding was only a fortnight away when she dumped me for Ballistrat. I thought I'd never gotten over her and what she did. Which is why I came down here. But I soon realised I had. Well and truly. Still, when she came up to me and asked me to dance with her, I thought it would be a good idea to make certain.'

'And?'

'And nothing. She's pathetic. More than pathetic. She's so rotten to the core, I can't believe I ever loved her.'

'But you did.'

'I thought I did. But I was also only twenty-five years old, and even back then she was very sophisticated in matters of men and sex. Maybe that explains it. It wasn't love. It was a sexual infatuation.'

'And you don't desire her any more?'

'I almost felt sick tonight, touching her.'

Funny. He hadn't looked sick when she saw him. But he always was good at putting on a façade.

'I'd much rather touch you,' he said, sitting down beside her on the bed and running a tantalising finger around the deep neckline of her dress.

'No, don't,' she protested weakly, despite her pulse-rate immediately taking off.

'Don't be silly. You want me to.' And he rolled her over and began slowly unzipping her dress.

'Oh, God,' she gasped when he bent his mouth to the nape of her neck. It moved inexorably down her bared spine as he peeled the dress back with his hands.

Abby was instantly breathless with desire, spellbound with a heart-pounding excitement.

Yes, kiss me there, she moaned silently. Then *not* so silently.

'Don't stop,' she gasped on one occasion. 'Please don't stop.'

He kept her face down while he stripped her, sensitising each square inch of her body as it became exposed to his mouth and his oh, so clever hands.

He did not stop the erotic torment. Not for a moment.

By the time he finally fused his flesh with hers she was writhing beneath him, grasping the quilt with clenched fists, her cheek hot against the pillow. Her only consolation was that he appeared as mindlessly impassioned as she was, blind to everything but her body and the pleasure he seemed to find there.

She cried out his name as she came. Then simply cried, her face buried and turned away from him. She tried to resist his taking her in his arms afterwards, but she was too exhausted to resist.

'Hush, my love,' he soothed, rocking her in his arms. 'Hush.'

But she cried till she fell asleep. For she knew that she was not his love. And never would be.

CHAPTER FOURTEEN

'I DIDN'T do it,' Abby cried aloud in her sleep. 'I didn't. You have to believe me. Oh, God, why don't you believe me?'

'Abby.' Ethan shook her by the shoulder. 'Abby wake up. You're having a nightmare.'

She sat bolt-upright in the bed, staring around her for a few confused seconds before she realised where she was, and that the real nightmare she'd once lived through was not actually happening all over again.

It was just a dream that came whenever she was upset. In it, she would be back in that courtroom, trying to convince everyone of the truth, but no one would believe her. No one.

The worst thing was that it always *seemed* so real!

'Oh, thank God,' she cried with a rush of relief.

When Ethan's arms went round her she shuddered, then with a strangled sob buried her face in his chest. 'It was just a dream,' she cried in muffled tones. 'Just a dream…'

He gathered her tightly to him and began stroking her hair back from her face. 'Just a dream, my love.'

Abby stiffened at the endearment and went to pull away, but he would have none of it, holding her even more tightly.

'Tell me about it,' he insisted.

She looked up into his shadowed face, unable to see the expression in his eyes, the only light in the room some faint moonlight coming through the window.

'I…I don't think so.' It was all very well for Dr Seymour to say be honest, but being honest didn't automatically mean being believed.

'Tell me, Abby,' he urged.

'You…you called me Abby?'

'Mmm.' He kissed her on the forehead. 'You seem to be breaking down all my defences. Next thing you know, I'll be telling you I love you.'

Abby froze in his arms. 'Don't say things like that!'

'Why not? You don't still hate me, do you, my love?' he asked, so tenderly that her own defences suddenly crumbled.

'You know I don't,' she choked out.

He sighed. 'I'm afraid I don't know any such thing. I don't really know anything about you. I certainly don't know your innermost feelings.'

'Are…are you saying you want to?' she asked tentatively, hardly daring to hope that she might really mean something to him.

'Yes. Yes, I do,' he said, sounding almost surprised at himself, yet quite pleased. 'And you can start by telling me about that nightmare.'

Abby wanted to. But she was still afraid.

'Don't be afraid,' he said gently, as though reading her mind. 'I'm not shockable.'

She breathed in deeply, then let it out in a shuddering sigh. 'You might be more shockable than you realise. But all right, Ethan, I'll tell you why I keep having this nightmare.'

'It's always the same one?'

'Always.'

'That sounds pretty traumatic,' he said thoughtfully. 'Want me to put on a light first? Or get you a drink?'

'No. Just hold me and listen.'

'My pleasure.'

'God, I don't know where to start.'

'Why not at the beginning?'

'The beginning?' she repeated.

Where on earth was the beginning?

For some strange reason, her mind flashed to that day when she'd come home from her Wednesday afternoon ballet lesson to find that her mother had left and wasn't coming back.

'She's run off with her current lover,' her father had bluntly told her, in that coldly aloof manner of his.

'But…but where's she gone?' she'd asked, dismayed and devastated. Her mother hadn't been much of a mother, but at only eleven she hadn't been quite sure of that yet. Though chronically self-obsessed, Stephany Richmond at least had a warmer and more engaging personality than her husband.

'I don't know and I don't care,' her father had returned coldly. 'She always was a slut. I only married her because she was pregnant with you. There hasn't been a decent-looking man visit this house she hasn't tried to seduce, and I dare say she succeeded more times than she failed.

'I see *you've* taken after her in looks,' he'd sneered. 'God knows what awaits me as a father in a couple of years. But be warned, Abigail. Shame me once with your behaviour and you'll be out on your ear without a penny. I won't be shamed by my daughter as well as my wife!'

And that had been that. Not a word of sympathy or comfort for the shocked and equally abandoned child, only abuse because she looked like her mother. The following day Abby had been sent off to boarding-school.

Now, why should that be the beginning? Abby puzzled.

Because, she finally realised, that had marked the start of her long, lonely, loveless teenage years which had produced the perfect victim for a man like Dillon.

She glanced up at Ethan in the darkness.

'You promise you won't misjudge me again? You promise you'll hear me out properly?'

'I promise.'

She sighed, and began at the beginning while Ethan listened.

She told him of her mother's defection and her dismissal to boarding-school, and of how her father's accusations and threats had made her fearful when boys had started being attracted to her. She had become reticent with the opposite sex and very wary, especially when she'd found herself having feelings she'd thought were a sure sign that she was a slut, like her mother.

So she spurned having a boyfriend to become a type of bluestocking, and in doing so found a certain satisfaction in her father's surprised praise. He gave her a year's trip overseas when she gained an excellent pass in her HSC—an elderly chaperon filling most of her time with visiting art galleries and museums and the great theatres of the world. Even so, men paid her attention, but once again she spurned them, despite feeling attracted to more than one.

On her return to Sydney, she began a science degree at university, and after two years' successful completion her father presented her with a red Mazda RX7 for her twentieth birthday, telling her it was because he was so pleased at how well she'd turned out.

Ironically, it was her car which first drew Dillon's attention. He came over to look at it in the uni car park, took a long second look at the pretty but naïve girl behind the wheel, then moved in for the kill.

Dillon.

A glamorous name for a very glamorous young man. Blond and bronzed and so beautiful, he took every girl at uni's breath away. And he wasn't just gorgeous to look at. He was intelligent and witty and charming as well, filling his days doing an endless engineering degree after failing several times. He even made his failing sound glamorous.

Abby didn't stand a chance once he directed his dazzling charm and personality full-blast upon her that day in the car park.

Yet she wasn't easy, sexually speaking. Heck, no. She'd built up quite a reserve against male overtures over the years. Dillon had to work damned hard to seduce her, gradually breaking down those quite unnatural barriers till she became the girl she'd probably been meant to be all along. Passionate and loving and sensual. Warm and affectionate and generous.

Once they became lovers, she really blossomed, physically speaking. She started dressing a little more sexily, leaving her shoulder-length hair down for a change, and generally being much more confident and comfortable with her female attractions. She even became a bit of a flirt, although her eyes were only ever for Dillon. He was her miracle-worker. She was mad about him.

When Dillon first asked her for small loans she simply gave him the money, telling him not to worry about repaying it. He always said he would but he never did, and soon he was spending more of her allowance, not to mention driving her car—his own being always in the smash repairs place. She often came home on public transport, which might have been a problem if her father had been around to notice, but he rarely was.

Abby kept on being putty in Dillon's hands for several

months. Life had never seemed so wonderful. She was loved and needed and wanted.

Abby never realised that he was merely using her for the things a wild young man of his ilk couldn't get enough of or do without. Money. Sex. Decent wheels. Designer clothes.

And designer drugs.

God, but she was so naïve not to see that he was high on drugs a lot of the time. The way he drove. The way he could dance all night. The way he sometimes wasn't able to make love all that well.

Though perhaps that was due to his having already made love to someone else earlier on that day. She was later to discover that he had girls all over the place. She wasn't his only prey.

They were coming home from a dance party one Saturday night during her last year at uni when disaster struck. It was four in the morning and Dillon was speeding as usual. Abby tried to get him to slow down, but he merely laughed at her.

She looked down at her feet because she was afraid to watch the road and the oncoming traffic.

'I was still looking down when we ran a red light and smashed into another car,' she told Ethan. 'I hit my head on the dash and was knocked out cold. When I came to I was in the driving seat, my hands wrapped around the steering wheel. Dillon was nowhere to be seen. The woman driver in the other car was dead.'

Ethan switched on the bedside lamp and she glanced warily up at him. But he only looked shocked, not sceptical.

'When I was released from hospital after spending the night in with concussion,' she continued carefully, 'I was arrested.'

Ethan was frowning now. 'What was the charge?'

'Charges,' she corrected grimly. 'Culpable driving. Manslaughter and possession of narcotics. Dillon had kindly left his personal supply of cocaine tucked under the driver's seat,' she finished bitterly.

'Good God.'

'There were no other witnesses, you see,' she explained further. 'And it *was* my car. Dillon must have walked home. We weren't that far away from his parents' place. He told the police I'd dropped him off first. At that hour of the morning there weren't many people awake to corroborate or deny what he claimed.'

'What a bastard! Oh, you poor darling. I hope you had a good lawyer. Sounds like you needed one.'

She stared up at him. 'You...you believe me...'

'Well, of course I do. No one would make up a horror story like that! Besides, you're honest as the day is long. Even an old cynic like me can see that.'

Her eyes swam with tears, several spilling over.

'Hey!' he said softly, dashing them away with gentle fingers. 'What's all this about?' His fingers froze suddenly and he stared down at her. 'Hell, Abby, they found you guilty, didn't they? That bastard let you go to gaol for something he did.'

'Yes,' she choked out. 'I was sentenced to eight years. I...I got out in four. That was six months ago.'

'Oh, you poor darling. God, what a bastard. So what happened to *him*, do you know? I hope he died of an overdose, the creep.'

'No, I don't know what happened to Dillon and I don't really care any more.' And, strangely enough, she didn't.

'Don't care! Hell, he should be made to suffer for his

crimes! I'd like to strangle him with my bare hands. Send the bastard straight to hell.'

'People like Dillon find their own hell on earth, Ethan.'

'You don't really believe that, do you?'

'Oh, yes. You take your Vanessa. She's not happy, you know. And as she gets older and loses her beauty she's going to be downright miserable. No one will love her or want her. You wait and see.'

'I've waited ten years and it hasn't happened yet,' he said drily. 'Anyway, I'd rather not talk about that witch, if you don't mind. Let's get back to you. You must have been absolutely devastated when you were first arrested.'

'Absolutely. My father refused to hire a decent lawyer for me. I had to settle for legal aid, but the lawyer assigned to me seemed to bitterly resent a millionaire's daughter using their services. Both the judge and jury appeared biased against me for the same reason. I was held up as an example of true justice—a spoilt rich bitch going to gaol for her selfish and amoral ways. Eight years was a pretty harsh sentence.'

'Oh, Abby... I'm so sorry... You make me feel terribly small. You've been through hell, whereas I—' He broke off suddenly, his dark brows drawing together in another puzzled frown.

'Now hold on, there! What about that story you told me about that rich older guy and his giving you all that jewellery and—?' He broke off again and glared at her, his expression becoming exasperated. 'That was your father, wasn't it? You played with words when you told me that, didn't you? Dillon was your only lover and your father paid for your trip overseas. Plus your pearls. Some sugar-daddy,' he scoffed. 'He was your *real* daddy!'

Abby gave him a sheepish look. 'Are…are you angry with me?'

'I should be furious. Instead I'm merely flabbergasted. What a wicked little minx you can be sometimes, Miss Richmond!'

'Well, you had such an awful opinion of me, and I rather wanted you to go on thinking that way to keep you at bay. You see…I wanted you to make love to me so badly. I was almost at screaming point for the wanting…'

'You wouldn't have kept me at bay forever, believe me,' he said thickly. 'I'd just about reached my own tether where my feelings for you were concerned.'

'We don't have to hide our feelings any longer, though, do we?' she murmured, placing her head on his bare chest and sighing a sigh of utter peace and contentment.

'Never.'

'I'm so happy you believed me, Ethan.'

'And I'm so happy you told me. Don't ever be afraid to tell me anything, my love.'

Abby's heart swelled with joy. He'd called her his love again, and this time she believed him. He did love her. He just wasn't ready to say it yet.

'And don't you be afraid to tell *me* anything,' she countered sleepily.

If she hadn't already been drifting off she might have felt the abrupt stilling in that stroking hand, might have worried when he made no reply.

CHAPTER FIFTEEN

THE golf-course was a picture—green and lush, with each fairway bordered by rows of those same pines that encircled the tennis courts. Clearly the drought hadn't affected this part of the countryside.

'Who's going to partner whom?' Henry asked as they assembled on the first tee.

'I'm easy,' Ethan said, and smiled at Abby.

She smiled back, her heart fairly bursting with happiness. It had been a marvellous day so far—had been since the first moment she woke that morning and remembered what had happened the night before. It was as though a great weight had been lifted from her shoulders in telling Ethan the truth, even better than when she'd told Miss Blanchford.

It had been equally marvellous to see how Ethan had ignored Vanessa's blatant overture towards him at breakfast, then at the barbecue lunch which had followed the morning's lectures. Ethan's ex had seemed most put out by his blunt rebuff on this last occasion, clearly stunned that he wanted nothing to do with her. She'd given Abby the most vicious look.

Abby had half expected the woman scorned to show up at the tennis courts that morning, where she and Ann had been having a re-match while the men were in conference, but there hadn't been a single sight of her. With a bit of luck she'd given up on Ethan and settled on seducing some other poor fool.

'If Abby plays golf like she plays tennis,' Ann

warned, 'then I think we'll play the boys versus the girls.'

'She doesn't,' Ethan replied. 'Do you, darling?'

'Er…no. I'm a bit of a duffer.'

'Then she'd better play with you, Ethan,' Henry suggested.

'Fine by me,' he agreed happily. 'Don't look so worried, Abby. I don't mind if you can't play very well.'

Abby tensed inside. Gone was any idea of making Ethan look a fool by beating the pants off him. Now she had to concentrate on making him *not* look a fool by actually playing too well.

Hopefully, her rustiness would help her nonperformance. She hadn't played golf in years. But she would still have to watch it. She'd been damned good once, her father having sent her to a sporting camp every summer for six years, where she'd been given professional lessons in all sorts of sports.

By adopting an appallingly crooked stance and a wayward elbow, Abby managed to hook her first drive out of bounds. Everyone commiserated on seeing her crestfallen face, then proceeded to show her what she should have done.

Ethan's ball sailed straight down the fairway for a couple of hundred yards and Henry's landed only a little shorter; even Ann's went a respectable distance, despite it scrubbing along the top of the ground.

'It's all in the swing-through,' Ethan explained patiently as they set off at a brisk pace to find her ball. 'I'll show you when we find your ball. *If* we find your ball,' he amended drily as they headed towards the pines. 'And you must keep your feet straight!' was his last piece of advice.

It wasn't her feet that she had trouble keeping straight

for the eighteen holes, but her face. She hadn't realised how much fun it could be playing badly. Or having Ethan show her how to putt—his arms wrapped tightly around her, his body pressed against hers. Sometimes she genuinely played a bad shot, she was so distracted.

She almost made it round without raising Ethan's suspicions. The eighteenth hole was her undoing. It was a difficult par four, with a dog-leg corner to the right. A clump of tall trees made it very hazardous to cut the corner in an attempt to reach the green in one. Henry, by this time very smug at their imminent victory, suggested a bet on this last hole, placing a fifty-dollar wager on their combined scores.

When Ethan magnanimously agreed, Abby decided that his male pride had had enough to bear. So, when it came her turn, she lined up her ball and hit it with a great whack which sent it flying over the trees in a high arch—virtually the same shot Ethan had chosen earlier. Her ball landed right on the green, less than a metre from the hole and a couple of metres inside Ethan's ball. Both Henry and Ann had taken the conservative route—their balls down in the fairway at the corner, still a hundred metres from the green.

'Holy hell,' Henry said succinctly.

'Heavens!' Ann exclaimed.

'Did I do that?' Abby gasped, hoping she was using the right amount of astonishment in her voice. 'Your tips must be doing me some good, Ethan.'

Ethan remained suspiciously silent, though his suddenly narrowed eyes spoke volumes.

'Bit of a duffer, eh?' he muttered under his breath as they strode off the tee together, Ann and Henry going in a different direction. 'I hope you've had a good time, laughing at me behind my back.'

'Actually, I have,' she confessed impishly.

He shot her a savage look, which quickly dissolved into a helpless smile when she giggled. 'What on earth am I going to do with you?' he said, shaking his head.

'You could kiss me, if you like,' she said, puckering up.

'You're incorrigible.' But he did kiss her, with all the hunger and passion the Ethan of last Friday would never have displayed in private, let alone public. One kiss followed another, then another, his hands reaching down to curve over her buttocks and pull her into him as much as clothes would allow.

'You want to win this hole or don't you?' Henry shouted from the dog-leg corner after playing their shots.

'Coming!' Abby shouted back.

'Almost,' Ethan muttered blackly, and Abby burst out laughing. After a second so did Ethan, his face showing a startled delight at his own spontaneous humour.

He took his buggy with one hand and hers with the other. 'You know, Abby,' he said warmly as they walked companionably along, 'I could get used to this.'

I hope so, she thought. I sincerely hope so.

The evening was as successful and happy as the day, with cocktails followed by a formal five-course dinner. Abby's black crêpe sheath gown was as big a hit with Ethan as the coffee-coloured lace—her over-indulging herself at lunch and dinner resulting in another tight fit.

He seemed to like things tight on her, all night whispering erotic promises in her ear of what he was going to do to her later. And how often.

She laughed at his outrageous boasting at one stage, but he had the last laugh when he lived up to his promises, reducing her to a state of exhaustion.

'No more,' she said limply, some time after midnight.

'Chicken.'

'No—duck. A dead duck. So you can stop your cock-crowing. You win.'

'I didn't realise it was a competition.'

'You know it was. You were paying me back for this afternoon.'

'You know me well, Miss Richmond.'

'Too well, Dr Jekyll. Though I think it's back to Mr Hyde tonight.'

'What on earth are you talking about?'

She told him and he laughed. 'I always loved that story. And I always liked Mr Hyde better than Dr Jekyll. Which one do you prefer?'

'Not telling,' Abby said, yawning. 'Now, could we turn off the light and get some sleep? Henry tells me you have a riveting video of one of Dr Ballistrat's operations to watch tomorrow morning. You might need a few live brain cells if you're going to get anything out of it.'

'There's nothing Ballistrat can teach me that I'd want to know,' he scoffed. 'What are you and Ann doing tomorrow morning?'

'Ann's taking me into Bowral with her,' she mumbled into the pillow. 'She wants to visit the antique shops before we go back to Sydney after lunch.'

'Do you want any money to buy something?'

Abby knew that he was probably only being nice but she wished he hadn't offered. 'I don't want to buy anything.'

'You might want to stop off at one of those tea-houses, though, for morning tea.'

'I have enough of my own money for that.'

'Just asking. Don't get defensive.'

'I don't ever want you to think I want you for your money, because I don't!'

'I never thought that for a moment,' he returned drily. 'I know you only want me for my body.'

She rolled over, an exasperated glare in place, only to find him grinning down at her, dancing teasing lights in his beautiful blue eyes.

'Why, you!' she squealed, and began pummelling him in the chest and stomach.

He laughed and grasped her wrists, whipping her over onto her back and holding her arms up on the pillows above her head. When he secured both in one iron hold and began touching her again, she groaned her total exasperation. 'No, don't. I couldn't bear it again. I simply couldn't.'

She twisted beneath him, trying to get away from that merciless grip, that harassing hand and that marauding mouth. But his hold on her remained invincible, his ruthless attentions gradually achieving their aim.

'No, I told you,' she cried in fury and frustration, when it soon became obvious that it was her own feelings she was having to fight. 'No, no, no!'

'Yes, yes, yes, Abby,' he bit back, his lips and teeth momentarily stopping their torment of one of her nipples. 'Your body speaks far more truthfully and eloquently than your tongue. Shall I prove it to you?'

She was about to scream when he let her go, reaching over to switch off the light and leaving her to lie there, panting, for several long, agonising minutes, the dark and the quiet making her even more hotly aware of every throbbing, re-aroused nerve-ending she possessed.

And there seemed to be millions.

'So what's it to be, Abby?' he taunted at last from the black stillness of his side of the bed. *He* didn't seem to be breathing hard, or silently screaming with frustration. 'Sleep? Or me?'

'I see you've reverted to Mr Hyde again,' she bit out.

'Ah, but Mr Hyde does have his attractions for you, doesn't he?' And with a swift, savage movement, he pulled her over on top of him.

'Tell me you love me,' he rasped as he manoeuvred his steel hardness into her stunned body.

'You know I do,' she admitted on a raw whisper.

'Then say it!'

'I love you, God forgive me.'

'Then let God forgive the both of us, Abby,' he growled. 'For I love you too. More than I would ever have thought possible. No, don't say anything now, for pity's sake. Just keep doing what you're doing,' he urged, with his voice and his hands. 'This is how we found each other and this is all I want for tonight. We'll talk of the future on our way back to Sydney. *After* we've left this place well behind.'

'You're off in another world, Abby, aren't you?' Ann said, looking up from the table of knick-knacks she'd been browsing over. 'Making mental plans for your wedding?'

'In a way,' Abby confessed, still a little bewildered by Ethan's passionate declaration of love the night before. She couldn't help hoping that his plans included marriage, but something—some instinctive wariness, perhaps born of her bitter experience with Dillon—made her hesitate to hope too much.

She might have asked Ethan this morning to elaborate, except they'd slept in, then had to rush to get down to breakfast where the presence of Ann and Henry had rather precluded such a strange question. After all, they were supposed to be already engaged.

'And when is the wedding?' Ann persisted. 'Soon, I'll bet. If I know Ethan, he won't want to wait long after waiting all these years to find the right girl.'

'I'd marry him tomorrow, if I could,' Abby said with a quiet intensity.

'Oh, to be in love like that again!' Ann sighed expressively. 'It does wear off, though, that madness when you can't keep your hands off each other. Still, if you really love someone, that initial burst of uncontrollable lust gradually settles down to the most wonderful relationship, which includes the occasional burst of lust, a lot of contentment and companionship, and scads of security.

'There's nothing like that feeling of security—especially these days. The knowledge that you can trust your partner, both with your body and your life. Henry might look at other women, but I know he would never, ever touch one. He's my best friend, is my Henry. I will love that man till the day I die.'

'Oh, that's so beautiful,' Abby cried, tears flooding her eyes. 'That's what I want with Ethan, more than anything. That feeling of security. But I'm so afraid that he won't…that he might not…' She choked back a sob and dived into her handbag for a tissue.

Ann bustled her out of the antiques shop, murmuring apologies for having made her cry. 'You think Ethan might look at other women?' she asked when Abby had stopped weeping.

Abby shook her head. 'No. Not really…' If Vanessa had failed to turn his head this weekend, she couldn't see any other woman doing so easily. But the type of relationship Ann had just described seemed unattainable with Ethan. He'd said that he never trusted women. How could they be best friends without trust?

'You'll be all right,' Ann said, patting her hand. 'Trust me. I've seen a good few couples together in my life, and you two are the real McCoy. Let's forget the antiques and go have one of those Devonshire teas. There's a cute little tea-house just down the road. That's what you need—a cup of tea and a good dose of calories.'

Abby had to laugh. 'I think that's the last thing I need. Didn't you see me in that black dress last night?'

'Sure did. And so did all the men in the room,' Ann added drily. 'My Henry was most amorous last night, thanks to that dress of yours.'

Abby blinked her shock and Ann chuckled. 'You know, for a sophisticated-looking girl you have a way to go to learn about men and sex. Let me give you a piece of advice—never worry about a man looking. If he stops looking, then it's a good bet he's dead from the waist down and not much good to you anyway.'

'I…I'll keep that in mind.'

'Of course, that doesn't apply to a man-eater like Vanessa Ballistrat. If your man starts looking too closely at something like that, then you need to bring out the big guns.'

'The big guns?'

'Yeah, you either shoot her, or you get your man a hundred miles away. Quick smart.'

'Then it's as well we're going back to Sydney this afternoon,' Abby said thoughtfully.

'And none too soon, I'd say,' was Ann's final comment on the subject.

But it was already too late, Abby was to find out less than an hour later. Too late…

CHAPTER SIXTEEN

ANN dropped Abby off at the front of the hotel shortly after eleven. They hadn't spent nearly as long in Bowral as they'd intended, but that was all right by Abby. She still hadn't packed, and was anxious not to do anything to delay their departure after lunch.

'Thanks for the tea, Ann,' she said through the passenger window. 'See you at lunch.'

Ann drove off to park the car in the basement car park, Abby hurrying up the steps and into the hotel foyer. She moved quickly across the tiled floor and down the central hallway, and was approaching the door which led out to the back when it opened abruptly and an incoming person collided with her.

'Sorry,' she automatically apologised.

Vanessa seemed to take a moment to realise who she'd run into, while Abby could only stare at the woman.

There was no doubt that she was frighteningly beautiful, even in her present slightly flushed and flustered state. She looked decidedly dishevelled as well—her hair messy, her lipstick smudged, and the zipper on her black cat-suit open well past her bustline.

Abby was sure the creature was naked underneath the skin-tight outfit—her cleavage looked braless, her nipples starkly pointed, and not a pantie line showed anywhere. She looked as if she'd just had a hurried amorous rendezvous with someone. But not with her husband,

173

obviously, since he was still at that moment delivering his last lecture. Probably some poor fool she'd picked up down here.

A malicious smile began tugging at that sinfully sensuous mouth, a cold, cruel gleam entering those beautiful blue eyes.

'You're home early, sweetie.' She wagged a scarlet-tipped finger back and forth. 'Tut-tut. Never come home earlier than the boyfriend or hubby expects. It leads to trouble. After all, you told Ethan you'd be away all morning. But not to worry. It won't happen again. Not with me, anyway. I'm leaving shortly, and, frankly, I've outgrown men like Ethan. Still, the poor darling was desperate for one last sample of what he once couldn't live without, so I gave it to him. Wasn't that sweet of me?'

Abby tried not to believe the poisonous words. Tried with all her heart. Ethan loves me, she kept telling herself. He would not do this. She's lying.

But Vanessa's softly knowing laugh undermined her confidence. 'I wouldn't say anything to Ethan if you want to keep him, honey. I won't be back, after all. Phil and I are off on a world tour tomorrow. And so what if he thinks of me while he's doing it to you? What do you care? You'll be Mrs Ethan Grant. That's all you want, isn't it?'

Looking back, Abby would never know how she found the courage or the strength to do what she did. Somehow she dredged up a haughty yet at the same time pitying look, accompanied by a mocking laugh of her own.

'What a pathetic liar you are. Truly, you must think I don't know everything about you, you vile creature! My

Ethan would never make love to you. He *despises* you. And you're quite wrong about my only wanting to be Mrs Ethan Grant. That's not it at all. I just want to be with him, to be his woman and the mother of his children.

'If you must know,' she added, out of some kind of desperate defiance, 'I'm already having his baby. Yes, that's right. I'm pregnant. Ethan truly loves me and I love him, and no scheming witch like you will ever break us up. So go round the world with your poor, pathetic husband. Keep screwing every man you fancy and keep screwing up your life. You'll end up a lonely old woman—a lonely, ugly woman whom no one will ever really want.

'Yes, go!' Abby raved on, finding some triumph as the blonde paled at her words. 'And be thankful that I'm letting you get away with your precious face and your precious boobs still intact. The only reason I am is that you're not worth going to gaol over. Heaven forbid!'

And, with another scornful laugh, she whirled and marched off, not once glancing behind, determined not to let that evil woman win in the smallest possible way.

But by the time she reached the door of her room Abby's courage was failing. Her head was whirling, her stomach churning, her heart pounding. What would she do if Ethan was inside...in this room...at this hour... when he should still be at the conference?

Abby's hand shook as she tried the door.

It was locked. Ethan wasn't inside after all. Vanessa *had* been lying!

She leant her head against the door and almost cried. How could she have ever let that woman make her doubt Ethan?

Sliding her key into the lock, she opened the door and walked in, a quick glance showing that the room was indeed empty. She had just closed the door behind her when the distinctive smell hit her nostrils.

It was Vanessa's perfume, the overpoweringly cloying perfume that she always wore. It permeated the whole room, its sickeningly sweet scent hanging in the air.

Abby clamped her hand over her mouth and slumped down on the side of the bed, gulping to stop herself from being sick. Closing her eyes, she tipped back onto the bed, only to be assailed by an even stronger whiff. She jerked upright as though stung, staring down at the quilt, knowing that Vanessa had lain there only recently.

She jumped to her feet and was staring despairingly down at the bed when the bathroom door was wrenched open and a naked Ethan just stood there. She stared, round-eyed at him, at the droplets of water still clinging to his body, at his appalled expression at finding her there.

'You weren't supposed to be back till twelve!'

Abby wanted to kill him. She wanted to kill them both. For clearly Vanessa hadn't lied. She'd lain here on this bed and Ethan had put his body into that vile woman's flesh.

Slowly, Abby became aware of a trembling deep inside, despite seemingly being in control. 'I'll be asking Ann and Henry if I can go home with them,' she said in a low, quavering voice. 'I don't want to ever see you again after this.'

'After what?'

If looks could have killed, he would have perished on the spot. 'Don't bother to lie,' she said coldly. 'I've just left Vanessa's charming company along the way. She told me what happened in here, but stupid me didn't believe her till I walked into this room. Now I know she *was* here. I can smell her. I can smell her on that bed. I can smell her everywhere. Is that why you had a shower, Ethan? To try to wash the smell of her off you?'

'I didn't touch her,' he denied fiercely. 'You have to believe me, Abby.'

When he took a step forward she put up her hands to ward him off. But she rather fancied it was the look on her face which did that. She could feel the bitterness burning in her eyes, the cold fury twisting her heart.

'I don't *have* to do any such thing,' she bit out. 'I won't be used and betrayed by a man a second time, Ethan Grant. I'll kill you first, do you hear me?' And, having said so, she felt her control break and she rushed at him—arms flailing, fists pounding, uncaring that she was the one sustaining the bruises as she struck out blindly and wildly. The pain in her heart was far greater than any pain in her body. He absorbed her blows for a while before stopping her, after which she sank down to the ground at his feet, sobbing hysterically.

'How could you?' she moaned when he sank to the floor next to her and gathered her up into his arms. 'How could you…?'

'I didn't, Abby,' he insisted brokenly. 'I swear to you. On my love for you, my honour as a doctor and my Hippocratic oath, I did not touch her. Do you think I could do such a thing after making love to you in that bed? Do you think I could ever go from your truly loving embrace to that slut's evil arms? God, Abby, I would rather die than be guilty of such treachery. I would rather die than have you lose faith in me and my love for you. Please, darling, say you believe me, say you still love me. I can't bear to think I might lose you. I just can't bear it.'

Abby heard the despair in his voice, saw the torment in his face, felt the trembling in his body.

He's telling the truth, she realised. He didn't touch Vanessa. He loves *me*.

All the pain drained away immediately, replaced by the deepest, sincerest regret. He'd believed *her* when she'd said she was innocent, whereas she hadn't believed him. 'Oh, Ethan...' She reached up and laid a gentle, apologetic hand against his grey, strained cheek. 'I'm so sorry for doubting you, even for a moment... Of course you wouldn't do a thing like that. Forgive me, my love. Forgive me.'

'Forgive you? I'm the one who should beg for forgiveness. I should never have let the bitch into the room, should never have given her the slightest opportunity to hurt you like that. I knew what she was like. How wicked and selfish she could be. But I wanted the chance to redress the mistaken opinion I might have given her the other night when I danced with her. I wanted the chance to tell her what I really thought of her.'

'What happened, Ethan?' Abby asked.

His shudder showed true revulsion. 'I still can't believe what she did. The woman is sick, I tell you. Sick.' He shook his head in disbelief.

'How did she get into the room with you? How did she know I wouldn't be here?'

'She must have overheard you and Ann at breakfast this morning, discussing your outing to Bowral, and planned her strategy accordingly. When we came out for morning tea from the conference, I was handed a written message from her. It said she needed to see me urgently—there was some crisis—and was waiting for me at the door of my room. I knew in my heart I should ignore the note, but I just couldn't. Curiosity, I guess, and that niggling need to have a type of revenge—even if it was only seeing the look on her face when I told her that I thought she was disgusting.

'She took my showing up as a sign I still wanted her, of course. Vanessa had snapped her fingers and stupid Ethan had come running. Once inside the room, she put on an act which would make your mind boggle. She tried tears at first—told me she still loved me, that she'd made a terrible mistake in marrying Ballistrat. She said he'd seduced her with the help of drugs, that he'd even made her into an addict for a while. She also said that he was a drunk and mistreated her, and that she wanted to leave him but was afraid.

'When that tack didn't seem to be working—I don't think I'd said a word at this stage—she turned to sex, as usual. I should have been expecting it, but I was still stunned when she pulled down the zipper of that disgusting outfit and stepped, totally naked, out of it. Perhaps she took my shock for a reluctant interest, for she started running her hands all over herself, reminding me that she used to do the same to seduce me when we were living together and I wanted to study but she wanted to make love.

'Which was true, I'm ashamed to admit. She knew all the tricks to turn on a man. She'd do anything, any time, anywhere to get what she wanted. What I didn't realise was that she'd do the same with any*one*. Back then, I was fascinated by her beauty, plus her total lack of sexual inhibition. What young man wouldn't be? This time, however, I felt nothing but revulsion. When she lay down on the bed and started touching herself more intimately, I actually bolted into the bathroom and started dry-retching into the basin.'

Abby could feel his disgust as he shuddered at the memory.

'When I came out,' he went on, 'she was gone. I dare say my actions spoke much louder than any words could have. Yet I felt no triumph, only a long, lingering revulsion and the feeling that I'd been made unclean by watching her, even for a moment. I locked the door, stripped off and had a shower. Even after I'd switched off the water I just stood there, unable to dry myself or function. Then I heard someone in this room. I thought maybe she'd hidden in the room somewhere, so I dashed out. Only to find you standing next to the bed, looking devastated.'

'I *was* devastated,' she admitted.

He held her close. 'God, I'd give anything to go back in time and just stay in that conference room. How could I have been so stupid? My only excuse is that I'd wanted some kind of revenge for so long, Abby. For what she did to me. She almost destroyed me all those years ago. I can't tell you…'

'But you can, Ethan. Tell me like I told you everything about Dillon. What else did she do to you, besides what you've already told me? I know there has to be something else…something awful.'

And he told her, in a hushed, hurt voice. How she'd been pregnant with their baby at the time of Philip Ballistrat's arrival at the hospital. She seemed thrilled, he said, almost as thrilled as he was.

Just that week, however, she'd found out that he wasn't as rich as she'd thought, that it would be years before he made that sort of money she wanted. He had watched her change before his eyes; watched her ruthlessly set out to seduce their famed visitor; watched his own future being slowly destroyed.

'Though she wasn't slow to destroy my baby,' he bit out. 'She got rid of that, quick smart.'

'Oh, Ethan, how horrible for you.'

'Seeing her again after all this time made me see it wasn't such a tragedy. Who would want *that* as the mother of his child?'

'It was still wicked.'

'She *is* wicked.'

'She didn't love you, Ethan. No woman who loved a man would do a thing like that. I would never get rid of your baby. Never!'

He hugged her to him. 'I know that.'

'I...I might even be pregnant now,' she confided to him. 'It's not all that likely, but it *is* possible. I'm notoriously irregular when my equilibrium is upset. And you've been upsetting my equilibrium for some time, Ethan.'

He held her away from him and stared down at her. 'Are you saying that when I offered you that morning-after pill the other day you might actually have conceived the night before?'

'Well, probably not...'

'But there *was* a risk?' he asked, frowning.

'Well, yes. You're...you're not mad with me, are you, Ethan? I mean, don't you want me to have your babies?'

His face was disbelieving. 'Don't I...?' His answer was to hug her again, so tightly that she could hardly breathe. 'Of course I want you to have my babies,' he said thickly. 'And I want you to be my wife. As soon as possible. Say yes, Abby. Please say yes. Make our engagement real.'

Abby shook her head in disbelief that he would think there was any other answer.

'You won't marry me,' he said bleakly. 'You don't trust me enough. And I don't blame you. I don't deserve you. I've been a pig. And a fool. God, I've been a fool for so damned long!'

She cupped his face firmly with her hands. 'Shut up, you silly man. Of course I'll marry you.'

'You will?'

'Yes, of course.' And then she laughed.

Ethan looked mildly affronted. 'This is a very serious moment, Abby.'

'I was just thinking of the expression on Sylvia's face when we tell her we're engaged. Not to mention Miss Blanchford.'

'Who's Miss Blanchford?'

'Don't worry. You'll know soon enough. By the way, how big is your house?'

'Too big.'

'Then you have a spare downstairs room for an old lady in a wheelchair?'

He smiled. 'Ah, so there really *is* an old lady with a wheelchair.'

Abby bristled. 'Did you ever doubt it?'

'Not really. Yes, of course we'd have a spare room downstairs.'

'That's wonderful!'

'I think I'm acquiring more than a wife here,' was his rueful remark.

Abby bit her bottom lip. 'She's like my family, Ethan,' she said pleadingly. She didn't add that her real

family didn't want her any more, had never really
wanted her.

'Well, why didn't you say so, darling?' was his wonderfully warm reply. 'Your family is my family, and my
family is your family.'

'You don't think Sylvia will mind?' she asked hesitantly.

'Mind? She'll be delighted! She's been delighted with
you all along. It was only her fool of a brother who
couldn't see what a treasure she'd found for him. A treasure which I will guard and cherish all the days of my
life.'

She snuggled into him and thought that it was she who
had found the treasure. 'You're going to become my best
friend, Ethan,' she said, remembering Ann's heart-
wrenching words.

'I thought I was going to become your husband!'

'That too. And my lover. And the father of all my
children.'

'Well, I'd better be or you're in big trouble. *How*
many children did you say?'

'How many bedrooms does that house of yours have?'

'Oh, God, not that many!' he groaned.

'How many, Ethan?'

'Twelve.' His voice sounded very fragile.

'That many! Oh, I don't think I want that many children.'

'Thank God,' he muttered.

'I've only ever wanted ten.'

'Ten!' he squawked.

'Too many, still?'

'I think so.'

'How about eight?'

'Eight!'

'Six, and that's my final offer.'

'Six it is,' he sighed.

Abby snuggled into him again, feeling well satisfied. She'd only ever wanted six anyway.

'Ethan,' she said softly after a minute or two.

'Mmm.'

'What *did* you have in mind when you first came down here last Friday? I mean...you weren't ever really going to do anything bad, were you?'

'I won't lie to you, Abby. I wanted revenge. I wanted to make her suffer as she had made me suffer. I had a suspicion that she might make a play for me if I turned up. I'd heard the rumours about her husband's finances. I planned to lead her on for a while if she did, then crush her totally once she'd burnt her bridges behind her with Ballistrat.'

'But if that was your plan why did you hire me to come with you? Wouldn't you have been better by yourself?'

'Of course. But it seemed my feelings for you were already beginning to vie with my so-called feelings for Vanessa. I told myself you were the perfect salve for my male pride, plus a possible weapon to spur Vanessa on— since she always did enjoy ensnaring a man who belonged to someone else. Frankly, I told myself a whole lot of garbage just so I could be alone with you, Abby, my love.

'Once I found some excuses to kiss you, my need for revenge soon took a back seat. In fact, my intense hatred for Vanessa quickly watered down to nothing more than a cynical curiosity and a rather confused revulsion. That's why I danced with her. To ram home just how revolting I found her. My one regret is that I didn't tell her in so many words.'

'Don't worry, Ethan, I did it for you.'

'You what?'

Abby told him then—everything that she'd said to the woman.

'You didn't!' He sounded both astonished and admiring at the same time.

'I did, indeed.'

'Even the bit about her…um…'

'Boobs, Ethan. The word is boobs. I think I worried her slightly about that. She was certainly hugging her chest as she raced off,' Abby lied outrageously as Ethan's delight grew.

He laughed and hugged her tightly. 'Oh, that's priceless! I wish I'd been there to see it. There again, you *are* priceless, my darling.'

'Well, not quite, Ethan. I do have a price. Or I *did*. Which reminds me. I have a confession of my own to make about that.'

He looked alarmed.

'It's nothing terrible,' she soothed. 'But I don't think I agreed to come with you just because I needed that money. I think, underneath, it was because I wanted to go to bed with you.'

'Well, I certainly don't mind *that* confession.'

'But I don't think I loved you back then, Ethan. It was just sex to begin with.'

'It often is, my darling. That's the way of nature, and men and women. But it's not just sex now, is it, for either of us?'

'Oh, no,' she assured him. 'It certainly isn't.'

'I really, truly love you, Abby.'

'And I really, truly love *you*, Ethan. Only…'

'Only what?'

'Do you think you might put some clothes on? It's very distracting and disturbing.'

'I will, darling. I will…afterwards.'

MILLS & BOON®

Presents...™

THE COZAKIS BRIDE *by Lynne Graham*

Olivia had no choice: her mother urgently needed expensive medical treatment, so she'd have to beg Nik Cozakis to marry her. Nik agreed, but only if Olivia bore him a son…

ROMANO'S REVENGE *by Sandra Marton*

When Joe's new cook turned out to be blonde, beautiful—and useless in the kitchen—he knew it was the work of his matchmaking grandmother. So he decided to add posing as his fiancée to Lucinda's list of duties. Lucinda could cope with a pretend engagement—but she drew the line at sharing Joe's bed!

THE MILLIONAIRE'S VIRGIN *by Anne Mather*

Nikolas has obviously not forgiven Paige for walking out on him four years ago. So why has he offered her a job on his Greek island for the summer? And what exactly will he be expecting from her?

THE PLAYBOY'S PROPOSITION *by Miranda Lee*

Tyler Garrison was impossibly handsome, and heir to a fortune. So Michele was touched by his plan to escort her to her ex-boyfriend's wedding as her pretend lover. But she was shocked when he proposed they become lovers for real—what was his motive?

Available from 7th July 2000

0006/01b

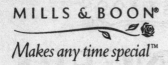

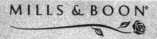

SUMMER'S CHILD
DIANE CHAMBERLAIN

Early one morning on the beach beside her home,
eleven year old Daria finds an abandoned new-born
baby. When no-one identifies the baby girl, she is
adopted by Daria's family.

Now, twenty years later, someone has returned to
investigate the mystery of Shelly's birth. But
someone doesn't want the secret uncovered…

MIRA®

Published 23rd June

M182

ON FIRE

CARLA NEGGERS

An uneasy alliance, an unexpected passion…

When a dead body washes up it opens up an incident Riley St. Joe wants to forget. Her only hope of finding the answers means working with FBI agent Straker. He is rude, cynical, frustrating…but they share a desire to find the truth. And a surprising passion that sets them on fire…

Published 23rd June 2000

M183

HELEN R. MYERS

A teenage girl has disappeared and it's happened before.
Police chief Jared Morgan cannot see a connection, Michaele, the missing girl's sister, suspects the worst. She's sacrificed everything—including her feelings for Jared—to bring up her sister. She won't believe Faith has simply run away.

lost

Published 23rd June 2000

MIRA®

M184

MILLS & BOON®

Enchanted™

HIS DESERT ROSE by Liz Fielding

When Prince Hassan al Rashid drew the world's media attention to the abduction of well-known foreign correspondent Rose Fenton, he also lost his heart. And, kidnapped by Hassan, Rose was surprised to find that beneath the designer suit lay the heart of a true desert prince!

TOM BRADLEY'S BABIES by Marion Lennox

Tom isn't happy to be stranded with a heavily pregnant woman—especially when he finds himself delivering twins! Tom soon realises that Rose is alone and in trouble, and proposes a marriage of convenience. However, keeping his distance isn't as easy as he thinks…

WIFE ON APPROVAL by Leigh Michaels

Paige was shocked to see Austin again. It was seven years since she'd called him husband—now he was only a client! Except he wanted to give their marriage another try…or did he just want a mother for the little girl now in his care?

BACHELOR IN NEED by Jessica Steele

Jegar Urquart needed Fennia's help in looking after his niece while her parents were in hospital. Jegar clearly found Fennia attractive…but while she could answer Jegar's need for a live-in nanny, Fennia felt she must resist slipping into the role of live-in lover as well!

Available from 7th July 2000

Available at most branches of WH Smith, Tesco, Martins, Borders, Easons, Volume One/James Thin and most good paperback bookshops

0006/02